KU-568-211

Friends of the Earth

The Rainforest Harvest

Sustainable Strategies for Saving the Tropical Forests?

Including the Proceedings of an International Conference held at the Royal Geographical Society, London 17-18th May 1990

ISBN 1 85750 0555

February 1992

Published by

Friends of the Earth Trust Ltd

26-28 Underwood Street London N1 7JQ

Editors

Simon Counsell and Tim Rice

Design and typesetting

Julie Berg

Printed by

LAC Litho

Printed on 100% recycled material

The Rainforest Harvest

Foreword

"In the so-called developed world, we are all becoming far more familiar, not just with that fascinating list of rainforest products which already enrich our lives in one form or another, but with the ever-growing list of products that one day might enrich our lives yet more.

That we should treat this profusion of natural wealth with such utter contempt continues to astonish me. It isn't as if we don't know its value, for we do - if not always in monetary terms, then certainly in ways that cannot so easily be reduced to the convenience of a pound or dollar symbol. It isn't as if we can't guess at some of the potential consequences of eliminating this diversity at the rate of literally thousands of species every year...

The rainforest must not be seen as just another 'investment opportunity', however environmentally aware the investor may be. Equitable compensation for forest peoples' knowledge and discoveries is essential, as is the need to ensure that a fair proportion of the profits are returned to the local communities involved. This is the only means by which their economic advancement and welfare can be underpinned, while simultaneously ensuring that the forest base is maintained intact...

I can, with the utmost enthusiasm, commend to you the proceedings of this Conference, for it seems to me to offer some realistic hope, at a somewhat gloomy time, both for the rainforests themselves and for the people of those countries on whom we depend to act as guardians and stewards of the forests in all our interests."

Extract from the Keynote Address at this Conference by HRH The Prince of Wales, and reprinted with his kind permission.

Table of Contents

Foreword *i*
Acknowledgements *5*
List of illustrations *6*
Acronyms *8*
Biographies of speakers *10*
Preface - The Rainforest Harvest - Sustainable strategies for saving tropical forests? *17*

PART 1 New Directions for Rainforest Conservation: People, Governments, Corporations and Development Organizations

(Conference Chair: *Hugh Prysor-Jones*)

Rainforest Harvest: An Overview *21*
Professor Ghillean Prance, Royal Botanic Gardens
Genetic Materials and the Climate Connection *26*
Professor Norman Myers, Environment Consultant
Keynote Speech *30*
His Royal Highness, The Prince of Wales
The Future of Amazonia *37*
Dr José Lutzenberger, Secretary for the Environment, Government of Brazil

PART 2 The View from the Forest Floor: A Community Perspective

Definitions of Extractive Reserves in the Context of the Alliance of the Forest Peoples *44*
Antonio Macedo, National Council of Rubber Tappers
The Development Project of the Poyanawa Association *46*
Mario de Lima, Leader of the Poyanawa community in Brazil
The Work of Northwestern Bee Products, Zambia *47*
Bob Malichi, Northwestern Bee Products
The Utilization and Trade of Non-Timber Products in South-east Asia *51*
Dr Noraini Tamin, University of Kebangsaan, Malaysia
Discussion *58*
Dr José Lutzenberger, Bob Malichi, Dr Noraini Tamin, Mario de Lima, Antonio Macedo

PART 3 Official Strategies: Government Policies and Development Organizations

Colombia: Setting a Precedent for the World 61
Martin von Hildebrand, Head of Indian Affairs, Government of Colombia
Forestry and Non-Wood Products: A Developing Country's Perspective 64
Dr Otto Soemarwoto, University of Padjajaran, Indonesia
The Tropical Forestry Action Plan and Non-Wood Forest Products 70
Michael Flint, Consultant to the Overseas Development Administration, Government of the UK
The Role of the European Commission in the Conservation of the Tropical Forests 83
Catherine Guibourg, DG1 of the Commission of the European Community
Discussion 86
Michael Flint, Catherine Guibourg, Martin von Hildebrand, Dr Otto Soemarwoto, Manuel Paveri-Anziani (FAO), Axel Peuker (World Bank)
Address from the UK Minister for Overseas Development 93
The Rt Hon Lynda Chalker MP
Discussion 101
The Rt Hon Lynda Chalker MP

PART 4 Business Opportunities: Marketing and Development of Rainforest Products

The Practical Realities Affecting the Marketing of Food Products as Part of a Sustainable Strategy for Saving Tropical Rainforests 103
Paul Beresford, The Food Business
First Experiences: Trading in Sustainable Rainforest Timbers 109
Chris Cox, Ecological Trading Company
Sustainable Marketing and Development of Rainforest Products: The Path Taken by The Body Shop 114
Robert Forster, The Body Shop, for Dr Jason Clay, Cultural Survival

PART 5 The Science, Social Organization and Economics of Extractive Production

Conference Chair: ***Dr John Hemmings***

Quantitative Ethnobotany and the Case for Conservation in Amazonia 117
Dr Brian Boom, The New York Botanical Garden

Tropical Forest Products and Extractive Resources in Xishuangbanna, China 130
Xie Jiwu, Kunming Institute of Ecology, China

A Study of the Non-Timber Forest Products of Ghana's Forest Zone 135
Julia Falconer, Overseas Development Administration

Community Versus Company-Based Rattan Industry in Indonesia 142
Yance de Fretes, Yale School of Forestry

Game Harvesting in Tropical Forests 150
Dr Kent Redford, Centre for Latin American Studies, University of Florida

Public Awareness and Extractive Economies 155
Anna Lewington, Consultant to the World Wide Fund for Nature UK

The Economic Importance and Marketing of Forest and Fallow Products in the Iquitos Region, Peru 177
Dr Christine Padoch, The New York Botanical Garden

Discussion 198
Dr Brian Boom, Dr Kent Redford, Yance de Fretes, Xie Jiwu, Julia Falconer

PART 6 Local Economic and Social Organizations: the Impact of Expanding Extra Economies

Indian Reserves: A Feasible Alternative for the Conservation and Proper Use of the Colombian Amazon Forests 202
Thomas Walschburger, Fundacion Puerto Rastojo

Social Movements and Natural Resource Conservation in the Brazilian Amazon 207
Dr Stephen Schwartzman, Environmental Defense Fund

Land-Use Strategies for Successful Extractive Economies 213
Dr Anthony Anderson, The Ford Foundation

Extractive Reserves and the Future of the Amazon's Rainforests: Some Cautionary Observations 224
Dr John Browder, Virginia Polytechnic Institute and State University

Indigenous Peoples and the Marketing of the Rainforest 236
Dr Andrew Gray, International Work Group for Indigenous Affairs

Land Security, Self-Sufficiency and Cultural Integrity in the Philippines *247*
Reverend Delbert Rice, Kalahan Educational Foundation
Building and Supplying Markets For Non-Wood Tropical Forest Products *250*
Dr Jason Clay, Cultural Survival
Discussion *256*
Thomas Walschburger, Dr Andrew Gray, Dr Jason Clay, Dr Stephen Schwartzman, Antonio Macedo, Dr Anthony Anderson

PART 7 Additional Papers Received

Sustainable Strategies for Saving Tropical Forests: The Ghanaian Case *262*
Professor Kwabena Tufuor, Ghana Forestry Commission
The Feasibility of Developing Borneo's Non-Timber Forest Products for the United States Market *267*
Anthony Dixon, Project Borneo

Appendix
The Rainforest Harvest: three briefings prepared for the Conference by Friends of the Earth *272*
- Medicines
- Industrial Products
- Agriculture and Food

Acknowledgements

The Tropical Rainforest Campaign of Friends of the Earth has always considered as part of its role to help promote and encourage the sustainable use of the world's rainforest. The proceedings of this Conference, we hope, will unite environmentalists, government officials and business people in an agenda that is both practical and visionary - a sustainable 'Rainforest Harvest'.

To this end, Friends of the Earth would like to thank the many contributors to the Conference, who stimulated two days of constructive discussion and debate. Special gratitude is extended to the representatives of Southern Non- governmental Organizations (NGOs) and organizations present. Their views, infinitely greater knowledge and wisdom of the rainforests are crucial in the development of sustainable strategies for saving the tropical forests. Their voices should be leading this debate.

A Conference of this scale would not have been possible without the generosity, participation and sponsorship from a large number of individuals and organizations. Friends of the Earth would like to thank, in particular: Dr John Hemming and the Royal Geographical Society for agreeing to host the Conference; Emma O'Bryen, Heather Cannon and all at Media Natura for their organizational skills and expertise; and the main sponsors - the Overseas Development Administration, The Body Shop and The Ford Foundation. Special thanks also to Hugh Prysor-Jones for his expert chairing of the first day of the Conference.

Friends of the Earth would like to acknowledge the invaluable work of all those who contributed to the production of the proceedings, especially to those who gave their time and resources free of charge. Our thanks go to David Edwards, Charlotte Smith, Kathy Daniels, Glyn Walters, Jonathan Selwyn, Illiera Margaritas, David Smith, Sara Tyack, Barbara Spivey, Niall Mitchell, Tony Juniper, Adrian Barnett, Helen Leith, Peter Philip, Aubrey Meyer, Neil Verlander, to the Friends of the Earth publications team Athena Lamnisos, David Caines, Julie Berg, Vicki Hird and Penelope Mawson and to Sue Cunningham for providing many of the photographs used in the publication.

Simon Counsell and Tim Rice, Friends of the Earth

List of Illustrations

Plate 1 Açaí palm fruit *(Euterpe oleracea)* [1]

Plate 2 Kayapo woman preparing açaí[2]

Plate 3 Cupuaçu fruit *(Theobrama grandiflora)* [3]

Plate 4 Guaraná fruit *(Paullinia cupana)* [4]

Plate 5 Aguaje or buriti fruit *(Mauritia flexuosa)* [5]

Plate 6 Rosy periwinkle *(Catharanthus roseus)* [6]

Plate 7 Zambian bee-keepers extracting honey from artificial hives [7]

Plate 8 Rattan in Sumatra, Indonesia [8]

Plate 9 Lauraceae (*Neolitsea* sp.) Potential producer of essential oils for the pharmaceutical industry [9]

Plate 10 Herbal remedies in South American market [10]

Plate 11 A Nepali woman tells a British aid worker about preferred fodder species [11]

Plate 12 The Ecological Trading Company in operation with the Trekkasaw, El Pan Project, Esmeraldas province, Ecuador[12]

Plate 13 'Heart of Palm' *(Euterpe precatoria)* [13]

Plate 14 A maize storage barn. Walls are con structed from split bamboo. The roof is made from leaves of the raphia palm which have been woven into tiles [14]

Plate 15 Tree bark (mahogany) used in medicinal preparations sold at Kumasi's Central Market, Ghana [15]

Plate 16 West African women processing the roots of the forest tree *Parkia bicolor* to make a sponge. The roots are soaked, pounded and teased [16]

Plate 17 Several types of sponge made from the processed fibres of several forest climbers sold at Central Market, Kumasi, Ghana [17]

Plate 18 A plant medicine trader in Central Market, Kumasi, Ghana [18]

Plate 19 Weaving a large cane basket of the climbing palm *Erythmospatha hookeri.* It will be used by fishmongers who trade fish in northern Ghanaian markets. [19]

Plate 20 Don Calazacón - Colorado Indian from lowland Ecuador (with achiote paste on his head) [20]

Plate 21	Caju (cashew) nut *(Anacardium occidentale)* [21]
Plate 22	Achiote or urucu flower *(Bixa orellana)* [22]
Plate 23	Papaya tree *(Carica papaya)* used for treating stomach disorders [23]
Plate 24	Rubber tapper in the Alto Juruá Extractive Reserve, Acre, Brazil, scoring the bark of a rubber tree *(Hevea brasiliensis)* [24]
Plate 25	Pouring the rubber latex over a mould prior to smoking [25]
Plate 26	'Pearl of the Amazon' - the seed of *Hevea brasiliensis,* the rubber tree [26]
Plate 27	Brazil nut tree *(Bertholletia excelsa)* [27]
Plate 28	Brazil nut oil extraction equipment in situ (Kayapo village) [28]
Plate 29	Fruit of the Peach palm *(Bactris gasipaes)* [29]
Plate 30	Jatoba seed and seedling (*Hymenaea* spp). Some species of this genus are known to produce a viscous resin which is used to produce varnishes, paints and lacquers. [30]

Photo credits

1. Simon Counsell
2. Sue Cunningham
3. Sue Cunningham
4. Sue Cunningham
5. Sue Cunningham
6. Sue Cunningham
7. David Wainwright
8. M Rautkari/WWF
9. N Tamin
10. Sue Cunningham
11. ODA
12. C Cox
13. Sue Cunningham
14. Julia Falconer
15. Julia Falconer
16. Julia Falconer
17. Julia Falconer
18. Julia Falconer
19. Julia Falconer
20. Edward Parker
21. Sue Cunningham
22. Sue Cunningham
23. Sue Cunningham
24. Edward Parker
25. Edward Parker
26. Sue Cunningham
27. Sue Cunningham
28. Sue Cunningham
29. Sue Cunningham
30. Sue Cunningham

Acronyms

ACP - Africa, Caribbean and Pacific (states)
ASEAN - Association of South-east Asian Nations
AWARE - Association of Wood Users Against Rainforest Exploitation
CAP - Common Agricultural Policy
CEC - Commission of the European Community
CEDI - Centro Ecumênico de Documentação e Informação (Ecumenical Centre of Documentation and Information)
CEPASP - Centre for Research and Union and Popular Support
CFC - Chlorofluorocarbons
CIDA - Canadian International Development Agency
CITES - Convention on International Trade in Endangered Species
CNS - Conselho Nacional Dos Seringueiros (National Council of Rubber Tappers)
COICA - Co-ordinadora de las Organizaciones Indígenas de la Cuenca Amazónica (Co-ordinating Body for the Indigenous Peoples' Organizations in the Amazon Basin)
DBH - Diameter at Breast Height
ECU - European Currency Unit
EEC - European Economic Community
ETC - Ecological Trading Company
FAO - Food and Agriculture Organization of the United Nations
FBPR - Fundacion de Biologia Puerto Rastrojo
FoE - Friends of the Earth
FRIM - Forestry Research Institute of Malaysia
FRMP - Forest Resource Management Project of Ghana
FUNAI - Fundação Nacional do Indio (National Indian Foundation of Brazil)
GTZ - Deutsche Gesellschaft für Technische Zusammenarbeit
IBAMA - Instituto Brasileiro de Meio Ambiente (Brazilian Environmental Institute)
IBGE - Fundação Instituto Brasileiro de Geógrafia e Estatística
IBPGR - International Board for Plant Genetic Resources
IDB - Inter-American Development Bank
IEA - Instituto de Estudos Amazônicos (Institute of Amazon Studies)
IIED - International Institute for Environment and Development
INCRA - National Institute for Colonization and Agrarian Reform
IRRDB - International Rubber Research and Development Board
ITTA - International Tropical Timber Agreement
ITTC - International Tropical Timber Council
ITTO - International Tropical Timber Organization
IUCN - International Union for the Conservation of Nature and Natural Resources
MAB - Man and Biosphere Programme
MIRAD - Brazilian Ministry of Agrarian Reform and Development
NDI - Núcleo de Direito Indígena (Nucleus for Indigenous Rights)
NFAP - National Forestry Action Plan
NGO - Non-governmental Organization
NTFP - Non-timber forest products
NWBP - Northwestern Bee Products
NWFP - Non-wood forest products
ODA - Overseas Development Administration
ODI - Overseas Development Institute

Acronyms cont.

ODNRI - Overseas Development Natural Resources Institute

OFI - Oxford Forestry Institute

PAE - Projeto de Assentamento Estrativista (Extractive Settlement Project)

PNG - Papua New Guinea

PSP - Permanent Sample Plot

RGS - The Royal Geographical Society

STR - Sindicato Dos Trabalhadores Rurais (Union of Rural Workers)

TFAP - Tropical Forestry Action Plan

TFP - Tropical Forest Products

TST - Temporary Sample Plot

TTF - The UK Timber Trade Federation

UK - United Kingdom

UN - United Nations

UNDP - United Nations Development Programme

UNEP - United Nations Environment Programme

UNI - União Das Nações Indígenas (Union of Indigenous Nations)

USA - United States of America

WRI - World Resouces Institute

WRM - World Rainforest Movement

WWF - World Wide Fund for Nature

A Note on Vocabulary

A billion is one thousand million.

Unless otherwise stated, all dollars are US denominations.

Biographical Details of Speakers*

Dr Anthony Anderson
Programme Officer
The Ford Foundation

Currently Programme Officer at The Ford Foundation, having been a forest ecologist in the Amazon for 15 years. Since 1980 his interests have focused on the use and management of extractive forest products by forest inhabitants.

Paul Beresford
Managing Director
The Food Business

Paul Beresford has more than 20 years experience in the UK food industry which began with seven years retail operations and buying with J Sainsbury. He then moved into Marketing Management with Nestle followed by an extensive period with the Nabisco Group managing a wide range of brands.

The Food Business is a specialist consultancy working with established companies at every level of the UK food and drink industry in the creation and evolution of new products and new business development.

Dr Brian Boom
Assistant Curator
The New York Botanical Garden

Previously Research Associate, Institute of Economic Botany, The New York Botanical Garden; currently Visiting Senior Researcher, Depto de Ecologia, Instituto Nacional de Pesquisas da Amazonia, Manaus, Brazil; Commission Member, Organization for Flora Neotropica; Council Member, Torrey Botanical Club, Professional Society Ethics Group, AAAS, representing the Botanical Society of America; Visiting Lecturer in Tropical Studies, School of Forestry and Environmental Studies, Yale University; Adjunct Assistant Professor, Department of Biology, Lehman College, City University of New York. He has received various grants, fellowships and awards from, amongst others, the National Science Foundation and is author of a number of publications covering Amazonian plants.

Dr John Browder
Assistant Professor
Urban Affairs and Planning
Virginia Polytechnic Institute and State University

Prior to this appointment, Dr John Browder has had academic appointments at the Universities of Michigan, Pennsylvania and Tulane in Brazil. He is currently Chairman, Task Force on Natural Resources and the Environment, Latin American Studies Association and is the author of a number of publications on Latin America and the rainforest.

The Rt Hon Lynda Chalker MP
The UK Minister for Overseas Development

Previously a statistician, Lynda Chalker became a Member of Parliament for Wallasey in February 1974. She has served on the committees of many voluntary bodies particularly in the field of social services and foreign affairs. In May 1979, she became Parliamentary Under-Secretary of State for Social Security and in

March 1982 was appointed Parliamentary Under-Secretary at the Department of Transport, and then Minister of State in October 1983.

Mrs Chalker was appointed Minister of State at the Foreign and Commonwealth Office in January 1986 and in June 1987 was made a Privy Counsellor. Her responsibilities included western and southern Europe, the European Community, International Trade and Economic Relations, sub-Saharan Africa and Commonwealth affairs. She became Minister for Overseas Development in July 1989.

Dr Jason Clay
Anthropologist
Director of Research at Cultural Survival

Educated at Harvard University and the London School of Economics as well as Cornell University, he has conducted research in Brazil, Djibouti, Mexico, Ruanda, Somalia, Sudan and Uganda. Most recently Dr Clay has developed a project to expand the market for sustainably produced rainforest products - a project which aims to demonstrate that a healthy rainforest can generate more income and employment than a razed one.

Chris Cox
Director
Ecological Trading Company

Founder and Secretary of AWARE - Association of Woodusers Against Rainforest Exploitation - since 1987, Chris Cox has been a full time joiner and cabinet maker for the last ten years.

The lack of clear information about the availability of tropical timber from sustainable sources led him and Hubert Kwisthout to form the Ecological Trading Company in March 1989 and the first load of timber from a co-operative in Peru has now arrived in the UK and is being kilned and will be ready for sale shortly.

Yance de Fretes
Yale University
School of Forestry and Environmental Studies

Actively involved in different kinds of environmental activities which have been organized by both Indonesian institutes and NGOs. His professional experience includes the preparation and implementation of management plans for nature reserves in Irian Jaya and community organizer in the social forestry programme there. He has produced a number of reports on forestry, farming and land tenure as well as nature conservation.

Mario Cordeiro de Lima
Local Co-ordinator of the Union of Indigenous Nations and leader of the Poyanawa Community in Brazil

Since 1983 he has been leader of the Poyanawa community of the Barao Indian Reservation. Has served as an officer of the local Rural Workers' Union since 1975.

Dr José Lutzenberger
Special Secretary for the Environment, Government of Brazil

Attended the Universities of Porto Alegre and Louisiana State in the United States between 1947 and 1953. Prior to his activities as an environmentalist, Dr Lutzenberger worked for two fertilizer companies - CRA and BASF.

In 1987, he founded Fundacao Gaia and received

the Right Livelihood Award in the following year. In March 1990, he joined President Collor's government as Special Secretary for the Environment.

Antonio Luiz Batista de Macedo
Forest People's Alliance, Co-ordinator of the National Rubber Tapper's Council and Advisor to the Union of Indigenous Nations in Brazil
Born the son of a rubber tapper and brought up with Kaxinawa Indians of the area, Antonio Luiz Batista de Macedo was in a variety of professions, including rubber tapping, before eventually founding the Acre Pro Indian Commission of which he remains a leading member. He set up 35 co-operatives, 31 schools and 13 health centres in Indian areas, initiated the legalization of 45 indigenous areas and set up the rubber tapping co-operatives as well as organizing several forest people's meetings. In 1986 he agreed to join FUNAI, heading the agency's department of community development and directing operations for the Jurua Valley before accepting an invitation from Chico Mendes to move to the National Rubber-tappers' Council, which he has coordinated in the area since 1988.

Julia Falconer
Technical Co-operation Officer
ODA Forest Management Project Ghana
Has a masters in Forestry Sciences from Yale University. In 1986 she was a senior scientist at the International Institute for Environment and Development in Washington building a database for Botswana and the Philippines. In 1987 she became a research assistant at the Overseas Development Institute working on the Social Forestry Network, then she moved to the Oxford Forestry Institute, where she produced reports for the FAO on Forestry and Food Security. Subsequently she became consultant, Community Forestry Unit, Forestry Department, FAO Rome, Italy, where her research included work on non-timber products in the West African humid zone before moving to her present position.

Michael Flint
Economist and Independent Consultant
Micheal Flint is a natural resources socio-economist, now working as an independent consultant. He has spent four years in Botswana working on a farming systems project and has since undertaken a number of short-term assignments in Asia and Africa for the ODA and other organizations. Recent work includes research into common property issues and biodiversity and he is involved in preparing a forestry project in Tanzania as a follow up to the National Forestry Action Plan.

Dr Andrew Gray
International Work Group for Indigenous Affairs
Formerly Director of The International Work Group on Indigenous Affairs, Dr Gray has carried out extensive research in Peruvian Amazonia on social organization, cosmology and the impact of development.

Katherine Guibourg
DGI (External Affairs)
Environmental Unit
Commission of the European Communities

Dr John Hemming
Director and Secretary
The Royal Geographical Society

Dr John Hemming has been Director and Secretary of The Royal Geographical Society since 1975. He was leader of the Maracá Rainforest Project in northern Brazil, 1987-88, which was probably the largest research effort mounted by the UK in Amazonia. He has participated in many previous expeditions to rainforest regions in Amazonia and South-east Asia and is the author of several books on the treatment of Brazilian Indians and the history of Amazonia, including *Red Gold, Amazon Frontier* and as Editor, *Change in the Amazon Basin.*

Martin von Hildebrand
Head of Indian Affairs
Colombian Government
Executive Secretary of the Special Commission for Indian Affairs of the Amazonian Pact

Since 1972 Martin von Hildebrand has been directly associated with the Indian communities of the Colombian Amazon. Over the years he has conducted anthropological research and collaborated with the Indians in their search for autonomy. He has been instrumental in the demarcation of 18 million hectares of Indian Amazonian territory as Indian collective property, several laws in favour of Indian rights and government Indian policies over the last eight years.

Since 1987 he has been head of Indian affairs for the Colombian government. He is the Executive Secretary of the Special Commission for Indian affairs of the Amazonian pact and the personal adviser to President Barco on Indian matters and Amazonian management.

He obtained his doctorate at the Sorbonne, Paris and has published chiefly on Indian cosmology and their use of the rainforest.

Anna Lewington
Ethnobotanist and Writer

After studying Amerindian languages, Anna Lewington began ethnobotanical research amongst Machiguenga Indians of the Peruvian Amazon in 1981, investigating the importance of manioc *(Manihot esculenta)* in their society. She administered the Cusichaca Project in the Peruvian Andes in 1985 and conducted an ethnobotanical survey of medicinal plants for the Rio Mazan Expedition in southern Ecuador in 1986. She is author of *Plants for People* written for the Royal Botanic Gardens, Kew, and is Consultant to WWF on Latin America with a particular interest in Amerindian affairs.

Bob Malichi
Assistant Manager
Northwestern Bee Products Zambia

Bee-keeping is a traditional activity in his home area in Chizela, Northwest Province, Zambia. He worked as a mechanic on the Copperbelt before returning to Northwest Province where he is now responsible for buying honey and wax and liaising with the bee keepers. Northwestern Bee Products was formed by the traditional bee-keepers, together with their district council, in order to market their honey and wax throughout Zambia and abroad.

Professor Norman Myers
Consultant in Environment and Development
Professor Norman Myers has been a consultant for over 20 years with emphasis on species, gene reservoirs and tropical forests. As well as publishing over 200 papers in the professional literature and several hundred articles in magazines and newspapers, Professor Myers has written several notable books including *The Sinking Ark, A Wealth of Wild Species, The Primary Source* and *Conversion of Tropical Moist Forests* and was Editor of the *The Gaia Atlas of Planet Management.* He has received several awards for his environmental work.

Dr Christine Padoch
The New York Botanical Garden
Christine Padoch is an ecological anthropologist and Associate Scientist at the Institute of Economic Botany of The New York Botanical Garden. She has done field research on many aspects of traditional resource management in the tropical forests of Amazonia and South-east Asia. Studies of local marketing patterns have been an important part of that research.

Professor Ghillean Prance
Director
Royal Botanic Gardens, Kew
Spent 25 years working at The New York Botanical Garden where he became Senior Vice-President for Science and Director of the Institute of Economic Botany. He was the founder Director (1973-75) of graduate studies at the Instituto Nacional de Pesquisas da Amazonia in Manaus, Brazil, and is a foreign member of the Academy of Sciences of Brazil, Denmark and Sweden. His honours include the Distinguished Service Award of The New York Botanical Garden (1986), the Henry Shaw Medal of Missouri Botanical Garden (1988) and the Diploma Honra ao Merito of the Instituto Nacional Pesquisas da Amazonia (1978). Professor Prance has published over 200 papers and 9 books on Amazonian plants. He is deeply involved in the issues of conservation and sustainable development of tropical forests.

Dr Kent Redford
Director Programme for Studies in Tropical Conservation, Centre for Latin American Studies, Florida
After receiving a PhD from Harvard University and completing a post-doctorate at the University of Florida, Dr Redford has worked for the Programme for Studies in Tropical Conservation dedicated to training and research in wildlife conservation in tropical countries. He has also recently concentrated on subsistence and commercial uses of wildlife in Latin America.

Reverend Delbert Rice
Received a Bachelors degree in electrical engineering from Oregon State University. After obtaining a Master's in Divinity from the Western Evangelical Seminary, he and his wife came to the Philippines in 1958 where they have resided ever since. In 1972, Reverend Rice received a Masters degree in Anthropology from Silliman University in the Philippines.

In 1965 the Rices began working with the Ikalahan people, a tribal group in northern Luzon. Reverend

Rice helped establish a school for the Ikalahan people and serves as the Executive Officer of the Kalahan Educational Foundation. Realizing that the tribe had no legally recognized right to the land they had inhabited for centuries, in 1974 Rice assisted them in obtaining from the government a Communal Lease Agreement to their 14,000 hectare area. Subsequently he assisted them in conserving and developing the area. Rice helped other tribal groups obtain land rights through his work with the Philippine Association for Inter-Cultural Development, a non-governmental organization for which he serves as Executive Director. He has published many articles based on his work with the tribal people of the Philippines.

Dr Stephan Schwartzman
Environmental Defense Fund
Washington
He has a PhD in Anthropology, from the University of Chicago. He has organised field research in the Xingu Indigenous Park, Mato Grosso and Xapuri and Rio Branco, Acre, Brazil.

Dr Otto Soemarwoto
Head of the Research Institute for Ecology
Padjajaran University
Bandung Indonesia
Dr Soemarwoto was first appointed as Professor to Padjajaran University in 1972 and is presently serving as the Institute's Director. Previously he was Professor at Gajah Mada University in Indonesia, served as Director of the National Biology Institute in Bogor, Indonesia between 1964-72 and obtained a post-graduate degree from the University of California. In 1980, he was Visiting Professor at the same institution. His current specialist subjects are ecology and environmentally sustainable economic development.

Dr Noraini Tamin
Biology Department
Universiti Kebangsaan Malaysia
Dr Tamin received a BSc and a PhD from the University of Malaya specializing in plant ecology. She has been employed at the Universiti Kebangsaan Malaysia (UKM) since 1977, initially as a lecturer in the botany department and subsequently appointed head of the biology department from 1979-81. She was later promoted Associate Professor in 1984. She was appointed Visiting Fellow Wolfson College, Oxford in 1989 and is currently attached to the Oxford Forestry Institute as Malaysian co-ordinator of the British Council CICHE programme between UKM and Oxford University, involving forest research.

She has participated in many local and international seminars, symposia and congresses and is the author of several scientific papers on plant and forest ecology.

Thomas Johannes Walschburger Bergdoff
Director
Foundation Estacion de Biologia Puerto Rastrojo, Colombia
He has worked on numerous projects investigating Amazonian rainforest management and utilization, and has produced many reports and publications as a result of this work. He is presently working on a conservation and management strategy for the lower Caqueta region, Amazonas, Colombia.

Xie Jiwu
Tropical Plant Ecologist
Kunming Institute of Ecology
Has been involved in natural conservation work in Xishuangbanna, China, and research into tropical forests including planting of economic crops, agri-system engineering, artificial ecosystems in the tropics and a study on the structure and functions of the rubber-tea community for a UNESCO project. He also took part in an international symposium on Man-made Community in the Tropics and Rational Development of tropical and sub-tropical Lands.

The following Conference participants were sponsored by the Overseas Development Administration:

Brazil: Jose Carlos Carvalho, President, IBAMA. Indonesia: Mr Lakito Daryadi, Assistant to the Minister of Forests Ir Djamaludin, Director, Directorate of Utilization, Ministry of Forests; Dr Otto Soemarwoto, Director, Institute of Ecology, University of Padjarjan, Bandung. India: Shyam Sunder, Former Head of Karnataka Forest Department. Nigeria: Dr Jonathan Okafor, formerly Forestry Research Institute, Nigeria. (He has conducted 15 years research on tree breeding of indigenous tropical fruit trees used in Nigeria). Cameroon: Mr Mbenkum Fonki Tobias, joint author of the ODA funded study entitled Medical and Food Plants from Cameroon forests. Ghana: Julia Falconer, ODA Ghana specialist: Mr Jean Francois, Head of Ghana's Forestry Service.

* Editors' note: These details were accurate at the time of the Conference

Preface

The Rainforest Harvest

Sustainable Strategies for Saving the Tropical Forest?

Tropical rainforests are, almost exclusively, located in developing countries. They are under pressure from the expansion of agriculture, colonization, commercial logging, the activities of companies engaged in mining and exploration for fossil fuels, and development projects such as dams and roads.

Some countries, such as Costa Rica, have established extensive areas of totally protected forest as National Parks or wildlife reserves. However, whilst these nations continue to suffer enormous economic difficulties, protected areas often remain a luxury which they largely cannot afford. In many cases, the forests will only survive if they can be made to pay their way through the generation of economic wealth and employment for expanding populations.

Logging

The most obvious way to exploit the rainforest is for timber. The international trade in tropical hardwoods such as mahogany, meranti, iroko and sapele is worth about $8 billion annually. The timber is used in developed countries such as Britain for construction, furniture, window frames, replacement doors, kitchen utensils, musical instruments, coffins, and many other products. However, most of the tropical forests providing us with the raw material for these goods are being badly damaged by logging, and are not managed sustainably or with care for the ecosystem. Even in the few cases where logging is claimed to be conducted on a 'sustainable' basis, it may still involve massive modification of the ecosystem and the depletion of other, non-timber, resources.

Learning from Tribal People

Some tribal groups may have been living in the rainforests for thousands of years, and have learned to extract from their environment all the necessities of life without destroying the forest (see papers by Hildebrand and Rice, this volume). Most have developed complicated systems of beliefs and rituals which ensure that no more is taken from the forest than it can replace. They have an unparalleled knowledge of the forests' plants, animals and insects (see Hildebrand and Malichi). For example, Indian communities in the Amazon use up to three-quarters of the forests' different tree species for various purposes (see Boom). Ethnobotanists are beginning to understand how tribal communities use the forests' resources, but the tribes are often under threat from the degradation or destruction of their traditional territories.

The Genetic Treasure Chest

Tropical rainforests can be thought of as vast natural laboratories. Millions of years of gradual biological development in a hot and humid environment has given rise to an extraordinary diversity of species. The rainforests are estimated to contain at least one-half of all the wild species on the planet, including many which are potentially of enormous benefit to humanity. Indeed, many rainforest species are already widely utilized in industry, agriculture and medicine (see Myers).

Non-Timber resources

Trade in non-timber products (also known inappropriately as 'secondary' or 'minor' forest products) such as rattan, fruit, nuts, rubber, oils, foods, natural medicines and other plant extracts already thrives (see Tamin and Padoch). Tribal and other rural communities may rely heavily on such products for their subsistence and for income (see Boom and Falconer). Often, these products can be and are extracted without causing damage to the natural forest. Some, such as Brazil nuts, will not grow in intensive plantations and can only be collected from the wild. The plants from which they come rely on complex ecological relationships involving other wild species in order to flourish.

Economic development and conservation

Governments, scientists and environmentalists now generally regard 'extractive management' of tropical forests as a realistic and economically feasible alternative to conventional logging and clearance (see Walshburger, Schwartzman, Macedo, Browder and Anderson). Forest managed by local communities for non-wood products has the potential to allow for a sustainable economic use which leaves the ecosystems intact and maintains high levels of biological diversity.

A 1988 study by the New York Institute of Economic Botany suggested that the fruits, nuts, rubber, and other non-timber products in one hectare of Peruvian rainforest could provide six times more revenue than if the hectare were used solely in its timber producing capacity. The value of the extractable products was shown to be many times greater than the value to be gained by clearing the forest to create pasture for cattle.

Non-timber forest products have played an important role in Third World economies, and already provide a vital source of revenue and employment for many nations (see de Fretes). In India, in the early 1970s, 346 million person-days were spent in the non-timber forest product industry compared to 135 million for timber. In Ghana, the value of non-timber forest product exports is roughly equivalent to exports of timber. In 1982 $120 million worth of non-timber forest products were exported by Indonesia. The State of Sarawak, in Malaysia, exports more than $15 million worth of these goods every year. In Brazil, thousands of people earn a living by tapping naturally occurring rubber trees for their latex. These people have been in the forefront of efforts to counter the destruction of parts of Amazonia (see Macedo and de Lima).

Hidden resources

Scientists are only now beginning to understand the full richness of the rainforests ecosystem. Studies conducted in the rainforests of Central America suggest that the number of species to be found in the world's tropical forests may be many millions more than had been previously thought. New discoveries are constantly being made.

Many rainforest species thus remain to be identified, and only a small fraction have been assessed for their usefulness. The potential for uncovering valuable new products is immense. But as many as 50 species are becoming extinct each day as a result of tropical deforestation (see Myers).

In order to realize the full benefits of the rainforests' resources, Friends of the Earth will continue to stress the need to slow, halt and ultimately reverse deforestation. One strategy that may achieve this is to make greater use of non-destructively extracted non-timber forest products. There is an urgent need for an exploration of the practical ways in which business, governments, aid agencies and forest peoples can profit from and encourage sustainable rainforest conservation. Whilst many questions remain unanswered concerning, for example, the patenting of plant materials and the exposure of indigenous peoples to outside market forces (see Prance, Gray), Friends of the Earth hopes that the gathering of representatives from all these groups at the Rainforest Harvest Conference (and the publication of the proceedings) will go some way to achieving this aim.

The views expressed in this volume are those of the authors and are not necessarily endorsed by Friends of the Earth.

Simon Counsell and Tim Rice
Tropical Rainforest Campaign
Friends of the Earth
February, 1992

Rainforest Harvest: An Overview

Professor Ghillean Prance
Director, Royal Botanic Gardens, Kew, United Kingdom

Summary

This paper provides an overview of the many issues that will be discussed during the Conference. The challenge is to halt rainforest destruction and replace it with a management system that is sustainable in the long-term. Current literature is reviewed showing the extent to which forest Indians and non-indigenous populations in South America extract products sustainably. However, whilst research is conducted on rainforest products that could be marketed in the developed world, other local issues must also be taken into consideration; the social and environmental consequences of increased prosperity; the reliability of product supply; the effects of harvesting on the forests and local communities; and adequate recompense to the country of origin of plant materials.

Introduction

We are at this Conference because of a crisis in the rainforest areas of the world. With half the area that was originally covered by this luxuriant and species-diverse type of vegetation destroyed, at last the world is becoming aware that we might lose all the rainforest if we do not rapidly halt this destruction.

Unfortunately, this loss of forest has been generally of little permanent benefit to the rainforest countries. It has been for non-sustainable, short-term use that is often encouraged by the false economy of tax incentives or land speculation as, for example, in the large areas of cattle pasture that replace rainforest in the Amazon region. There are even ranches that have never sold a single cow.

The first owner of the Jari forestry project in Pará, Brazil, lost over 600 million dollars in his attempt to grow timber for paper pulp in the Amazon region. The internationally financed Balbina hydroelectric dam flooded a vast area of uncleared forest in the territory of the Waimiri-Atroari Indians and has been declared an ecological disaster. The indigenous populations of the rainforest have suffered terribly as the greed and thirst for gold has led to vast invasions of their territory by miners carrying a host of diseases that have greatly reduced their populations.

Many of the most useful rainforest products, such as some of the best timbers like mahogany, the latex that is used in chewing gum, and the Amazon rosewood whose oil is used in perfumes and cosmetics, have been mined out of the forest rather than treated as sustainable and manageable resources. Distilleries for rosewood oil *(Aniba rosaeodora)* are set up in the forest and every tree for miles around is cut and chipped to extract the essential oil linalol. However, this same product occurs in the common shrub of secondary forests, *Croton cajucara,* which could easily be managed in a sustainable fashion.

The challenge before us today is to halt unnecessary and unproductive destruction and replace it with a management system of the forest that is sustainable in the long-term. There are many ways towards sustainable use of the rainforest and this Conference is concerned with two of them: the direct harvest of timber and non-timber products from the forest without destruction of the ecosystem and the delicate balance of nutrient cycles.

Mining or Managing Rainforest

Most of the timber extraction from tropical rainforests is carried out in a non-sustainable way. An example is found in the *Virola* or ucuuba trees of the Amazon basin that are being eliminated by the demand for this wood for plywood and veneers. Sawmills are already having to switch to alternative woods because the supplies of *Virola* are running out. However, this is a fast-growing tree of the inundated riverside forests that could easily be managed, rather than mined. Species of *Virola* have been used for centuries by the Indians of the region without causing a reduction of the tree population. The Yanomami Indians of Brazil use *Virola theiodora* bark resin as the principal ingredient of their narcotic snuff that produces a chemical compound which is being investigated for the treatment of certain mental disorders. The Chácobo Indians of Bolivia use the resin of *Virola elongata* for the treatment of skin fungus. Western man eliminates the species from the forest because of his excess demand for timber products.

The paper by Brian Boom, in this volume, shows the extent to which forest Indians use the trees. In the case of the Chácobo of Bolivia, 82 per cent of the species and 95 per cent of the individual trees on a single hectare of forest are used by the Indians. Other studies of quantitative ethnobotany, such as those of William Balée with the Arawete and Tembé Indians of Brazil, have shown a similar dependence upon the forest (Balée, 1987; Prance *et al.*, 1987). A people that use so many of the trees for such a variety of purposes - edible fruits, building materials, craft fibres, medicines, etc - would hardly want to destroy all the forest upon which they depend. This gives us a hint for the future pathway; the use of many products from the forest without destroying any of the species that produce them.

The non-indigenous *campesino* or *caboclo* population of the rainforest also have much to teach us and have often been neglected by students of the rainforests. Anthony Anderson has carried out a most useful study of the sustainable extraction of the açaí palm (*Euterpe oleracea,* Plate 1) by the settlers of the Amazon estuary (Anderson, this volume). This palm is particularly suitable for the extraction of heart-of-palm because it is abundant in the flood plain forest and because it is a multi-stemmed palm that re-sprouts when cut. This is so different from the loss of many single-stemmed palms of the rainforests of Madagascar to provide palm hearts to France. The system of sustainable extraction of products studied by Anderson yields a remarkably good income to these farmers (over $10,000 a year).

A social problem that we must address at this Conference and in the future is; what happens when these peasant farmers prosper from their agroforestry systems? Will the next generation remain on the land to continue the good work? Will their newly found prosperity lead to more destructive methods? If we do not face up to this problem early in our search for sustainable systems of harvest, our work may be in vain.

During the Conference, we will discuss frequently the Amazon rubber tappers and Brazil nut gatherers who eke out a meagre existence from their sustainable harvesting of two products from the forest. Their life is humble and simple because they are still slaves of a system that takes their products from them through a long chain of middlemen, before they are sold in the markets of North America and Europe. The work that Jason Clay and Cultural Survival are doing to shorten the chain of middlemen is the crucial part of the creation of a sustainable harvest. This must, however, be balanced against the interesting paper by Christine Padoch about the market of Iquitos, Peru. She shows the large number of traders who are sustained by the elaborate market system and that the majority of them work extremely hard and competitively for their modest subsistence.

One of the main themes of this Conference will be the search for new rainforest products that can be marketed in the developed world. We will hear about timber products from the Ecological Trading Company, cosmetics from The Body Shop and food from The Food Business. The participation here of these companies that are willing to produce rainforest products is encouraging. We will also learn about some of the potential products such as cupuaçu pulp (*Theobroma grandiflora,* Plate 3) that furnishes the delicious ice-cream that will be served at the Conference lunch. Two other Amazon products of unrealized potential are oil of copaiba (*Copaifera* spp.) for cosmetic and medicinal development and the tasty fruit of the cocona *(Solanum sessiliflorum)* from the Peruvian Amazon. The vitamin-rich juice of this fast growing fruit is already canned and exported in a small way.

As we develop a market for products, the problem we shall face is the reliable supply of raw material for our ice-cream, beverages or cosmetics. Attempts to introduce to the developed world market the delicious, caffein-rich beverage guaraná (from *Paullinia cupana* var *sorbilis*, Plate 4) have already failed several times because, once a company became interested, the demand for powdered extract far exceeded the total production of Brazil! I recently interested a firm in using the seeds of cupuaçu that remain as waste after the pulp is extracted for ice-cream. The problem is that they are now asking me where they can obtain 60 tonnes of seeds! I hope that this Conference and our subsequent actions will take this problem of supply into account. Products that require small quantities of raw material will be the most successful, especially fragrances and flavours.

As we search for products to market, we must also encourage research on methods of harvesting and the effects of harvesting on the local forests and local communities. Some products that are potentially sustainable are often harvested in a non-sustainable fashion. For example, sorva latex *(Couma utilis),* which is used in chewing gum and exported from Manaus and Brazil in large quantities, is seldom tapped from the trees. Methods have now been developed to tap sorva trees and thus to encourage the use of this latex and so one must be sure that the product originates from tapped, rather than felled trees.

A further problem for us to address is one of the results of success with marketing. If a product becomes popular and the demand increases we are probably producing a future plantation crop, rather than a rainforest product. This is not necessarily a bad thing because some of these future crops may be the appropriate one for the restoration of areas of forest which have already been destroyed. The search for future agroforestry crops is another part of the overall conservation programme for tropical rainforests.

The topic of medical plants is not being discussed in great detail at this Conference, which is perhaps wise since they present their own particular problems and because not many medicinals are actually harvested in a sustainable fashion from the rainforest. The trees of *Pilocarpus* on the fringes of Amazonia are being destroyed through over-harvesting their leaves for pilocarpine to treat glaucoma. Many medicines from tropical plants have been developed by large pharmaceutical companies without any recompense to the country of origin of the plant material. Medicines are even sold back to the tropical countries at highly inflated prices.

If we discuss medicinal plants, it should be in the context of recompense to the countries of origin. The Royal Botanic Gardens, Kew, will not make a deal to work on medicinal plants without an agreement that includes royalties for the countries of origin. We hope that this will become the normal way of operation rather than the exception.

An important strategy for the development of new tropical rainforest products is the search for products that come from plants that are particularly abundant in the forests. We tend to emphasize the diversity of tropical rainforests. However, some species occur in natural clusters in special habitats within the rainforest. These so-called oligarchic forests, dominated by one or two tree species, occupy tens of millions of hectares in Amazonia, (Peters *et al.,* 1989). An example is the area in eastern Amazonia dominated by açaí palm, discussed by Anthony Anderson. Another good example is the rivers and lakeside clusters of camu-camu *(Myrciaria dubia)*, a fruit that contains 30 times more vitamin C than citrus, and that now has a substantial market in Iquitos, Peru. Throughout Amazonia, from Maranhão, Brazil to Loreto, Peru, there are large swamps dominated by the buriti or aguaje palm (*Mauritia flexuosa*, Plate 5) that has multiple uses (Padoch, 1988). This palm is also an example of the need for a change in harvesting methods. In Amazonian Peru, the trees are often felled to collect the fruits, leaving only the fruitless male trees standing in the forest.

Finally, I am glad that animals have not been forgotten in this Conference and that they will be discussed by Kent Redford. Animals are part of the rainforest harvest but present special problems, as we shall see from Dr Redford. Much of the deforestation of Amazonia has taken place to create pasture for an African savanna animal, the cow. Wild animals will probably only sustain light harvesting and the real challenge, at least for the Amazon rainforest region, is the domestication of other native animals that are ecologically more appropriate for the area than the cow. Those with the most potential include iguanas, capybara (Ojasti, 1973) and river turtles, all of which have already been experimentally raised in captivity successfully and all of which produce sufficient offspring to merit consideration. I am also pleased to see that we have a paper in this Conference on the production of honey in Zambia. The Amazonian Indians use and manage many native species of bees, and honey is certainly another sustainably harvestable rainforest product.

This Conference brings together a unique group of people of diverse interests that have never before gathered in this combination. It offers us the opportunity to advance the concept of sustainable management and harvesting from some of the rainforests of the world. Where the forests are used, they must be for the benefit of the local population and not to give extra tax breaks to the rich.

References

Balée, W (1987). A etnobotánica quantitativa dos índios Tembé (Rio Gurupi, Pará). *Bol. Mus. Par. Emílio Goeldi Sér. Bot.* 3 (1): 29-50

Ojasti, J (1973). *Estudio Biológico del Chiguire o Capibara.* Fona IAP, Venezuela, pp 265

Padoch, C (1988). Aguaje *(Mauritia flexuosa* Lf) in the economy of Iquitos, Peru. *Advances in Economic Botany* 6: 214-224

Peters, C M, M J Balich, F Kahn and A B Anderson (1989). Oligarchic forests of economic plants in Amazonia: utilization and conservation of an important tropical resource. *Conservation Biology* 3: 341-361

Prance, G T, W Balée, B M Boom and R L Carneiro (1987). Quantitative ethnobotany and the case for conservation in Amazonia. *Conservation Biology* 1: 296-310

Genetic Materials and the Climate Connection

Professor Norman Myers
Environment and Development Consultant, Upper Meadow, Old Road, Headington, Oxford OX3 8SZ United Kingdom

Summary

Tropical forests, with their 30 million species, support our daily welfare through their many contributions to modern health, agriculture and industry. In just the health sector alone, the cross-counter value of plant-derived products amounts to at least $20 billion a year world-wide. Yet we enjoy these contributions after scientists have taken an intensive look at only one species in 100 to assess their potential. We can surely expect cornucopias, pharmacopoeias and super-stocks of raw materials if scientists can get to the species before their habitats disappear. Regrettably a new threat, one of the biggest to overtake tropical forest species, could well lie with impending climate change.

This is a brief review of what we owe to genetic resources from tropical forest species. It links up with the climatic dislocations that are going to affect the survival prospect for tropical forests.

During the course of each day, we are surely losing between 50 and 100 species in tropical forests. Plants, as Professor Prance has described, will be widely affected. But more importantly, it is the loss of invertebrates, especially insects, that will be particularly severe. Of a minimum 50 species lost today, perhaps 45 will be insects.

Some people might wonder whether the loss of so many insects truly matters. Consider the following example. In Peninsular Malaysia, there are very extensive oil palm plantations. Until 1980 or so, pollination of these plantations was undertaken by human hand - a singularly inefficient and expensive process. The plantation owners asked themselves how the oil palm tree gets itself pollinated back in its native habitat in the rainforests of West Africa. So they went to Cameroon to investigate and they found the pollination job done by a tiny beetle; a weevil half the size of one's little fingernail. They took some weevils back to Peninsular Malaysia, made checks to ensure that there would not be any ecological backlash in the palm plantations, whereupon they released the weevil. The creature pollinated the oil palm trees successfully. The savings from the weevils' contribution each year are in the order of $125 million. Let us consider this fact next time we consume margarine, cosmetics or other products which may have a palm-oil ingredient. This is what is at stake when we lose some 45 insects every day.

So much for the bad news. The better news is that we are now becoming aware, thanks to occasions such as this splendid Conference organized by Friends of the Earth. We are at last witnessing a sunburst of interest and enthusiasm and awareness from people right around the world, from the top-most political level down to grassroots level.

Professor Prance has told us a good deal about certain plants. Let us consider one or two others. Each morning at breakfast we may have enjoyed the kiwi fruit. Ten years ago this was hardly known outside its native habitat in eastern Asia; but today it is available in supermarkets right round the world. In New Guinea there are 200 tropical forest fruits that have proved palatable to local human communities but are hardly known outside their native areas. There are probably 200 'kiwi fruits' awaiting us in New Guinea alone, provided the scientist and the food specialist can get to them before the chain saw man does. There is still more encouraging news. I was in Florida a little while ago, and in the supermarkets I noticed no fewer than 120 species of fruits and vegetables from the humid tropics.

The health sector also benefits from genetic resources of tropical rainforests. When we go to our neighbourhood pharmacy, there is one chance in four that what we purchase, whether it is an analgesic, antibiotic, anti-viral or diuretic, owes its manufacture to a basic raw material from tropical forest plants. The commercial value of these pharmaceutical products and medicines world-wide is in the order of some $20 billion per year. A particular example is the rosy periwinkle (*Catharanthus roseus,* Plate 6) whose success story has been proclaimed by conservationists for many years.

In 1950, the American pharmaceutical giant Eli Lily discovered that by using the rosy periwinkle's bio-compounds, they could develop two potent anti-cancer drugs, vincristine and vinblastine. The present commercial value of those two drugs in just the USA is in the order of $215 million per year. Since 1961, when these drugs were first released on the American market, the revenues from them have totalled $2 billion in the USA alone.

Of course it is not only the rosy periwinkle's materials that contribute to the revenues. There is also much research, development and marketing. Let us suppose the rosy periwinkle component is 1 per cent of the overall value, or $20 million. Yet none of this money has found its way back into Madagascar.

Within Madagascar's forests we can surely reckon that 1000 plant species are on the verge of extinction, and another 2000 species are likely to be severely threatened by the end of the century. Yet the incentive for the Madagascar government to take better care of its plant species is just about nil, insofar as it derives zero benefit from the commercial benefits that are being generated right around the world.

Note, moreover, that the National Cancer Institute in Washington DC believes that in Madagascar there could be at least another three plants with the capacity to generate superstar drugs against other forms of cancer. Again, what incentive does Madagascar's government have to do a better job of conserving its plants through the sort of economic argument that will no doubt be aired at this Conference?

So what more can we do to address this major problem - which we can still consider a splendid opportunity? How can we develop the international institutional mechanisms to ensure that when someone in this country benefits from those two anti-cancer drugs, some of the commercial transaction makes its way back to Madagascar? It is a difficult process, let us not shirk that. The issue has been on the agenda for the last 15 years and we have not yet devised a way of tackling it. The problem includes the questions of property rights and user fees. But we must confront this challenge if the problem of forest destruction is to be met. However difficult it is to stop deforestation, it cannot be half as difficult as trying to live in a world that has been denuded of its tropical forests and in a world which has lost tens of millions of plant and animal species with potential benefit for our economic welfare through agriculture, health and industry.

Let us now move on to consider the climate connection with tropical deforestation. This is potentially a serious situation. Again, it is balanced by some hopeful news. We are now learning that because of certain climatic linkages, many tropical forests could well be significantly and progressively depleted no matter how well we protect them - even by ceasing all deforestation forthwith, and declaring the forests a single global park. We know from the work of Professor Eneas Salati and his colleague Dr Carlos Nobre in Brazil, supported by Dr Jim Shuttleworth of Wallingford in Oxfordshire, that if a tract of forest loses a quarter of its expanse, then the remaining three-quarters may not be able to evapotranspire as much moisture as before. We could end up with a 'drying out' of the forest - which means that a rainforest would become a moist forest and then a woodland and so on.

A second climatic problem, or rather an atmospheric problem this time, lies with acid rain. It has been supposed that acid rain is a problem primarily of the industrialized countries in the North. But there is now evidence that quite extensive sectors of the tropical rainforest in China are dying back because of acid rain. A number of other tropical areas have been identified as subject to the same threat. These other forests, some of them already beginning to show signs of damage, include forests of western Indonesia, Malaysia, Thailand, south-western India, West Africa, parts of the Zaire basin and south-eastern Brazil. Overall, acid rain could, within the next two or three decades, eliminate as much as one million square kilometres of tropical forest out of eight million square kilometres remaining today.

A third climate connection lies with the greenhouse effect. Equatorial forests may well thrive in a greenhouse-affected world, due to a slight increase in temperature plus more rain. But away from the equator and towards the outer tropics and the sub-tropics, there is a region that may well be subject to quite acute changes in rainfall patterns as a result of the greenhouse effect. These are areas of seasonal forest with monsoonal precipitation patterns; there could be an intensification of monsoonal patterns, that is to say, rainfall arising sooner or later than usual, and in more erratic quantities. This could have a profoundly disruptive effect on tropical forest ecosystems in the outer tropics including areas such as Madagascar, Philippines, New Caledonia, Central America, the eastern Himalayas and many other hotspot areas that are exceptionally rich in species and that are already severely threatened by destruction.

But there is another side of the coin. It is becoming apparent that one of the best management responses we could generate to combat global warming lies with grand-scale reforestation in the humid tropics. A tree is half carbon. Through photosynthesis it soaks up carbon dioxide from the global atmosphere. If we plant enough trees we could sequester (*ie* lock away) quite a lot of the additional carbon dioxide that is being emitted each year primarily through the combustion of fossil fuels and through the burning of tropical rainforests. If we plant enough trees of that sort we could go a long way to reducing the carbon dioxide loading of the global atmosphere. Of course this would only work as long as the strategy were to be accompanied by a slowing of tropical deforestation.

The humid tropics are the main locale for a grand-scale reforestation programme, since it is in the tropics that trees grow faster than anywhere else on earth. To soak up one billion tonnes of carbon dioxide from the global atmosphere each year would take about one million square kilometres of fast-growing trees in the humid tropics. The amount we would need to sequester is in the order of four billion tonnes per year.

On lands that have already been deforested, the cost would be in the order of four or five billion dollars per million square kilometres. This is twice as much as is now going into the major initiative on tropical forests, the severely limited Tropical Forestry Action Plan. But compared with the concealed costs of inaction on the greenhouse front, $4 billion per annum is surely a give-away. It would offer a far better return than anything one could get on the London Stock Exchange. It appears to be cost effective as well, in that it is technologically one of the most feasible ways of countering the greenhouse effect.

If there were to be funds available on that scale for tropical reforestation, this would surely transform the outlook for tropical forestry. It would offer a marvellous financial incentive for tropical rainforest countries to do a much better job of retaining their remaining tropical rainforests, and would serve to relieve the other exploitative pressures on the remaining tropical forests.

In a report written by myself and commissioned by Friends of the Earth in 1989, I have concluded that tropical forests are being depleted faster than ever. It appears that tropical deforestation has increased by as much as 90 per cent during the course of the 1980s. That is the size of the challenge. Let's not keep talking about a problem; we must consider this an opportunity because we still have time, just enough time, to get on top of the problem before it gets on top of us. What better way than to demonstrate an economic rationale for safeguarding the forests.

While you are enjoying your next cup of coffee you might like to reflect again on the economic rationale for safeguarding tropical forests. Coffee plantations around the world are dependant - as are all modern crops - on regular infusions of genetic variability to sustain their productivity and increase their capacity to resist pests and adverse environmental conditions. The main coffee germ-plasm reservoirs are located in Ethiopia. In 1950, Ethiopia's forests still covered about 25 per cent of the country; today they are down to less than 3 per cent, and declining rapidly. If these final Ethiopian forests disappear with their coffee gene-pools, that could make it much more difficult to keep on growing coffee with the productivity that we have been accustomed to. We might eventually be faced with huge price increases for our cup of coffee.

Keynote Speech

HRH The Prince of Wales
St James's Palace, London SW1A 1BS United Kingdom

Ladies and Gentlemen,

I do congratulate the organizers of this Conference for having drawn together such a remarkable gathering of thoroughly sustainable people in order to discuss such an urgent and difficult subject. I say 'difficult' because it concerns other people's countries and other people's natural assets. None of us react very kindly to being told by people we do not know in far off countries that we ought to be doing things differently - particularly when these people are not very good at setting a sensible example by sorting out their own back yard. So we have to approach the subject with a certain degree of tact and diplomacy - and no-one, I can assure you, more so than me!

Those of you who may have had the misfortune of sitting through my lecture at Kew in February will perhaps have seen what a flourishing industry there is in marketing the meaningful misunderstanding, in order to make a better story!

So before I begin to talk about the prospects for sustainable utilization of the rainforests, I think it might be helpful to correct one or two of the misunderstandings which may have arisen following my speech at Kew. I am, of course, quite accustomed to anything I say being interpreted rather freely but when dealing with such an emotive subject, and in the knowledge that other countries will often reprint British news stories without checking them, I think it is important to be precise. I was therefore more than a little taken aback to see the headline *"Prince calls for a hardwood boycott"*. That is precisely what I did not do. What I actually suggested (and I hope you will forgive me if I quote verbatim, but there may be a better chance of it being taken down accurately!) was the following:

"Firstly, it would seem to me to be eminently sensible to work towards the restriction of timber extraction to secondary forest - to those forests that have already been logged over. We could then look towards future timber needs being met from hardwood plantations established on the vast area of already degraded land."

Secondly, I called for a labelling scheme so that consumers might be able to identify timber from sustainably managed forests, thus allowing the market to give additional encouragement to concession holders in rainforest countries to manage the forests differently. *"Failing such a scheme"*, I went on, *"a cautious consumer is almost certainly going to be more inclined to avoid tropical hardwoods altogether, rather than risk contributing to their unnecessary demise."*

That still seems to me to be a reasonable conclusion to draw about the likely reaction of many of today's environmentally aware consumers and I should add that I have heard nothing since then to persuade me that such a labelling scheme would be either impracticable or unworkable.

Neither of these two points would seem to be entirely synonymous with a call for a boycott! But if they have served to stimulate debate, so much the better, because in any discussions on the future of the timber trade, we need always to bear in mind those chilling reports, from the International Tropical Timber Organization (ITTO) itself, that less than 1 per cent of current forestry management can be described as genuinely sustainable.

And since I have been given the opportunity to stir this particular pot yet again, let me say that I consider one of the principal reasons for this to be the ludicrously short concession agreements that operate in most rainforest countries. Given that management for sustainable yield requires an interval of at least 25 years between one selective cut and the next, an agreement for anything less than 25 years gives no encouragement whatsoever to concession holders to ensure that productivity is protected for the next time around. Anything less than 75 years seems to me to be quite inadequate.

This Conference, of course, is not about the timber trade, but rather about all the non-timber products that can be harvested on a sustainable basis from the rainforest. There is nothing new or particularly revolutionary about such an idea. The annual value to Indonesia, for instance, of non-timber forest products is already something in the region of $120 million. But the value of such extractive utilization is rarely recognized. Exports of renewable resources such as rubber and Brazil nuts from Brazil have declined by about 25 per cent during the last decade.

In the so-called developed world, we are all becoming far more familiar, not just with that fascinating list of rainforest products which already enrich our lives in one form or another, but with the ever-growing list of products that one day might enrich our lives yet more.

That we should treat this profusion of natural wealth with such utter contempt continues to astonish me. It isn't as if we don't know its value, for we do - if not always in monetary terms, then certainly in ways that cannot so easily be reduced to the convenience of a pound or dollar symbol. It isn't as if we can't guess at some of the potential consequences of eliminating this diversity at the rate of literally thousands of species every year.

Perhaps I read too much into this, but I cannot help seeing our continuing acceptance of this insane 'biocide' as a chilling symptom of a much deeper sickness, in which more and more people seem to have fallen prey to the idea that our technological civilization is sufficiently independent of nature as to entitle us to put it to the sword - or in this case the machete and the matchstick.

I wonder how many of you are familiar with those science fiction novels in which human society has indeed succeeded in insulating itself from the rest of the biosphere, living under huge glass domes, regulating air quality artificially, and producing all its foodstuffs synthetically. Progress for some, a hideous dystopia for others - but whichever way you look at it, it is surely worth pointing out that it is in our attitudes and behaviour today that such a future is foreshadowed.

Such a distant thought should not distract us from

the contemporary reality of poverty and hardship in so many rainforest countries today. It is difficult for people in those countries to make sacrifices on behalf of an abstraction like the 'biosphere' or 'genetic diversity', let alone to worry about such theoretical problems as global warming, especially where children are dying of malnutrition or cities are being crushed by the weight of hundreds of thousands of ecological refugees.

During the last year, in Venezuela, Indonesia, Nigeria, and Cameroon, I have met people who care as passionately about the environment as I do, but are increasingly impatient at prosperous Northern countries wearing their green hearts on their sleeve, whilst doing much less than they could, in practical terms, to assist the poorer South to protect its own environment.

There is, therefore, a 'bottom line' to this idea of harvesting the rainforest: its cash benefits must be demonstrable (in local as well as national terms), and must be superior over a period of time to other potential uses of the rainforest. Evidence to that effect is of immense importance, and is, I know, a topic which will be much discussed at this Conference.

As, too, will the all-important observation that it is not enough just to identify suitable products for harvesting: ways must then be found of transporting them, marketing them and retailing them. Over the years, I have discovered that environmentalists often seem to feel ill at ease with the very idea of entrepreneurial flair, but a 'harvest' implies a 'market', and a market demands business and commercial skills to operate efficiently and to the benefit of those involved in the harvesting.

The fact that it is that well-known organization, Friends of the Earth (FoE), that has had the imagination to put on this Conference tells us a lot about the contribution that the environmental movement is now able to make to finding solutions to some of our problems - while continuing to highlight those problems in a characteristically forthright (and, for some, uncomfortable) way! Clearly, at the same time it is important that that movement should do its utmost to get its facts right before launching into anything too forthright! The list of supporting organizations is also a most impressive alliance of differing interests in a common cause.

One of the most important features of this Conference must surely be that it has brought together the environmentalists, the entrepreneurs, the harvesters, the financiers and even the politicians, from both North and South. And no venue could be more appropriate for this gathering than the Royal Geographical Society (RGS), which has taken such an inspiring lead in organizing multi-disciplinary research projects in the rainforest.

The Maracá Rainforest Project (of which I was delighted to be Patron) made the most intensive study ever undertaken of a forest at the northern edge of the Amazon Basin. It has already identified some 250 species new to science, including an *Alexa* tree that is rich in castanospermine, a plant alkaloid that may prove to be of great benefit to humankind in its fight against AIDS.

The Royal Geographical Society is currently embarking on another rainforest project (of which, believe it or not, I am also the Patron!). At the invitation of the Government and University of

Brunei, a permanent research centre will be created in the virgin forests of eastern Brunei. This new centre is intended to teach and train students from all Association of Southeast Asian (ASEAN) countries to understand and value their rainforest.

Whether we are talking about research, specific demonstration projects or full commercial schemes, it is impossible to over-estimate the importance of research and education. We all have so much to learn.

Of equal importance are those direct links between the countries involved in projects such as these. The Maracá Rainforest Project was organized by the Royal Geographical Society at the invitation of the Brazilian Environment Secretariat. I am therefore so pleased that Dr José Lutzenberger, the new Environment Secretary, has been able to come here at such short notice, especially in view of all the complicated issues he is obliged to tackle in Brazil.

I think I can safely claim that the Maracá Project was well received by the Brazilian authorities for many different reasons. It involved 30 British scientists working alongside 120 Brazilian colleagues and a further 50 Brazilian scientific technicians. Most of the British contingent knew (and loved) Brazil, so that all but two of them were able to present their papers at the first Review Conference, in Manaus, in Portuguese. The five research programmes which made up the Project were all carrying out work requested by the Brazilians themselves and the results are being published where it matters most: in Brazil.

The relationship was cemented when Britain and Brazil signed an inter-government agreement for environmental co-operation - the only such agreement that Brazil has so far undertaken with any country, which has, perhaps, something to do with the hard work of the Overseas Development Administration (ODA) and the persuasive charm of that mighty sustainable Secretary of State for the Environment, Mr Chris Patten! At a time when North and South find it hard to communicate on these issues, we should set great store on such practical initiatives.

My wife and I will be visiting Brazil at the end of October[1], at the invitation of President Collor, and look forward to hearing more about all the many developments that are taking place in that country. Amongst other things, I hope to hear more about the plans for the 1992 Conference on Environment and Development, which will take place in Brazil. Twenty years on from the 1972 United Nations Conference in Stockholm, I know that expectations for 1992 are already running very high, particularly amongst developing nations.

Their message to us is a simple one: fine words are simply not up to the job any longer - additional financial resources and specific initiatives to transfer environment-friendly technologies are urgently required if we are to avoid the progressive deterioration of the global environment.

Having followed the deliberations of the Bergen Conference[2] with interest, I can only say that it still seems to have escaped the attention of some Western politicians that it is literally impossible to control the emissions of greenhouse gases, to eliminate the production and consumption of ozone-depleting substances, let alone to protect the remaining rainforest, without the active co-operation of the Third World. That co-operation is not likely to be forthcoming unless we do everything in our power to put substantial additional financial backing behind the concept of sustainable development.

One message that came out loud and clear from Bergen was the need for the developed world to 'put its own house in order'. We really cannot go on taking other countries to task for not giving adequate protection to their priceless environmental assets when we still seem to be incapable of offering adequate protection to our own particularly precious ecosystems. In their own way, lowland peat bogs in Britain are as special a habitat as the rainforest, and the utterly unsustainable commercial utilization to which they are currently exposed is as bad, in its own way, as the burning of the rainforest or unsustainable logging operations.

But the notion of 'putting one's house in order' cuts both ways, of course. If it is true that we should not lecture Third World countries on their environmental responsibilities whilst we are still flagrantly disregarding our own, it is equally true that Third World countries should not be too strident in their denunciation of Western banks until they themselves are prepared to do something about the huge problem of 'flight capital'. This rather coy and innocuous sounding term refers to the devastating and debilitating phenomenon by which vast sums of money have left countries illegally. No one knows the sums involved but one contribution to flight capital is corruption. The environmental consequences of such corruption on a vast scale are immense in many countries and it is not surprising, therefore, that the innocent as well as the guilty are being invited to submit their proposed projects to independent auditing and proper accountability.

Although the international context is of enormous importance when talking about the rainforests, this Conference should also serve to remind us that the effectiveness of international agreements is eventually decided by what is then done, or not done, at the grassroots. The Brundtland Report laid great stress on this local dimension:

"Programmes to preserve forest resources must start with the local people, who are both victims and agents of destruction, and who will bear the burden of any new management scheme. They should be at the centre of integrated forest management, which is the basis of sustainable agriculture. Such a change would entail further changes in the way governments set development priorities, as well as the devolution of greater responsibility to local governments and communities."

'Top down' approaches are unlikely to work, and may, indeed, lead to costly and time-consuming projects which fail through lack of local support. Truly sustainable development must be based upon the wants and needs of local communities and must involve them at the earliest stages of planning, recognizing them as fully participating partners throughout.

That obviously poses quite a challenge to conventional business attitudes. The rainforest must not simply be seen as just another 'investment opportunity', however environmentally aware the investor may be. Equitable compensation for forest peoples' knowledge and discoveries is essential, as is the need to ensure that a fair proportion of the profits are returned to the local communities involved. This is the only means by which their economic advancement and welfare can be underpinned, while simultaneously ensuring that the forest base is maintained intact.

Many Third World NGOs and local communities are rightly apprehensive of the ability and readiness of commercial enterprises in the North to 'rip them off'. And there are certainly grounds for concern. One of the more inequitable aspects of human development over the last 500 years has been the transfer of genetic resources from the South to the North.

But now, with our more sophisticated financial systems and our recognition of the debt we in the North owe to those in the South for the contribution their gene-pools have made to our quality of life and general prosperity, it must surely be time to consider paying royalties for patented biological materials, especially from the rainforests. If plant breeders' rights can be justified in the North, it seems to me that the local protection and conserving of plant genetic material, should receive financial reward generated from taxes, royalties or patents from the North.

Perhaps one of the things that this Conference can come up with is some kind of recommended code of conduct for all companies operating in rainforest areas or through indigenous people or local communities. The whole concept of the extractive reserve is of such immense significance that it would be tragic were it to be undermined by the practices of those who do not share the scruples of most of us here today.

There are already several important case studies to which we can refer. The Kuna Biosphere Reserve in Panama seems to exemplify the effective combination of sustainable utilization and direct control by the people most immediately concerned. As the last representatives of the people that once occupied most of Panama, the Kuna were granted sovereign rights over a 200 kilometre stretch of the Caribbean coast. The General Kuna Congress owns and manages most of the tourist facilities on the islands off the coast and was instrumental in setting up the Kuna Wildlands Project, a 90,000 hectare natural reserve. To date, they have successfully resisted pressure from land speculators and colonizers and have been able to demonstrate that their kind of extractive farming works far better than conventional agricultural settlements.

The key to the success of the Kuna Project seems to be the security of land rights vested in the Kuna people. I am particularly delighted that Antonio Macedo and Martin von Hildebrand are here to tell us a little bit about what is going on in Brazil and Colombia respectively. In the lecture I gave at Kew, I paid tribute to the courage and vision of President Barco of Colombia in handing over 12 million hectares to the indigenous people of the Amazon region. And like so many people, I have been much impressed by the work of Brazil's Forest People's Alliance, which has managed to bring together the National Council of Rubber Tappers and the Union of Indigenous Nations in a remarkable example of solidarity and co-operation.

I need hardly say that I attach the greatest

importance to learning as much as we can from those whose direct, first-hand knowledge of the rainforest is infinitely greater than all that is contained within the dozens of rainforest books that have been brought out over the last couple of years.

The knowledge of tribal people is particularly valuable, not just because of what it tells us about the multifarious species which might be of use to us, but because of the way in which that knowledge is ordered and passed on from one generation to the next. Whilst we are accustomed to classifying things by botanical families, many Indian people classify plants in their own forest simply by use - as foods, medicines and so on. The challenge to the botanists is to escape their rather sterile academic strait-jackets and to learn from these traditional insights; to seek ways of adapting them, jointly, to new conditions and needs.

Ladies and gentlemen, one of the great problems the world faces, it seems to me, is that there is no shortage of people, nor of powerful lobbies for that matter, who would wish to persuade us that the world's environmental problems, about which some of us have been gravely concerned for many years, are not as serious as we fear. You would think, wouldn't you, that the millions of dollars spent in trying to prove that those who are concerned about the irreversible damage which is being inflicted on the earth are politically motivated or simply deranged could surely be far better spent on research and development into alternative ways of doing things? Environmental damage, they say, can be rectified. In some cases, they may be right - though the sums of money required to rectify the damage to Eastern Europe (and in the face of conflicting priorities) must be astronomical. But in the case of the rainforests, all the evidence is that once they have gone it is simply impossible to reconstitute them in their full richness.

On that score alone, I can, with the utmost enthusiasm, commend to you the proceedings of this Conference, for it seems to me to offer some realistic hope, at a somewhat gloomy time, both for the rainforests themselves and for the people of those countries on whom we depend to act as guardians and stewards of the forests in all our interests.

Editors' Footnotes

1. Their Royal Highnesses, The Prince and Princess of Wales postponed their planned trip to Brazil to April 1991.

2. Ministers from 34 countries in the UN Economic Commission for Europe (ECE) region met at Bergen, Norway from 14th to 16th May 1990 at the regional conference on 'Action for a Common Future'.

The Future of Amazonia

Dr José Lutzenberger
Special Secretary for the Environment, The Government of Brazil

Summary

Climate systems are highly complex but many areas of the world, particularly Europe and southern Brazil, are directly influenced by the Amazon rainforest. The new Brazilian government has introduced new measures which will contribute to the survival of the country's tropical forests. The First World is called upon to reform current unsustainable agricultural practices and consumption patterns. He argues that capitalism, and the dogma of continuous growth, cannot survive in its present form. He offers an alternative world view based on an all-encompassing holistic ethic.

I am very happy to be here with you again. We are all more concerned than ever with the preservation of rainforests and the people who know how to live in harmony with them. Today I am not bringing despair, like so often in the past, but a message of hope.

I was asked to say something about the significance of the rainforest with reference to world climate, a subject that is not at all well understood. You are aware of the controversy that is now raging, even at government level, about the possibility of global warming due to the emission into the atmosphere of carbon dioxide, chlorofluorocarbons (CFCs) and other gases. I have just come back from Bergen[1] where about 34 government ministers discussed the issue. Some countries say that we must take action immediately, some recommend precautionary action. Others, the USA for example, say that we have to wait for more scientific information because of the current uncertainties.

I would like to give you one more uncertainty that, to me, looks even more threatening than global warming, and one I have seen no mention of lately in any of these meetings around the world. Professor Salati has already done a great deal of work on this subject. He has calculated that the world's rainforests have a fantastic evapotranspiration, that is the sum of evaporation and transpiration. Of the rain that falls on the rainforest, about 25 per cent evaporates and never reaches the ground. It is just enough to moisten the layers of foliage from 40 metres up, down to the herbs on the forest floor.

Of the 75 per cent of water that does reach the ground only some 25 per cent ends up in the streams and rivers and goes back to the ocean, and even part of that evaporates on its way there. In the deepest of rainforests the remaining 50 per cent is pumped back up by the trees and transpired into the atmosphere, so a total of 75 per cent makes new clouds and more rain. The rainforest is therefore not only dependent on this precipitation, it also makes its own climate. It is like asking which came first: the chicken or the egg?

In South America, rainwater on its way from the Atlantic to the Andes is recycled 5 to 7 times. Professor Salati has shown this by analyzing isotopes of hydrogen and oxygen in rainwater but we can also make a very simple calculation. We know how much water falls on the catchment basin of this enormous river system - about five times as much as the water that flows out at the mouth of the Amazon. The flow of the Amazon river is about 200,000 m^3 per second or 20 per cent of the world's fresh water flow.

This sequence of condensation and evaporation involves a vast amount of energy. You know from your first classes in physics that it takes an awful lot more energy to raise water from its liquid stage to vapour than it takes to heat it up. In fact we need about 530 times as much energy to turn water at 100 degrees centigrade into steam than it takes to raise that same quantity of water from 99 to 100 degrees centigrade. On the way back from steam to water, as much energy is also released. Professor Salati worked out that the flow of energy over the Amazon rainforest is equivalent to something like 6 million Hiroshima-sized atom bombs per day. A huge amount of energy is captured from the sun and then transported from east to west.

Where does all that energy go? Today we have fantastic instruments which enable us to see the whole planet from satellites and the movement of these air masses from the Atlantic to the Andes. As they are brought in by the Trade Winds they are repeatedly dissolved and reformed, and we can see on the satellite pictures very clearly that when these air masses hit the mountain range of the Andes they split into three parts. A small part jumps over the Andes and goes into the Pacific, and is probably involved with the movement of the two currents, the Humbolt and the El Niño.

Another, almost a half, goes south and sweeps all over central and southern Brazil and far down into Patagonia, so that the climate in central and southern Brazil, Argentina and Uruguay is dependent on the rainforest. We, in Brazil, want to turn the cerrado (South American savannah) into a bread-basket for the world, but if we destroy the rainforest, the cerrado will probably become a desert.

The other half goes north, more or less parallel to the Gulf Stream. It 'licks' the eastern coast of North America and then goes into Europe - Scandinavia, northern and central Europe - all the way into the Soviet Union. Indeed the Scandinavian climate depends to some extent on what happens in the rainforest. I have just come from Norway, where there are long, cold winters, but they have beautiful vegetation, forests and highly productive agriculture. On the other side of the planet, on the same latitude, you have Labrador - Eskimo country. We can see quite clearly that the climate there [in Scandinavia] depends on the integrity of the rainforests and on what happens in the Caribbean. But we do not know how these two flows, the air masses and the Gulf Stream are connected, or how they influence each other.

All we know is that the world's climate system is highly complex, something that we cannot even begin to express in mathematical formulae. We would need inputs of unknown potency. We do know, however, that when we deal with highly complex, highly integrated, self-contained and self-regulated systems such as the world's climate, they do not react in the way that we expect them to.

The controversy about the greenhouse effect is based mostly on linear extrapolations. They tell you that we are introducing so much carbon dioxide, CFCs and methane into the atmosphere, that we will get a certain increase in mean temperature by the year 2020 and so on. Well, these systems just do not behave in that way. Highly complex systems do not react in a linear or even in an exponential way. Take an animal. It can take much abuse, battering and aggression, and remain relatively stable, up to a point! Then, you get sudden collapse. We can use a very simple image; I am a little midget who lives here and I make my living by pushing...pushing...pushing. [Dr Lutzenberger pushes book towards edge of podium - Editor]. I do not see the whole picture; past experience tells me that I can go on pushing...pushing; I can even accelerate. When this happens [book falls off the edge - Editor] it is too late; no use getting wise. I think we should really be aware of what we are doing. It is no use saying that we do not have enough information - that we must wait for more information. We have enough information to know that we must act.

Perhaps I should mention a fundamental tenet of wisdom. We are engaged in an experiment where we know beforehand that, if it is to go wrong, the result is unacceptable and irreversible and we had better get out as soon as possible. Our present modern industrial civilization - a consumer society - has a tremendous amount of knowledge, but we are a very dumb civilization - we have almost no wisdom. Wisdom and knowledge unfortunately do not always go together as they should. Well, the note of hope that I want to bring to you is that in Brazil we now have a new Government. We have a young President, the first President elected by the people in almost thirty years, who really is convinced that he has to do something about the problem, and he wants to. We have already initiated some concrete action. It is very little to begin with, but we really want to change, to make things better. We really want to save the rainforest.

Right now we are in the middle of positive action to remove the gold diggers from the Yanomami territory. This action has only just begun and the bombing of the airstrips is only part of what is necessary, it is only a small measure. What we have to do is control the flow of diesel oil from the larger airports, something we can do very easily. A more important measure taken by this Government was the elimination of the subsidies for so-called development in Amazonia[2]. Cattle ranching is probably the single factor that has caused most damage to the rainforest. Every one of those ranches requires forest clearance of tens of thousands of hectares and a few of them even hundreds of thousands of hectares. But they would be totally uneconomic if it were not for subsidies. Some of them even cleared the forest but did not put cattle there because their work was sufficient for them to get subsidies. Now this has been changed. The present Government has also changed the taxation structure and now taxes the profits from agricultural production. Up until recently, since our tax laws were mostly influenced by wealthy landlords, we had a situation where whenever somebody made a lot of money in town, for example lawyers or industrialists, he had to have a ranch.

That was where he could make his taxes disappear. Well, now they pay taxes just like everybody else. They have been protesting that such taxes would hurt the small guy, but it certainly will not because these people do not make enough money. Their produce is mostly for themselves, and they will pay very little tax, if any.

With the help of the airforce, the police action against the clearing and burning can be doubled, trebled or increased to whatever extent is necessary. This is starting now, in the coming dry season. We will also take steps as soon as we can against the thousands of illegal timber mills in Amazonia. Until recently the situation was so absurd that when a small farmer in the river valley of my home region cut three or four eucalyptus logs he had to have a licence, waste two or three weeks in bureaucracy, and often pay corruption money as well, while in Amazonia thousands of timber mills are under no control whatsoever. This must be reversed.

We will also see what we can do about the Carajas Project. Here perhaps you could help us by insisting that the pig iron that comes from Carajas is not produced in smelters that use charcoal. This is a very serious problem. It is not just that charcoal is very cost effective. We have discovered that the operation would be more efficient if we worked with Colombian coal, or perhaps if the boats that took the ore or pig iron from Brazil to Europe or Japan could bring us back mineral coal. But there are many interests behind this sort of forest clearing. People who want it cleared to make cattle ranches will get the clearing for free and the money from timber for Carajas charcoal production would be another form of subsidy.

We will also revise all the decrees that the previous Government issued in the last few months of its administration, in some cases crippling and in others eliminating Indian reserves. It is true, however, that the previous administration did establish a very large extractive reserve, and in June our new president will go there and inaugurate it as the Chico Mendes Reserve.

But we are only just starting with these positive actions. In the past, governments had all the information they needed to act. Every day, for example, satellites give us information on whatever happens in Amazonia. Nobody could burn a patch 5 x 5 metres without it being seen on satellite pictures. The information was there but the political will was not. Now, although the political will is also there, you must all help us. The time has come where it makes no sense to continue with the mutual recriminations any more, we are all sinners. What we must do now is to sit together, First, Second and Third World, and see how we can save the planet of which we are only a small part.

Flying over the land already cleared in Amazonia (something like 400,000 square kilometres - almost twice the size of the UK), most of which has been abandoned, you can see how much of it is already turning to bush.

This is because the soils under the rainforest, with few exceptions, are extremely poor. They are not only poor in nutrients, they are also poor in nutrient holding capacity. They are either pure sands or highly degraded clays. So conventional agrochemical methods do not work. In Rondônia, a large part of the State was cleared by migrants. People were sent there because they had been uprooted from other parts of Brazil, and because the authorities did not want to confront social justice in these areas.

Today, most of the small farmers can only survive by clearing new forest every year. The soil is so poor that it has to be abandoned after one or two meagre harvests. We must teach these people methods of regenerative farming, which is the only method that works on these soils; if agrochemistry worked, the chemical industry would be jumping on it. We must teach them organic soil management without insoluble mineral fertilizers, no till and maximum use of legumes. We are now discovering really great things about the recuperation of soils with some of our huge variety of legumes which will save on expensive nitrogen fertilizers. We must also teach companion planting, crop rotation and the message that much of the land should be allowed to revert to forest.

Natural reforestation first produces scrub and bushes that are a relative monoculture with only a few species, but as time passes it becomes more and more complicated and richer in species. If we leave it in peace, in 30 or 40 years people who are not familiar with the rainforest would hardly notice the difference. Of course there isn't anything wrong with commercial monocultures as long as they are done on the degraded soils, and not, as is often the case, at the expense of virgin forest. That is why I am very afraid of this programme of planting billions of trees in South America. When big money flows, the big programmes are usually very aggressive and when you want to plant 100,000 hectares of forest all in one place, you will usually cut down some of the remaining wilderness. This has happened in the past and caused tremendous devastation, only making richer those who were already too rich.

However, I would like to appeal to you to reform your agriculture. Not only do we have to do this all over South America and in the rest of the Third World, but also here in the Common Market. The form of agriculture that you practise today is totally unsustainable and reform must be led by the First World because what we practise in South America, Africa and all over the so-called Third World is the consequence of the model of development that you practise here. It is totally unsustainable and you cannot continue with it for much longer before you find yourselves facing collapse. Today it took me one hour to come from Hampstead [a suburb of London, some 10 kilometres away from this Conference - Editor] to here because of traffic jams - cars are the most absurd and inefficient way of transporting people. The implication of today's development policies, as practised here in the so-called First World and everywhere else, is that we want to give the guy behind the last mountain in the remotest place in the world, the kind of consumption pattern that we see here today in the UK, Germany and Holland, which is totally impossible.

Let us make a very simple extrapolation. If all the world had the density of cars that we have in Holland or in the USA, where you have one passenger car per 1.7 or 1.8 people, then we would not have 500 million cars as we have today, which is already much too much, but something like 3 billion. Then, if by the year 2020 as is foreseen, we have 10 or 12 billion people, with this kind of consumption pattern we would have something like 7 billion cars. The world would be dead. Fortunately, there is not enough in the way of resources and petroleum for that, but if it is impossible to give the whole world the patterns of consumption that we have today in the First World, perhaps we should think it sinful to live the way we do. We must re-examine the fundamental tenets of our economic thinking. We cannot continue much longer the way we are acting at present.

On our side of the now crumbled Iron Curtain most people seem to think that capitalism has won the race - that we are the victors. I would say that is not true. The victors are the people over there, they overthrew the tyrannies. We are in for our own perestroika. The way capitalism functions today has no future. We must rethink our basic postulates - for example, the dogma of the necessity of continuous growth. Governments like to speak of sustainable growth, but this is a contradiction in terms. Let us use another image. Of course it would be a calamity for a baby to stop growing, but if I, aged 63, had not stopped growing at the rate I grew when I was a baby (for I doubled my weight in the first six months), today I would be as big as the sun! So sustainable growth is a contradiction in terms, but sustainable development does not have to be if development is defined in different ways.

Life first appeared on this planet some 3.5 billion years ago and from then on became ever more complex, more highly integrated, more beautiful, more harmonious in this fantastic pageant of organic evolution of which we are only one of the latest outcomes. Life has always evolved and developed not in quantitative but in qualitative ways. If we learnt to base our economies on a sustainable logic, if we managed to have technical and organizational infrastructures that made it possible for our economies to be homoeostatic and not exponential, then we would have a future. What we are involved in today is the logic of the snowball. I cannot help the snowball by providing more snow and more mountain slope. That would only make things worse, but today our economists, all of them, east and west, seem to think that what we need is more resources, more growth. They think they can ride a snowball forever. But if we want to change we have to, above all else, look into our ethics, into our worldview.

From our remote Judaeo-Christian past we have inherited an anthropocentric view. Even when I listen to discussions such as these, here and in other seminars and congresses, much of the reasoning is based on the need to behave correctly because otherwise we lose our resources, the resources of our children and so on. It is always that anthropocentric view.

I do not know who it was that gave us a very beautiful example of this kind of thinking. Somebody argued that it would have been a catastrophe for humans if the armadillo had been exterminated. The armadillo is the only animal from which we can cultivate the bacillus of leprosy - the armadillo has made it possible for us to research the problems and cures of this disease. Are we really entitled to think that the armadillo - the result of hundreds of millions of years of accumulated natural wisdom in organic evolution - evolved only so he could be a 'guinea-pig' for humans to solve one of our small problems? No, the armadillo is just as important as we are. All species are important and we must begin to realize that we are one species among untold millions of species, and that we have no right to appropriate everything on this planet as our own.

It is not just a question of preserving resources, it is fundamentally a religious question. It is a question of how we look at the world, of going back to an all-encompassing holistic ethic which the forest people, whom we discuss today, in our arrogance based on ignorance, like to call 'primitive'. Most of the people we call advanced, however, do not have a holistic and all-encompassing ethic, but one that is limited to our species, whether or not we are believers in Christianity, Judaism or Islam. Our ethic is still limited and includes only human relations or relations between humans and God; but nature is left out.

Editors' Footnotes

1. Ministers from 34 countries in the UN Economic Commission for Europe (ECE) region met at Bergen, Norway from 14th to 16th May 1990 at the regional conference on 'Action for a Common Future'.

2. President Fernando Collor and Minister of Justice Jarbas Passarinho signed on 26th June 1991 Decree 153 which modifies article 15 of Decree 101 from 17th April. The new regulation *"bans the concession of fiscal incentives for activities resulting in deforestation of primary forests and destruction of primary ecosystems"*.

Definitions of Extractive Reserves in the Context of the Alliance of the Forest Peoples

Antonio Luiz Batista Macedo
Co-ordinator of the Conselho Nacional Dos Seringueiros (CNS) and advisor to União Das Nações Indígenas (UNI) in the region of the Juruá Valley, Acre. Conselho Nacional Dos Seringueiros, Rua Guanabara No. 150, Estação Experimental, 69.900 Rio Branco, AC Brazil

First of all I would like to thank you very much for the invitation extended to myself and Mario Puruaranha as representatives of National Council of Rubber Tappers (CNS) from the Juruá Valley in the State of Acre, to come to London to speak at this important Conference.

Secondly, I would like to extend my thanks to His Royal Highness The Prince of Wales, for his recognition of the importance of the Forest People's Alliance.

At this moment, with so many scientific experts meeting here, I would like to express the sentiments I feel about this subject. The feeling that I have is that the struggle of Chico Mendes has not stopped, and that the spirits of the forest have managed to illuminate our consciousness in such a way that we have come together at a global level to discuss the problems of our planet Earth. I believe that together we have a responsibility towards the forest, towards environmental questions, and towards the population of those regions of the Third World that have suffered so much.

I have worries relating to these discussions. Today is the 17th May 1990, the month that the clearings begin in the Brazilian Amazon region. When we return to Acre State, we will be witnessing the continuation of the process of clearing the forest and the setting up of more cattle ranches in the region.

Our struggle has been for the survival of Amazon people, and we have presented a proposal, not only for our survival but for everybody's. This proposal is for extractive reserves. Our basic priority continues to be to struggle for their creation. We wish to pursue the demarcation of those extractive reserves that we have identified, as well as the demarcation of indigenous reservations. We are clear in our own minds how we want to administer these areas. We, the rubber tappers, and the Indians are capable of administering our own riches through our own projects through the viable compatibility of growth and environmental protection.

It is very difficult for us to come to the UK and other countries as Chico Mendes did. Many children where I come from are dying or suffering from various diseases or from various degrees of parasitic infection and other types of illness without any medical aid.

The potential of the Amazon is not news to any of us

here; I am certain we all have interesting ideas about the future of its development. We from the Brazilian Amazon have created in São Paulo our representation, our delegation, to the peoples of the city. This is the Embassy of the Forest People's Alliance in São Paulo, co-ordinated by Ailton Krenak of the Union of Indigenous Nations (UNI). We have national offices of the CNS in the city of Rio Branco in Acre and in Cruzeiro do Sul. We also have the support of organizations like the Institute of Amazon Studies (IEA) in Curitiba. So I ask all of you here present, all of you with ideas about the preservation of our future survival, about this green universe that we live in, to come to us to discuss these ideas for we have many answers and ideas about the protection of the Amazon region and how to administer our future.

And, in closing, I would like to extend my good wishes to all participants of this Conference in the hope that the Queen of the Forests can illuminate our ideas and bring us together with the fertile ideas needed for a solution to the numerous problems confronting Amazonia. Also, I would like to extend an invitation to His Royal Highness the Prince of Wales to visit us in Acre - to visit the first extractive reserve in the world - in the Juruá Valley. Thank you very much.

The Development Project of the Poyanawa Association

Mario Cordeira de Lima
Local Co-ordinator of the União Das Nações Indígenas (UNI) and leader of the Poyanawa community in Brazil

My name is Mario Cordeira de Lima. I am leader of the Poyanawa indigenous community on the Barao rubber estate. I am also Co-ordinator of the Union of Indigenous Nations (UNI) in the Cruzeiro do Sul region in Acre.

We are organizing ourselves because we are going through a difficult period, as in fact all of our life has been. We want to free ourselves. We want the demarcation of our lands. We want the preservation of the forests. We need resources in order to be able to administer our communities. Because we have the knowledge, we have the certainty that nobody can administer an indigenous community in the way that we can. We want to live and survive in the forest because it is in the forest that we obtain the sustenance for our families.

The Work of Northwestern Bee Products, Zambia

Bob Malachi
Manager, Northwestern Bee Products, Kabompo, Zambia

with an additional paper from

David Wainright
Director, Tropical Forest Products, UK Agents to Northwestern Bee Products in Europe, Box 92, Aberystwyth, Wales

Summary

In the Northwest province of Zambia there are still many thousands of square kilometres of forest which are not used for forestry or farming. Bee-keeping is a traditional activity in the forest along with hunting and fishing. Despite advice to change to more modern hives, traditional beehives made from the bark of trees are still being used. These have proved to be more profitable because they cost very little to make. Bee-keepers in Africa are keen to link up with fellow comrades in the forests of South America; now that African bees have spread all over South America, they might be able to benefit from African types of hive and knowledge.

In the Northwest Province of Zambia we are still lucky to have many thousands of square kilometres of forest which we do not need for forestry or farming.

Bee-keeping is a traditional activity in the forest along with hunting and fishing. For a long time wax was collected in the forests and exported. This gave the people a chance to buy essential commodities which they could not make locally, such as soap, salt, bicycles and blankets. These simple things make a great difference to their standard of living.

However, the bee-keepers still had many problems. In the 1970s they complained to their traditional and government leaders. Prices were very low and the service provided by the government department and private businessmen was very unreliable. The Zambian government, with assistance from GTZ (Deutsche Gesellschaft für Technische Zusammenarbeit), set up a company owned by the bee-keepers and the district councils. The purpose was to buy the honey and wax from the villages and to find the best market for these products both inside and outside of Zambia. This company has been a great success. Every year increasing numbers of people are hanging more hives in the forest. Even in the most remote villages, people are able to buy essential commodities from the company.

All this would not have been possible without the skill and traditions of the bee-keepers who have been keeping bees in this forest for many generations. We have carried on using our traditional beehives made from the bark of trees (Plate 7) despite being advised by the experts to change to modern hives. Our hives are much more profitable as they cost nothing to produce and the bees seem happier in the traditional hives so that we do not need to spend money on protective clothing.

We would be very interested to link up with our friends living in the forests of South America because they might also find our type of hive useful, now that our African bees have invaded South American forests. Although the honey and wax that we produce is only a few hundred tonnes per year, which is insignificant on an international scale, it is very important to us. In our area of forest there are only a few thousand people; many of the men earn a bit of cash from bee-keeping and most enjoy the honey!

I would like to end with an appeal to the international delegates gathered here. Please help us by finding export markets for our products as exports are essential to the survival of our company. In Zambia today the economic situation is very difficult. For example, if I need to change the oil filter on one of our Land Rovers, I need foreign currency to buy such a simple thing! Without the Land Rover I cannot reach the people to buy their honey and wax.

I am very grateful to the sponsoring organizations, The Body Shop, The Ford Foundation, and the Overseas Development Administration (ODA) for bringing me all the way from Kabompo to London. It is a great honour to be chosen to speak as a representative of the bee-keepers. What would make me most happy would be to bring back something to benefit all the bee-keepers - your support as customers and consumers of our products is what we need most[1].

David Wainwright

By autumn 1990 shoppers in the UK will have a new opportunity. They will be able to pick a jar of honey from the supermarket shelf and know that this honey was produced by tribal bee-keepers, using their traditional techniques, deep in the forests of Central Africa. This honey is one of a new generation of products coming from the tropical forest; the promoters of these products believe that by harvesting the forest, rather than cutting it down and selling it, the survival of the forest ecosystem can be ensured and the basic human rights of the people who live there can be established.

In southern Central Africa, in what is now Angola, Zambia, Tanzania and Mozambique, beeswax is a forest trading product with a long history. Traders from Portugal, Britain and Zanzibar set up networks reaching from the coast to remote trading posts in the forest. Thousands of tonnes were produced from the large numbers of beehives, much of which ended up as candles in European churches. From their villages, the men would travel into the forest in small groups to collect the wax, setting up camps up to 50 miles from their homes. There they would stay for several weeks, cropping the honeycombs from wild bees nests, processing the wax, hunting, fishing and in the evening drinking beer brewed from the honey.

As production increased, there came a point where further production was limited by the number of natural nest sites available. Artificial hives were developed, usually made of materials readily available in the forest, such as bark and hollowed-out logs, normally in the form of a cylinder about 1.5 metres long. As bee-keeping became a common activity, it made a considerable impact on the forest ecology through changes in the pollination of many trees and plants, as well as the selective removal of individual trees for hive-making. It is not possible to know the nature or extent of the impact of bee-keeping on the forest ecology. However, it is important to stress that bee-keeping is not a cause of deforestation and bee-keepers have a vested interest in the conservation of the forest.

The newly made hives are hung high in trees scattered in the forest out of reach of forest fires, army ants and honey badgers. Successful bee-keepers, who may have up to 2000 hives, can leave the swarms undisturbed for 3 to 5 years before cropping them, and then harvest up to 20 kilogrammes from each hive. It is remarkable that, considering the dangerous reputation of African bees, most of the traditional bee-keepers have cropped honey for years without any protective clothing whilst climbing high in trees. It is a skilled operation which demands detailed knowledge of the history of each colony, the changing honey flow conditions in the forest and the behaviour of bees.

Many Western experts have assumed that the traditional village techniques need to be replaced by the 'advanced' frame hive used in Europe and the USA. This is justified by the assumption that the Western methods are more productive. However, only the rural elite could afford to invest in these more expensive hives, while the village technology, which uses local resources and requires no capital investment, allows the masses to participate fully in production.

The real problem faced by the villagers is often not producing a product - it is selling that product. For these people a source of cash income and a supply of essential commodities is vital. Since the late 1970s, many aspects of rural life have deteriorated; essential commodities such as salt, soap, bicycles and clothes have become scarce and expensive while government services like education and health suffer from a lack of most materials and equipment. It is this situation which motivates the people to struggle to obtain a little cash in order to buy essential goods and pay education fees.

Northwestern Bee Products (NWBP) was set up and organized to provide a market for the honey and wax produced by the forest bee-keepers in the Northwest province. The vehicles of NWBP travel to several hundred village-based bee-keeping groups to buy the honey and wax, bringing essential commodities needed by the bee-keepers. The company has to export honey and wax to earn the dollars with which to buy new vehicles and spare parts. Tropical Forest Products (TFP) act as an agent for NWBP and has succeeded in finding a high value market for all the honey the bee-keepers can produce[1].

Does tropical forest bee-keeping form a promising base for a renaissance of forest product harvesting? Will this persuade governments to halt the destruction of forests and provide forest peoples with a worthwhile way of life into the 21st century? Whatever happens, the rural industries offer more than just an opportunity to earn cash; they give the population confidence in the continued viability of rural life in a nation where education and culture have been biased in favour of an urban industrial development goal.

Editors' footnote

1. The first imports of honey from NWBP arrived in Europe in October 1990. Since then, a total of 54 tonnes has arrived. At present, demand for the honey has increased beyond the current production capacity of NWBP due to poor honey yields.

The Utilization and Trade of Non-timber Forest Products in South-east Asia

Dr Noraini Tamin
Biology Department, Universiti Kebangsaan, Malaysia 43600, Bangi Selangor, Malaysia

Summary

Rainforests in South-east Asia are the second most extensive in the world. These forests represent complex ecosystems, with great diversity of flora and fauna. In South-east Asia there are about 29 million forest dwellers, who over thousands of years have utilized a great range of non-timber forest resources for their daily needs, be they food, clothing or shelter, on a sustained yield basis that is intricately woven within spiritual and cultural practices without severe damage to the ecosystem. Trade in non-timber forest products has been in existence in South-east Asia since the fifth century, when resins and oils were exported from the western Indonesian islands to China. The height of the trade in non-timber forest products was during the 19th and 20th centuries between South-east Asian countries and Europe. Today, there is renewed interest in non-timber forest product extraction, development and trade, as an alternative to logging and forest clearance. The final objectives are to encourage multiple forest utilization, the conservation of biodiversity and greening of the environment. This paper also highlights various new business opportunities involving non-timber forest products from rainforests in South-east Asia and from heath forest in particular, as the latter is a diminishing and threatened resource in South-east Asia.

Introduction

The rainforests of South-east Asia are complex ecosystems, noted for their great biodiversity and timber resources. In the late 1960s it was estimated (Pringle, 1969) that forested areas covered about 250 million hectares of land surface, concentrated within a botanical region known as Malesia. This included present day Indonesia, Malaysia, the Philippines, Thailand, and Papua New Guinea, with outliers in the Seychelles, Sri Lanka, India, Burma, Kampuchea, Indo-China, Hainan, the Lesser Sunda islands, and north-eastern Australia. Two of the most important commercial tropical hardwood timbers, namely teak *(Tectona grandis)* and meranti *(Shorea* spp.) are from this part of the world.

Great demands for tropical hardwoods in the 1960s, along with the rapid economic development and population explosions of post-independent nations like Indonesia and Malaysia at about the same period, brought about extensive clearance of lowland and hill forests for infrastructural development of new villages, towns and cities, agricultural lands (rice fields and vegetable plots) and crop plantations (rubber, cocoa and oil palm). Today, in most countries in South-east Asia, the total land surface covered by natural forests varies from 20 to 30 per cent. The extent of forests in

Table 1. Forested areas in South-east Asia (square kilometres)

Country	Total Land Area	Permanent Protection Forest	All Production Forest	Virgin Forest Remaining
Indonesia	1,930,270	1,439,700	644,036	524,000
Malaysia				
Peninsular	131,596	63,532	43,607	9,600
Sabah	73,711	44,869	34,064	7,815
Sarawak	123,253	94,484	70,184	50,387
Papua New Guinea	468,860	359,900	?	?
Philippines	300,000	63,830	44,030	10,420
Thailand	513,115	142,958	?	?
Total	3,540,805	2,209,173	835,921	602,222

various countries in South-east Asia is given in Table 1.

In Malaysia and Indonesia there is a policy of reservation of permanent forests for productive and protective purposes. In Thailand and the Philippines all land not alienated is declared to be forest land. The Governments take no positive action to constitute forest reserves and thus forests may be alienated whenever a potentially valuable use develops. In Papua New Guinea about 97 per cent of the land is owned by clans or individuals who for centuries have utilized it for hunting or subsistence farming. Subject to the owner's agreement, the forest utilization rights may be bought by the Government for limited periods. Thus there are no permanent forests in Papua New Guinea except where the Government has bought timber and land rights over limited periods and areas (Poore, 1989).

The forests of northern Thailand, Burma and Indo-China are known as 'monsoon forests' as these are located in areas with marked annual dry seasons. On the other hand, the forests in Malaysia and Indonesia are known as tropical rainforests as these are confined to areas with hot, humid and ever-wet climates. Generally, rainforests are evergreen but differ slightly in structure, physiognomy and species composition depending on their altitudinal location, which influences edaphic and microclimatic regimes. Thus one can identify various forest types for example heath, mangrove, limestone, hill or montane forests (Whitmore, 1984).

Resource utilization

The rainforests of South-east Asia support about 29 million dwellers, not including transmigrants. The breakdown of the population in various countries is shown in Table 2. Large numbers are found in Indonesia and the Philippines, followed by Thailand

and Vietnam. They belong to various tribes (Senoi, Jakun of Peninsular Malaysia; Punan, Bidayuh, Bajau of Borneo; Kubu of Sumatra; Acta of the Philippines) and lead a traditional farming lifestyle including hunting, fishing and gathering non-timber forest products for their daily needs. These activities, together with farming, form an integrated system of resource utilization. Several tribes lead nomadic lives while others have been resettled in new villages by local governments, where they farm small plots of land.

The non-timber forest products utilized by forest dwellers consist of all biological materials which are extracted from natural forests for human use. These include foods, medicines, spices, essential oils, resins, gums, latexes, tannins, dyes, ornamental plants, wildlife (products and game), fuelwood, fodder, and raw materials such as rattan (Plate 8), bamboo and fibres. A comprehensive account of the economic value of non-timber forest products in South-east Asia has been documented (de Beer and McDermott, 1989).

Table 2. Forest dwelling populations in South-east Asia

Country	Number of People ('000s)
Brunei	20
Burma	2,600
Indonesia	7,500
Laos	1,000
Malaysia	770
Philippines	7,000
Thailand	5,000
Vietnam	5,000
Total	28,890

Source: de Beer and McDermott (1989)

■ Edible plant products

In South-east Asia, particularly in Papua New Guinea and Borneo, the most important staple food is wild or semi-wild sago from *Metroxylon sagu* and other palms like *Caryopha, Arenga, Caryota* and *Eugeissona* spp. which grow in freshwater swamps. Sago is processed into flour for making savoury or sweet puddings. Tapioca, maize and yams are the main staple food for traditional farmers. These are boiled or roasted and eaten with side dishes of fish, vegetables or pickles.

The most abundant food resources, available throughout the year from the forests, are vegetable material from many species of ferns *(Athyrium esculentum, Achrosticum aureum)*, herbs (*Ipomea* spp.), shoots of woody plants *(Manihot esculenta)*, flowers (*Musa* spp.), or seeds of legumes *(Parkia speciosa, Pithicellobium jiringa)* and young jackfruits (*Artocarpus* spp.). Others include tubers *(Ipomea batatas)*, roots, rhizomes (*Zingiber* spp.) and corms (*Dioscorea* spp., *Colocasia* spp.) which are usually extracted for starch or pickled. Most of the vegetables are eaten raw or blanched as salads, or used for flavouring food. Occasionally, mushrooms (*Cantherullus* spp.) are harvested off fallen tree trunks or from termite mounds (*Termitomyces* spp.), then made into soups.

Some forest fruits like banana and citruses are available throughout the year but others like durian (*Durio* spp.), mangosteen *(Garcinia mangostana)*, rambutan *(Nephelium lappaceum)* and mangoes

(*Mangifera* spp.) are seasonal. These fruits are eaten fresh, roasted, boiled, made into cakes or preserved. The preserved fleshy aril of durian seeds is a delicacy, used for flavouring curries. Fruits of *Gnetum gnemon* are commonly eaten as crisps. Various nuts from *Castanopsis, Canarium* and *Dacryodes* spp. are harvested for snacks.

Sugar, syrup or juices are obtained from boiling liquids of incised palm inflorescences until a thick mixture is formed. Sometimes these liquids are fermented to produce an alcoholic beverage known as 'toddy'. Honey is obtained after burning beehives (*Apis* spp.) and is frequently used as a medicine sweetener.

Edible oils are obtained from fruits of *Shorea* spp., *Aleurites moluccana* trees or seeds of *Pangium edule.*

Finally, there is a variety of spices that can be harvested from the forest for daily use. The most common are stems and rhizomes of *Languas galanga*, *Zingiber* spp., the leaves of *Pandanus odoratissimus*, and the bark of *Cinnamomum burmanii.*

■ Edible animal products

Forest dwellers eat a wide range of bushmeat from wild animals like: mammals (including: pigs, *Sus barbatus;* sambar deer, *Cervus unicolor;* and macaque, *Macaca fascicularis*); birds (argus pheasant, *Argusianus argus*); crocodile, *Crocodylus porosus*; snakes, *Python* spp.; frogs, *Rana* spp.; insects (grasshoppers, larvae of palm weevil, *Rhynchoporus ferrugineus*); a variety of freshwater fish (carps, cat fish); cockles (*Anadara graciosa*); and mud crabs (*Scylla serrata*).

■ Medicinal products

A great variety of plant and animal products are utilized as medicines, charms, aphrodisiacs or for treatment of superficial wounds. In Thailand, *Rauwolfia serpentina* is collected for use in local medicine or exported to national and international companies. The root of this plant contains alkaloids such as reserpine and rescinamine which are components of sedatives. In Indonesia and Malaysia, certain plants (*Pandanus* sp., *Dracaena* sp.) are planted around the huts of families with new born infants, to ward off evil spirits.

■ Non-edible plant products

The most important non-edible plant products are those used as building materials like rattans (*Calamus* spp., *Korthalsia* sp *Daemonorops* sp., *Plectocomia* sp.), bamboo (*Bambusa, Dendrocalamus* and *Gigantochloea* spp.) and wood. Some of these are used in basketry, household utensils, canoes, bows and arrows, blow pipes and traps. Bamboo poles are usually cut into half metre lengths for baking glutinous rice or tapioca. Wood from mangrove species like *Rhizophora* spp. are harvested periodically for fuelwood and charcoal.

Forest dwellers depend on a variety of herbs, ferns, grasses and lianes as fibres for clothings, fishing nets, clothes lines or goat leads. *Pandanus* leaves, stems of lianes and pitcher plants (*Nepenthus* spp.) and bark of *Gnetum* are commonly interwoven for these purposes.

A great variety of ornamental plants can be harvested from the rainforests of South-east Asia, like ferns (*Asplenium nidus, Cyathea contaminans*), herbs (aroids, grasses and sedges), shrubs (*Ixora* sp.) and palms (*Licuala* sp., *Cyrtostachys lacca*). Exotic flowers (orchids and gesneriads) are much sought after by nurseries, both locally and abroad.

Plant products and exudates are also extracted from various species to be utilized as preservatives, adhesives or varnishes. Some important plant extracts are resin (from *Balanocarpus, Hopea, Shorea, Dipterocarpus* and *Agathis damara*), camphor (*Dryobalanops aromatica*), gum (*Styrax* sp.), incense (*Aquilaria* spp.) and latex (*Palaquium gutta, Dyera costulata*).

Important animal products include wax secreted by bees which is extensively used in batik-printing, polishes, cosmetics, candles and castings. Also, pollen, royal jelly and venom are used as medicines in Thailand.

Forest dwellers have a good working knowledge of sustainable resource management. They only harvest the required amount of plant or animal extracts without severe damage to the species' populations. They are fully aware that their survival depends on the survival of the plants and animals within their environment. This innate ecological consideration is indirectly expressed in the forms of taboos or spirit appeasement which, in a way, discourage excessive exploitation.

Trade

In South-east Asia, trade in non-timber forest products has been in existence since the fifth century, when resins and oils were exported from western Indonesian islands to China. Later, around 850 AD, there was active trade between the middle-eastern countries, and Peninsular Malaysia. This continued to flourish in South-east Asia until its height in the 19th and 20th centuries when non-timber forest products were exported to Europe. However, after the Second World War, the export of these products began to decline as there were greater demands for tropical hardwood timber instead. In the late 1980s, as a result of global recession, low market prices and great concern for rainforest conservation and management, the demand for tropical hardwood timber also declined. Currently there is renewed interest in non-timber forest product extraction, resource development and trade, as alternatives to traditional logging and forest clearance. The ultimate objectives are the promotion of multiple resource utilization, maintenance of biodiversity, the greening of the environment and to perpetuate a desirable quality of life for the present and future generations.

In South-east Asia, barter trading is common in remote areas. As goods are seldom exchanged for money, forest dwellers have little knowledge of the true value of their market goods. Another aspect of great relevance to these people is the fact that these non-timber forest products are free, abundant and accessible. Usually, goods collected by remote forest dwellers are bought by village middlemen who act as liaisons between collectors and village shopkeepers in larger trade centres. The goods are subsequently sold to urban buyers who have links with foreign importers.

The export values of non-timber forest products

from South-east Asia range from $11 million in Malaysia and $32 million in Thailand to $238 million in Indonesia - the leading exporter of these products (de Beer and McDermott, 1989). Commercially, rattan is the most important non-timber forest product exported from South-east Asia. The total value in export trade of finished rattan product is about $2.7 billion per year. The major producers of rattan are Indonesia while secondary producers include Malaysia, Thailand and the Philippines.

Business Opportunities

One way of conserving natural forest is to identify, develop, promote and market various non-timber forest products to obtain better revenues than timber. The main object is forest conservation and management. Scientists, businessmen, economists and advertising agencies should work closely together to promote this idea.

Based on previous studies in lowland, montane and recently, heath forests in Malaysia, the following business opportunities should be considered:

■ Food industry

There are untapped potentials for food flavouring, colouring, preservatives, preserves and jams and light snacks. Some species to consider are *Parkia speciosa, Averrhoa bilimbii, Rhodomyrtus tormentosa, Garcinia* spp., *Gnetum gnemon* and *Salacca conferta.*

■ Pharmaceutical industry

New scents for perfumes, soaps, shampoos, powders and lotions. *Neolitsea* sp. (Plate 9) and *Melaleuca cajeputi* are tree species that should be studied. There are several herbaceous plants which should be considered as well, for example lemon grass, gingers and asters.

Male aphrodisiacs sell very well. Currently in Malaysia *Eurycoma longifolia* has received much publicity although the potency of the roots as aphrodisiacs has yet to be verified scientifically. There are plans to grow this tree commercially.

Herbal tonics and post-natal herbal treatment are consumed or practised regularly by village and forest womenfolk. However, there is a growing trend among educated women in towns and cities to do likewise especially after discovering the benefits derived from doing so.

■ Ornamental plants

There are many tree species from heath forests which are suitable ornamentals for exposed areas such as road-sides and city parks, for example *Garcinia homroniana* and species of *Ancistrocladus* and *Ploiorium.* Herbs with great potential as ornamentals include species of *Hoya*, gesneriads, *Nepenthes*, and *Eriocaulon.*

Conclusion

The rainforests of South-east Asia are too valuable a resource to be destroyed for timber. There are hundreds of useful non-timber forest products that have been utilized by mankind over thousands of years. There are perhaps even more useful forest products which have yet to be identified and developed. It is therefore our duty to pave the way for future extractive management and the perpetuation of rainforests.

References

de Beer, J H and M J McDermott (1989). *The Economic Non-timber Forest Products in Southeast Asia with Emphasis on Indonesia, Malaysia and Thailand.* Netherlands Committee for IUCN, Amsterdam, p 175

Poore, D (1989). *No Timber Without Trees: Sustainability in the Tropical Forest.* Earthscan Publications Ltd, London, p 252

Pringle, S L (1969). World supply and demand of hardwoods. In T C Whitmore (ed) (1984). *Tropical Rainforest of the Far East.* Clarendon Press, Oxford

Whitmore, T C (1984). *Tropical Rainforest of the Far East.* Second edition, Clarendon Press, Oxford

Discussion

Panel
Dr José Lutzenberger, Bob Malachi, Dr Noraini Tamin, Mario Cordeira de Lima, Antonio Macedo

Anthony Dixon, Project Borneo, Harvard Business School. I have a question for Bob Malichi. I sampled some of your delicious honey, and unlike much of the forest honey in Borneo, it is not fermented. My question is a technical one. What procedures do you use to ensure that the honey does not ferment, especially when the source of the honey is decentralized?

Bob Malichi. That is a very important question. We usually teach the bee-keepers to select the type of honey to crop in the hive. Honey is produced in stages, forming layers as it ripens and eventually becoming uniform. If this ripe honey is mixed with some other that is still in the process of ripening, then you are bound to get fermentation which is not suitable for the world market. The bee-keepers know which type they can sell and which they can use for other purposes - beer brewing for example.

Questioner, Management Today Magazine. A question for Dr Lutzenberger. There have been proposals for a huge debt swap for half of Brazil's debt to save the rainforest. Do you see this as a way forward?

Dr José Lutzenberger. Yes, I see this as one of the mechanisms that we can and must use, not only to solve the debt problem, but also to help protect what has to be preserved. Our Government is looking into this question.

Dr Anthony Anderson, The Ford Foundation. Dr Lutzenberger, today we had an opportunity to hear from the presentations of Mario de Lima and Antonio Macedo how the Alliance of Forest Peoples is actually working. At the present time in Brazil, FUNAI (the National Indian Foundation) is within the Ministry of Justice and I know that there is interest on the part of the Indians to come under the auspices of the Secretary of the Environment. This is due to the fact that many indigenous groups can identify with the ideals of the rubber tappers and the concept of extractive reserves which are now being legalized by IBAMA (Brazilian Environmental Institute) and which comes under your Secretariat. Is there any prospect from your point of view of FUNAI being put under the Environmental Secretariat?

Dr José Lutzenberger. I had a conversation with our President on Friday, and I suggested to him that FUNAI now be simply abolished. FUNAI is so corrupt and disorganized, and such a meaningless organization that it would make little difference to the Indians if it disappeared. In the past it has almost never worked for the Indians, only for the *garimpeiros*, the ranchers and others, and it would be almost impossible to reform the organization. There was talk that it should come to my

Secretariat, but I would prefer to have it abolished and then do something new - maybe a small secretariat at the level of the Presidency or within my Secretariat. We could obviously use all the good anthropologists at FUNAI, but most of the others will have to go. I hope that we can work out something in the near future that will really work. Even the Indians have proposed that an Indian Secretariat be set up instead of FUNAI. I do not know yet whether this will happen or not but this is the idea that is now being discussed.

Dr Maria Allegretti, Institute of Amazonian Studies. Various Brazilian, North American and European environmental organizations have given considerable thought and attention to the possibility of transforming extractive reserves into a government priority.

I would like to know if this idea is a strong possibility and if the forest peoples will be allowed to participate in the administration of such areas, perhaps alongside the Environmental Secretariat. Is this a priority or does the economic situation in the Brazilian Amazon mean that such plans will always be a dream?

Dr José Lutzenberger. NGOs are a priority of our Government - I can only assure you that they are. The President is very concerned about these questions and he has given me assurance that he will do what he can.

Nicholas Guppy, Associate Centre for Human Ecology, Edinburgh University. A question for Dr Lutzenberger. It strikes me that all the problems of tropical rainforest destruction stems from one underlying issue, which is that they have no economic value as living forests. We have not given them that. How can we change that? Every year, for example, agriculturists know the costs of seeds, for tillage etc, but there is no relationship between demand and supply for forests because the regrowth period is so long. We cannot forecast it, it does not exist. We need, I believe, to create, world-wide, a sort of economic buffer for natural ecosystems.

Dr José Lutzenberger. You touched on a very fundamental point about our present economic thinking. Now that the eastern countries have begun to accept that central planning does not work, they seem to expect market forces to provide a solution to their problems. The market really is a cybernetic instrument for finding the balance between supply and demand, but only when it is complete, and most of our markets are not. An American economist conducted a very interesting thought experiment some years ago. He said, supposing the Mona Lisa was auctioned with only shoeshine boys in the room, it would probably only go for five dollars, if not less.

This is the situation of many of our markets today. A cattle rancher near Amazonia cuts down nearly ten thousand hectares of forest to sow grass for his cattle; for him the forest has a negative value, he spends money to make it disappear. There is therefore something very wrong with the way we handle our present markets and we must find ways of putting representatives of other forces into the market. There are several 'bidders' that should be in the market that are not. For instance, future generations are not in our markets; if they were here, we certainly would not be doing the things that we are doing. Nature is not present; if all the other creatures had something to say in our markets they would not accept what we were doing. And a sizeable fraction of present humanity is not present either; the market only sees demand expressed in money terms. We have millions of people who have a tremendous need for food and commodities, but because they have no money to pay, they are not present in our markets. So we must really re-think modern economics and perhaps we could introduce some regulatory market mechanism to take these absentees into consideration. How, I do not know, but I am making an appeal to the economists present today; let us work something out. We must find some way to make the market respond to what is really important to Gaia and the living planet as a whole.

Colombia: Setting a Precedent for the World

Martin von Hildebrand
Head of Indian Affairs for the Colombian Government

Summary

Martin von Hildebrand has spent most of the last 17 years living with Indian communities in the Amazon where he has supported their fight for self-determination. This presentation outlines Colombia's official policy on tropical rainforests, the defense of Indian rights and the conservation of the Amazon ecosystems.

First of all, I would like to thank Friends of the Earth for giving me the opportunity to speak about Colombia's policy on tropical rainforests. In a few words I will attempt to outline the situation in general and then concentrate on the Colombian Amazon.

In Colombia, 2 per cent of the population are Indians, that is, people who define themselves as such. These people have all the rights of other citizens but also have further special rights which the state recognizes because they maintain their status as descendants of this territory. These rights encompass collective land rights over the traditional territories they occupy; cultural and social rights such as the legal recognition of their political, educational and health institutions; and other rights such as being exempt from paying taxes or doing military service.

The Indian land rights were already recognized by the Spanish Crown, that is, they recognized that the Indians owned the territories that the Spaniards had not conquered. In conquered areas, the Indians were recognized in titles over reservations where they lived and produced food for their conquerors.

After independence, at the beginning of the 19th century, all the land entered into the market and during the 150 years that followed, the Indians lost much of their land in the Andean area. There was no pressure on the Amazonian area. During this time the Indians kept on struggling for their land and insisting on the validity of the titles issued by the Spanish Crown.

In the 1960s, with the beginning of the Agrarian Reform, the Indian land rights were recognized again - that is, their right to the territories they still occupied and the validity of the Spanish titles. During the 1970s and 80s, the Government recognized these rights and bought land from landholders to hand back to the Indians. This has been a long and costly process from an economic and political point of view. The process was definitely stimulated by the continuous pressure of the Indian organizations, members of whom have lost their lives claiming their rights.

The result now is that 2 per cent of the population owns 18 per cent of the country's territory, that is 257,174 square kilometres of which the majority is in the Amazon forest (180,000 square kilometres). The Colombian tropical rainforest covers about 8 per cent of the Amazon basin and 33 per cent of the Colombian territory. The total area is 400,000 square kilometres of which 10 per cent has been occupied by settlers at the foot of the Andean mountains. The remaining 90 per cent is practically untouched rainforest, mainly inhabited by Indian communities. These communities have kept their traditional way of life, in spite of the outside pressures to which they have been exposed during this century.

In this area the first Indian land rights were recognized at the beginning of the 1980s. But it was not until President Barco's Government of 1986-1990 that an official policy recognizing Indian land rights in the Amazon was implemented. During this period 130,000 square kilometres were recognized and they have the right to administer their territories according to their customs and traditions.

This policy of the Government is not only the recognition of Indian rights but seeks the conservation of the rainforest. About 55,000 Indians, belonging to 50 different cultures, inhabit the area. For the Government to protect 180,000 square kilometres of rainforest is an impossible task. For the Indians on their own it is also very difficult. But the Indians, as owners of the land and supported by the Government, can manage. This is possible because they live along the rivers which are the only way of access to the forest. No roads exist in this part of the country.

The Government had tried other resources to protect the forest, such as declaiming it by law as a general forest reserve or by creating large national parks. But in both cases it did not have the capability to patrol such huge areas, nor were many people willing to go and live in isolation out in the wilderness. The combination of Indian land rights and the protection of the forest by those who, over the centuries, have learned how to live as part of it, seems to be the most responsible solution.

Even from the political or economic view, we know that the forest offers a great deal to the world and that we are only familiar with about 10 per cent of its species. We could benefit greatly by preserving and studying the rainforest in greater depth, which would make good business sense in the long term.

Forming national parks is not really an option, because 200,000 square kilometres is far too large to be given the term 'park' and we would not be able to police an area of that size. 'Reservations' would be no better. Government control of any description is inherently uncertain because one never knows what a future government might do. Recognition of the rights of Indian communities over the land is the most secure way of ensuring that the forest will be preserved.

But this also implies, in fact it is imperative, that we recognize and support their way of life and traditions. To suggest that the Indians use the forest sustainably is to simplify the issue because theirs is a holistic, spiritual relationship with the land which goes far beyond our normal understanding of the word 'sustainable'.

For the Indians the forest is inhabited by guardians and spirits. There are guardians for different animals - tapirs, jaguars, deer - and each guardian has a right to the food energy from the plants in this area and a responsibility to those plants and other animals. When an Indian walks through the forest, the moment he leaves his own territory of a few hectares around his house, he immediately enters a new territory and has to respect the domain of the people and animals that occupy it. He knows that if he is going to hunt he must ask permission and make an offering in exchange for what he is going to extract because he is going to take energy from the plants and animals and use it in his own community. If he fails to ask for permission then the owner of the area can induce sickness in him and regain that energy back when the person dies.

The Indians believe that the energy in the forest is finite and entrust its protection and distribution to a wise man in the community who is highly trained, religious, sensitive and experienced in observing the environment. He advises on where to hunt and fish so that these activities are carried out in a sustainable way, in order that the energy of the different species is not depleted.

In the West we have lost our spiritual relationship with the environment because we attach such great importance to a pragmatic, materialistic way of seeing the world. Both our Government and the West in general must re-assess all their projects to ensure that we are not guilty of imposing this upon the Indians without reference to their culture, religion, social organization and economy. We need to listen to the people and work with them. In Colombia this approach has now begun.

In the Colombian Amazon we have field officers, consisting of NGO and Government staff, who visit the Indian territories and discuss their ideas so that the Indians begin to administer their own territory and the services (education, health, production) within them. It is not at all easy; we are used to thinking that we have all the answers and we have to be careful that we are not simply changing the way in which we impose our ideas on the Indians, rather than actually rethinking what we are doing.

Dr Lutzenberger put it very clearly when he suggested that the way we think and act in our own economies is wrong. I believe that this is very important because we are centralizing everything and not giving other people and species a chance to survive. If we want the rainforest to be harvested by local people, we have to stabilize colonization, give the Indians their land rights and back them to administer the forest in the way they have always done but with far less outside pressure. If it is left to the free market, local control will be lost and with it the forests themselves.

The Colombian policy is attempting to address the ecological and cultural importance of the forest, rather than merely short-term economics. We are trying to establish a moratorium to give the Indian people, the Government, the scientists and all of us who are conscious of the importance of the rainforest, time to rethink, to listen to each other and to come up with policies that recognize its real importance and that of the forest people.

Forestry and Non-wood Products: a Developing Country's Perspective

Dr Otto Soemarwoto
Director, Institute of Ecology, Padjajaran University, Bandung, Indonesia

Summary

Historically, forests have been used in development as a source of fuelwood and construction materials and have been converted to other land-uses in the development process. Because the developed countries started to develop earlier, deforestation in the non-tropics has been much more extensive than in the tropics. Consequently, it has been suggested that the deforestation problem should be looked at in a holistic way rather than focusing solely on tropical areas. The concept of the global forest should be developed.

Sustainable production of non-timber products directly from the forest to serve the international market, which demands huge quantities, cannot possibly be achieved. It is recommended that plantations and/or small home-gardens are developed which should be designed in such a way that they can ensure the maintenance of biodiversity and other ecological functions of the remaining forest at a high level. It is also essential to manage population pressure in order to keep it as low as possible.

Introduction

Indonesia is becoming increasingly aware of environmental issues. Laws have been enacted although, unfortunately, their enforcement is still weak not only in the field of the environment but in other areas as well. Lately, however, strong measures are beginning to be taken. For example, a logging company was recently fined about 1 million US dollars for not complying with the existing regulations. Techniques are also being developed to improve the methods of monitoring and controlling logging with the use of aerial photographs and satellites.

But in spite of these positive actions there has been much hesitation about moving ahead more vigorously, partly because of economic reasons and partly because of a sense of being treated unfairly. Questions are being asked. For example:

- If the developed countries are really serious in wanting to save the tropical forests, why don't they remove trade barriers and farm subsidies to enable us to gain more access to international markets and earn more hard currency from our non-timber exports?

- Why should we serve as the filter or the lung of the world, while the developed countries are pumping tons of carbon dioxide into the air daily from their industries and cars?

■ Why should we stop development at a time when millions of people still suffer from malnutrition, infant mortality is still high, infectious diseases are still rampant and many children cannot go to school?

■ Why do they insist that we should have sustainable development (a very elusive term which can be interpreted in many different ways to suit one's need) while their consumerist way of living, which is highly polluting and which rapidly depletes the world's resources, cannot possibly be sustainable?

Of course, the classic answer of the developed countries has been: we are not accusing you and we are not asking you to stop development. This finger-pointing on both sides is unfortunate because with environmental problems becoming so serious and extensive, unless they are checked adequately and in time, there will be no winners, only losers.

Holistic approach

Focusing on the tropical forests creates the impression that tropical countries are the culprits in global problems such as global warming and the mass extinction of species. Indeed, the general public tends to hold this view as it does not have a sufficiently broad information base about these problems and their causes, and are exposed almost daily to television programmes which depict tropical deforestation and burning. Even among scientists such an erroneous view is not uncommon. When we look at deforestation in a historical perspective it becomes apparent that it has been the 'normal' way of development since forests are the source of wood for fuel and building materials for houses, factories and ships, and provide land for settlements, agriculture, pasture and roads.

Matthews (1983) reported that from the pre-agricultural era to the present, deforestation in the non-tropical countries has been much larger than in the tropics (6.5 million square kilometres in the non-tropics compared to 0.5 million square kilometres in the tropics)[1].

It is no wonder, therefore, that only 33 per cent of Europe as a whole and 30 per cent of the United States is covered with forest and woodland, while Brazil, Indonesia and Malaysia are 67 per cent covered while Zaire is 78 per cent covered (World Resources Institute [WRI] and the International Institute for Environment and Development [IIED], 1986). Even in recent times, deforestation in the United States and Australia is comparable to that in Brazil and much higher than in Indonesia (Williams, 1989).

It is understandable, therefore, that the developing countries are using the forests for their development and that, since many have started to develop only in the last decade or so, their present rate of deforestation is high. It is also unfortunate that the development of these countries coincides with a time when the atmosphere is already loaded with increasing concentrations of greenhouse gases, primarily carbon dioxide from the industrialized countries, and secondly, when the developed countries have been greatly in need of genetic resources for their industries and agricultural improvement.

Consequently, the developing countries are facing severe criticisms, especially because there are now vocal NGOs and a world-wide network of mass media which can broadcast the news instantaneously throughout the world, while in former times the developed countries could deforest without any protest. It should also be noted that before the Second World War, deforestation in the now independent countries of the tropics was carried out by the Europeans who colonized these countries for the establishment of plantations to serve their economies. In Indonesia, the Cultuurstelsel, which was instituted by the Dutch in the 1800s, in which the indigenous people were compelled to grow estate crops, also had a disastrous effect on the forests.

However, it is surprising that the recent large-scale deforestation in the developed countries escapes the severe protests which are being levelled at the developing countries. Furthermore, the forests in the northern hemisphere are now being threatened by acid rain and ozone pollution and the damage is progressing at a disturbing rate (Agren and Pape, 1989; WRI and IIED, 1986). In 1988, in Europe alone, almost 50 million hectares, comprising 35 per cent of the total forest area, were suffering to a greater or lesser degree. Eight regions, namely Czechoslovakia, Greece, the United Kingdom, Estonia (Soviet Union), West Germany, Tuscany (Italy), Liechtenstein and Norway, had 50 per cent or more of their forests damaged (French, 1990). The carbon from the dead trees will eventually enter the atmosphere while the still living but damaged trees are reduced in their capacity to sequester carbon.

With respect to species extinction, on the basis of Matthews' data and the species-area relationship, it can be estimated that deforestation has caused about 6 per cent of the total species in the non-tropical areas to become extinct, but in the tropical countries, about 1 per cent. Acid rain has also reduced the number of species in many lakes, or even rendered them completely unsuitable for aquatic life (French, 1990).

It should also be taken into account that it is not only the abundance of species in the tropics that is important, but also their degree of endemism and their relation to economic value. Endemic species are more prone to extinction because their distribution is limited to certain areas and their adaptation to unique environments. Many such species are found on isolated islands. Hawaii, New Zealand and Australia, for example, have a high degree of endemism and many endemic species live in these areas which are not in the underdeveloped countries. Many have become extinct before and after contact with Americans and Europeans.

Scientists have identified regions of diversity of domestic plants and animals which originally were proposed by Vavilov (*eg* Cox and Atkins, 1964, Hoyt, 1988, Reid and Miller, 1989). These so called Vavilov centres, which have since been modified in the light of new findings, are extremely important because the genetic resources which they harbour are closely related to our economic plants and animals, *eg* rice, maize, wheat, tea, citrus, sheep, goat, and fowl. These centres are located not only in the tropics but also, for example, in the Mediterranean and China. Crops which originate in the Mediterranean centre include cabbage, lettuce, cauliflower, radish and beet. These species are also important in Indonesia although habitat destruction and acid rain are causing genetic erosion there.

The above discussion is not intended to justify deforestation in Indonesia and the tropical countries, but rather to show the importance of looking at the global problems in a holistic manner. Such an approach prevents us from having tunnel vision. Instead of just focusing on the tropical forests, we should develop a concept of the global forest. This would then enable us to examine the problems in a holistic and balanced way, to refrain from accusing others and instead to ask ourselves what each of us can do to contribute to the solution of the global problems facing us, because it is quite clear that the achievement of this goal requires global solidarity.

Non-timber production

Traditionally, non-timber production from forests has always been carried out by forest dwellers for their own use, such as food, medicine and ritual items, and goods to barter with traders who frequent their settlements. Because of the destructive effects of logging, the interest in non-timber products has recently increased as observations have shown that the extraction of these products causes little damage to the forests. It is generally assumed that, in contrast to logging, non-timber production is a sustainable means of forest exploitation.

Studies have also shown that these products can have higher economic values than timber (*eg* de Beer and McDermott, 1989) and an increasing shift from timber to non-timber production has been suggested. So far, sustainable non-timber production has been carried out at low intensities to satisfy the daily needs of the local people. But it can equally be said that timber production by the local people for their own use has also been sustainable. Due to market forces, however, when production intensities increase, control of harvesting is weak and the ecological conditions for their growth are little known, this sustainability becomes questionable.

This is what has happened with logging in the past few decades. If the market demand for the non-timber products were to increase sharply and prices increased accordingly, a rush for these products would presumably follow which would cause over-exploitation with detrimental effects, and the local people would benefit little from the rush, if at all. Even if there were no rush, it would still be difficult to assess the environmental impacts of production, if it were increasing to satisfy the demand of the international market. This is because the level of sustainable yield, the ecological requirements for growth and the ecological functions of many of the non-timber species in the forest ecosystem are little-known, or even completely unknown. The over-exploitation of a key species could also cause a cascade effect in endangering other species. Conversely, it could cause an outbreak of a prey species with all its adverse consequences (Reid and Miller, 1989).

Experience has taught us that large-scale sustainable production of non-timber forest products for the international market can be achieved by cultivating the plantation plants such as cocoa, palm oil, quinine and rubber. These plantations have been in existence for more than a hundred years without signs of decline. Sustainable production can also be achieved on a small scale by individual farmers and this has been demonstrated in the home-gardens. In Java, for example, these have existed for more than a thousand years. Home-gardens have been shown to play an important role as a source of nutrition, income, fuelwood and various other items for the villagers (Soemarwoto, 1987; Soemarwoto and Soemarwoto, 1984).

From the above experiences, a sensible way of increasing the production of non-timber materials would be to establish either large scale plantations of the desired species and/or small scale ones such as home-gardens. Ideally, these home-gardens should be planted with a mixture of species in which the canopies form a multi-storey structure mimicking the forest and the species should be chosen to serve the nutritional, economic and socio-cultural needs of the people. An additional advantage of the multi-storey structure is that it can effectively control soil erosion.

The plantations and the home-gardens should have a spatial design which can maximize the number of species in the remaining forest. Fragmentation of the forest, for example, should be avoided and corridors should be established between parts of the forest. In order that the biodiversity and ecological functions of the remaining forest can be maintained at a high level from the very beginning of the development process and as an integral part of it, plans should be made for the establishment of national parks which cover a sufficiently large forest area.

Management of population pressure

Mounting population pressure will continue to increase, and sooner or later the people will encroach on the forest to obtain additional land for growing their crops. Plans should therefore be made to deal with this problem. A quantitative model has been developed to serve as a planning tool for keeping the population pressure at a low level (Soemarwoto 1985, 1990). Essentially it aims to minimize population demands on the land by a combination of agricultural and non-agricultural development. This development aims to improve agricultural technology in order to increase productivity and development of rural industries for the post-harvest processing of the produce. This would add value which would be enjoyed by the people and would generate employment, keeping the number of farmers low. Non-agricultural activities which have high economic potential in the area should be enhanced, so long as preventive measures are taken against potential adverse environmental impacts whenever necessary.

Effective co-operatives should also be developed with the aim of providing credits, developing markets and organizing training courses for the people, in farming and industrial techniques and management. Naturally, family planning programmes should be initiated as soon as possible. It should be noted that the management of population pressure is people-centred, ie the primary aim is to provide the people with sources of income which will enable them to maintain an adequate living standard which will in turn remove the need for bringing additional forest into cultivation.

Editors' footnote

1. Professor Norman Myers estimates, in a report for Friends of the Earth entitled *Deforestation Rates in Tropical Forests and their Climatic Implications,* that only 7.8 million square kilometres of the world's original tropical moist forest cover (approximately 16 million square kilometres) remains.

References

Agren, C and R Pape (1989). Accelerating damage seen. *Acid News* 1: 3-5

Cox, G W and M D Atkins (1964). *Agricultural Ecology.* Freeman and Company, San Francisco

de Beer, J H and M J McDermott (1989). *The Economic Value of Non-timber Forest Products in Southeast Asia.* Netherlands Committee for IUCN, Amsterdam

French, H (1990). Clearing the air. In L Starke (ed), *State of the World.* Worldwatch Institute, Washington DC

Hoyt, E (1988). *Conserving the Wild Relatives of Crops.* IBPGR/IUCN/WWF, Rome

Matthews, E (1983). Global vegetation and land use: new high-resolution data bases for climate studies. *American Meteorological Society* 22: 474-487

Reid, W V and K R Miller (1989). *Keeping Options Alive. The Scientific Basis for Conserving Biodiversity.* World Resources Institute, Washington DC

Soemarwoto, O (1985). A quantitative model of population pressure and its potential use in development planning. *Demografi Indonesia* 12: 1-15

Soemarwoto, O (1987). Home-gardens: a traditional agroforestry system with a promising future. In H A Steppler and P K R Nair (eds), *Agroforestry, A Decade of Development,* ICRAF, Nairobi, pp 157-170

Soemarwoto, O (1990). *Rural Industrialization as a Means for Managing Population Pressure.* Paper presented at YIIS-EUR Symposium on Small Industries. Foundation for Social Sciences, Jakarta, Indonesia

Soemarwoto, O and I Soemarwoto (1984). The Javanese rural ecosystem. In A T Rambo and P E Sajise (eds), *An Introduction to Human Ecology Research on Agriculture Systems in Southeast Asia.* University of the Philippines, Los Banos, Philippines, pp 254-287

Williams, M (1989). Deforestation: past and present. *Progress in Human Geography* 13: 176-208

World Resources Institute and the International Institute for Environment and Development (1986). *World Resources 1986.* World Resources Institute and the International Institute for Environment and Development, Washington DC

The Tropical Forestry Action Plan (TFAP) and Non-wood Forest Products

Michael Flint
Overseas Development Administration, 94 Victoria Street, London SW1E 5JL United Kingdom

Summary

This paper reviews the way TFAP has addressed the issue of non-wood forest products in eight countries in Latin America, Africa and Asia. The quality and coverage of these national TFAPs is highly variable, and the economic data on non-wood products extremely limited, but on balance non-wood forest products have been inadequately covered. Reasons include the widespread ignorance and undervaluation of non-wood products, the low priority generally accorded by governments, and the narrow composition of most TFAP review teams. However, the need for TFAPs to concentrate on the priority issues affecting forest degradation may justify the low priority initially given to non-wood products. Furthermore, while there is a strong social and environmental case for increased emphasis on non-wood products, the economic potential may be limited. Recommendations for improving the TFAP process with respect to non-wood products include:

i) Increased support for the establishment and operation of national TFAP Co-ordination Units.
ii) Higher priority for the collection of data on non-wood forest products and for research into existing and improved agro-extractive systems.
iii) Supplementary guidance notes on non-wood forest products should be produced by the TFAP Co-ordinating Unit at FAO.
iv) Broader multi-disciplinary involvement is required throughout the TFAP process.
v) Increased resources for consultations with forest users, and for the involvement of national and international NGOs, should be provided to national TFAPs.
vi) Greater attention should be paid to the issue of forest use rights and land tenure.

A comparison of early and later national TFAPs shows that TFAP is improving. It offers national governments - assisted by international donors and NGOs - an unparalleled opportunity to review and reform policies affecting the forestry sector. Despite its shortcomings, it remains potentially the most important and influential mechanism for ensuring that non-wood forest products, and those dependent on them for their livelihoods, are given increased consideration in the design and implementation of development policies and projects.

Introduction

The Tropical Forestry Action Plan (TFAP) was launched in 1985 as an international initiative to address the problems of forest destruction and degradation. Its main objective is to assist developing countries to review and revise national policies and programmes affecting forest resources, and to provide a framework for securing international financial assistance (FAO, 1989a). TFAP Review Missions have now been completed in 21 countries and are in progress in a further 42 countries (TFAP, 1990)[1].

Non-wood forest products are extracted from forests without involving the removal of woody stems. Timber, fuelwood, and construction wood are excluded from this discussion, as are non-wood products from agroforestry systems outside forests and ecosystem services (watershed protection, climatic stabilization etc). This still leaves an enormous and diverse range of products: fruits; nuts; roots; leaves; fibres; animal fodder; oils; resins; tannins; gums; fungi; latex; spices; medicines; poisons; sweeteners; fish; birds; butterflies; live animals; meat; tourism; and scientific research. This diversity of products is matched by great variation in the economic importance of non-wood products in local, regional, national or international economies, and in the characteristics of product collection, marketing and utilization. Some meet essential basic needs as non-traded subsistence goods; others are internationally traded commodities worth millions of dollars. This diversity makes generalization across products and countries extremely difficult.

The existing role and further potential of non-wood products and extractive reserves as a means of protecting forest ecosystems and sustaining livelihoods has received wide attention (Peters *et al.*, 1989; Fearnside, 1989; Prance, 1990). This increased interest in non-wood products coincides with continued general criticism of TFAP, including its concentration on the timber sub-sector (WRM, 1990). The question of the extent to which TFAP can or should assist in the development of non-wood products is thus highly relevant.

The objective of this paper is to review the way TFAP has addressed the issue of non-wood products in a range of countries and to make proposals on how TFAP could improve its consideration of this issue in future. TFAP documentation and available supporting literature on non-wood products were studied for eight countries: Peru, Costa Rica, Belize, Ghana, Cameroon, Tanzania, Nepal and Papua New Guinea.

The paper begins with a review of the coverage of non-wood products within the general TFAP documentation. Detailed consideration of non-wood products within the eight national TFAPs are reviewed and the possible reasons for inadequate coverage discussed. The paper concludes with an examination of the economic case for an increased emphasis on non-wood products, and puts forward proposals for improving TFAP.

The Tropical Forestry Action Plan (TFAP)

TFAP is a proposed framework for action by governments of tropical countries. Except at the very beginning - when the World Resources

Institute (WRI) and the World Bank drew up a proposed investment programme for 56 countries (WRI, 1985) - TFAP has never been a 'plan' as such. It consists of a recommended planning and implementation process for national TFAPs, together with generalized action programmes in five priority areas: forestry in land-use, forest-based industrial development, fuelwood and energy, conservation of tropical forest ecosystems, and institutions.

The central TFAP document produced in 1985 contained references to non-wood products in two of the five priority areas: 'Industrial Development' and 'Conservation' (FAO, 1985). The document recognized that non-wood products may be locally and nationally important, that utilization systems should be developed that enabled the production of wood and non-wood products on a sustainable basis, and that the needs of local people should be paramount. The TFAP for Latin America contained greater mention of minor forest products (FAO, 1988). Small-scale minor forest product enterprises were highlighted in the 'Introduction', and under 'Land-use', but surprisingly were not mentioned under 'Industrial Development' (except in the Summary Report) or 'Conservation'. The most recent 'Guidelines for TFAP Implementation' (FAO, 1989a) include explicit but limited mention of non-wood products in the suggested terms of reference for the TFAP country missions under 'Land-use', 'Industrial Development', and 'Conservation'.

Judged by these documents, TFAP has not treated non-wood products as significant. Non-wood products appear to be mentioned for the sake of completeness rather than as substantive components. The proposed programmes are dominated by timber and fuelwood, and there is little indication of any change in emphasis over the period in question.

However, there are compelling reasons for saying that TFAP should not be judged solely by this documentation. TFAP has never been more than a suggested framework for national plans, and the extent to which these documents actually guided the national TFAP exercises is open to question. TFAP should primarily be judged by actual outcomes at the national level. The general TFAP literature is nevertheless instructive in so far as it reflects the low priority accorded to non-wood products in the last three decades.

TFAP in practice

Two major problems were encountered in this evaluation: incomplete TFAP documentation and the lack of data on the economic importance of non-wood products in each country. At best there are official export statistics of variable quality, long lists of species known to be used, and a few usually anecdotal case studies. Reliable data on internal trade, employment, incomes, dietary or subsistence value - let alone studies of development potential - are universally absent. This makes it extremely difficult to assess objectively the adequacy or otherwise of the TFAP. It is also appreciated that TFAP documentation is not a full record of the TFAP process, and does not necessarily reflect the debate and discussion which took place. The best that is possible in these circumstances is a subjective assessment of the following:

1) the coverage of non-wood products within the

TFAP sector review relative to their (estimated) economic importance as documented;

2) the number of projects proposed under the TFAP solely or partly covering non-wood products;

3) the extent to which the TFAP involved and incorporated the views of local people using the forest and non-governmental organizations (NGOs).

The findings of the review with regard to the above criteria are tabulated below, with TFAPs ranked as 'poor', 'fair' or 'good' according to the author's assessment.

A major, but not unexpected, finding of this review is the enormous variation between countries in the economic importance of non-wood products, the coverage of non-wood products within the national TFAPs, and in the overall quality of the TFAPs. Non-wood forest products can be economically important at three levels: exports, domestic income and employment, and local subsistence. The latter can include central contributions to household welfare in terms of food security, dietary supplements, health care and raw materials. Non-wood products are only of major export importance

Table 1: The findings of the TFAP review

Country	TFAP date	Importance of NWFP	(1) Review of NWFP	(2) NWFP (a) Projects	(3) NGOs Involved	Overall NWFP (b) Assessment
Belize	1989	Low	Fair	Nil	(not known)	Fair
Costa Rica	1990	Medium	Fair	Fair	Fair	Fair
Peru	1988	High	Good	Good	Poor	Fair
Ghana	1987	Medium	Poor	Poor	Poor	Poor (c)
Cameroon	1988	High	Fair	Fair	Poor	Fair
Tanzania	1989	Medium	Good	Good	Good	Good
Nepal	1988	High	Good	Good	(not known)	Good
Papua New Guinea	1990	High	Poor	Nil	Good	Poor (c)

Notes:

(a) NWFP = Non-wood forest products

(b) Refers to the adequacy of the treatment of non-wood products, not the quality of the TFAP as a whole.

(c) Although not included in the TFAP review, both the Ghana and Papua New Guinea TFAPs have given rise to significant non-wood product initiatives (see below).

for Peru and Nepal, but are still a significant source of cash and subsistence goods for rural people in at least some parts of all the other countries reviewed, with the apparent exception of Belize. The explanation for the latter is the low rural population density and the relatively small number of indigenous forest peoples. However, even in Belize, and in other countries where non-wood products are apparently not of major national importance (*eg* Tanzania and Costa Rica), the value to local people has to be taken into account in planning forest development and conservation policies. Most national TFAPs did not do this.

The quantity and quality of coverage within TFAPs is extremely variable. Both the earliest (Ghana, 1987) and latest (Papua New Guinea, 1990) TFAPs reviewed barely mentioned non-wood products. Equally, there were three TFAPs (Tanzania, Nepal and Peru) with relatively extensive coverage. Where non-wood products are discussed, a more general criticism is the undue emphasis on wildlife conservation - with insufficient attention to who bears the cost or receives the benefit of conservation initiatives - and a lack of attention to the importance of existing (and potential) animal and plant extractive systems. This is linked to a more general lack of socioeconomic perspective. The consideration of non-wood products in the Cameroon TFAP is a particular example - the actual and potential uses of a wide range of medicinal and food plants were documented, but not their importance within agricultural and forest livelihoods. More seriously, no TFAP appears to have considered the interrelationships between the value of non-wood products and existing, or proposed, development programmes. Even where non-wood products are considered, they tend to be viewed in isolation, and the social and economic effects of, for example, increased logging or conservation on non-wood livelihoods is rarely considered.

Apart from the more recent TFAPs (*eg* Tanzania and Papua New Guinea), the record of NGO involvement and local consultation in the TFAPs is generally poor. This deficiency is particularly significant for the consideration of non-wood products: many non-wood products are only important to the poor in remote areas, rarely figure in official statistics, and tend to be ignored in mainstream planning, research and extension. To the extent that NGOs might be expected to be sensitive to these aspects, their limited involvement in many early TFAPs may have contributed to the lack of coverage.

The inclusion of non-wood projects or components in the proposed national Action Plans mirrored the weight given to the issue during the TFAP review process. While only a few project proposals were solely concerned with non-wood products, a greater number included mention of these products. On the assumption that all ecosystem conservation projects and all agroforestry projects involved non-wood products, between 3 and 10 per cent by value of the proposed Action Plans can be said to have a non-wood component. Furthermore, to the extent that the institutional support projects are intended to benefit the forestry sector as a whole, it would be fair to conclude that at least some of the general project investment would assist in the development of the non-wood sub-sector. This particularly applies to support directed at strengthening the research, policy and planning departments, where it is reasonable to assume that greater inputs will lead to improvements in the understanding and valuation of non-wood extraction.

A necessary qualification is that it is premature to judge most national TFAPs. TFAP should not be judged solely by the content of the TFAP sector review or by the lists of projects identified, but by the process set in train, and by the changes in institutions, policies and development priorities which ultimately result. The TFAP documents reviewed are no more than statements of intent and outlines of proposed projects. While some policy, and to a lesser extent, institutional reforms can be implemented relatively quickly, it would be unusual for a new project to proceed from identification to implementation in much less than two years. The projects in most of the TFAPs reviewed have yet to be implemented.

More significantly, even where non-wood projects or components have been identified by the national TFAP, there is no certainty that any donor will provide the funding. For example, it remains to be seen whether the funding for the bee-keeping projects identified during the Tanzanian TFAP will be approved. On the other hand, the content of TFAP projects can change considerably during design, preparation, appraisal and implementation. New non-wood components may be added, as in Ghana where two additional non-wood research projects were identified and funded following the TFAP. The same is likely to happen in Papua New Guinea. The final outcome in terms of the emphasis on non-wood products could therefore be much better (or worse) than implied by the national Action Plans.

The selection of national TFAPs reviewed reveal great variation between countries, non-wood products, and the quality of the TFAPs themselves. General conclusions about the adequacy or otherwise of the coverage of non-wood products need to be drawn with caution. It is certainly not the case that non-wood products have universally been ignored by TFAP, and indeed the coverage in most national TFAPs was superior to that in the general TFAP documents produced by FAO. That said - with the possible exception of Nepal, Tanzania and Peru - in most of the cases studied consideration of non-wood forest products probably was less than justified by their socioeconomic importance to the extent that this is known from available information. A more general criticism of all the TFAPs is that they did not adequately address the issues from the perspective of the rural people actually involved in non-wood extraction and processing, nor were the relationships between non-wood production and other land-use activities properly considered.

Why has TFAP given insufficient emphasis to non-wood products?

National TFAPs have generally been the most thorough review of the forestry sector ever carried out within the countries in question. They have been supported by considerable international technical expertise, and have resulted in extremely large proposed investment programmes. Why then have non-wood products not received more emphasis? Five reasons can be advanced.

The first reason is that non-wood products are not, in general, a national priority (as noted below, there are sometimes good reasons for this). TFAP is a national process, and while the major objective of

TFAP is to assist countries to review their priorities, the outcome in any particular country will be determined by prevailing national and donor priorities. While it is clearly intended that some priorities will change as a result of the TFAP process, it is inevitable that existing national priorities carry considerable weight, and that some reviews are more far-reaching than others. An appreciation of the constraints and competing priorities facing developing country government, and the fact that significant changes in forestry priorities require broad political and inter-ministerial consensus, is central to understanding why many national TFAPs have been less than radical. Some national TFAPs - such as Ghana and Cameroon - have initially followed conventional priorities and concentrated on forest management for large-scale timber exports of concern to national governments and business interests, rather than small-scale informal activities of importance to the poor in rural areas. The Papua New Guinea TFAP, on the other hand, has shown that some governments will consider radical policy changes provided international support is forthcoming. Provided the TFAP process works in the way intended, existing national priorities need not therefore be a binding constraint.

Second, non-wood products tend to be overlooked and undervalued. The lack of economic data and secondary sources means that there is very little of substance on which to base a reassessment of the role and importance of non-wood products within the framework of a TFAP review (de Beer and McDermott, 1989; Falconer, 1988).

Third, this general ignorance of non-wood products and extractive livelihoods has tended to be compounded by the composition and conduct of TFAP reviews. In many cases TFAP review teams have been narrowly drawn from forestry and wildlife professions, with little or no agricultural, sociological or economic input. The limited involvement of national and international NGOs (where the former exist), and the inevitably limited local consultation process which tends to characterize any national review and planning process, has further exacerbated these deficiencies.

The above three reasons explain much of the under-emphasis on non-wood products. There are, however, two further reasons which may justify the limited consideration of non-wood products. The first is that in some countries, such as Belize, non-wood products are of truly minor importance. More controversially, there will be many situations where the development potential of non-wood products is limited. This is discussed further in a section below. Both circumstances would, after careful review, justify a low overall priority on non-wood products.

Secondly, even where non-wood products are demonstrably important, the situation may demand that the TFAP addresses priority concerns first. The priority concern in Papua New Guinea, for example, was for immediate action to address the problem of uncontrolled logging. With the forestry sector in disarray, non-wood products were rightly considered as secondary to the need for priority action on policy, institutions and conservation. Such an approach does not rule out non-wood initiatives at a later stage of the TFAP, as in Papua New Guinea where supplementary projects are now in preparation. For this reason it would be a mistake to allow the pursuit of balance in TFAP to override the necessity for prioritization. There is little point in directing resources towards non-wood products if the major threats to the forest resources, and therefore to the future of extractive systems, are not addressed.

Economic issues

Much of the case for an increased emphasis on non-wood products rests on four assumptions:

i) that the current economic importance of non-wood products has been underestimated;
ii) that the extraction of non-wood products is a superior form of land use to timber extraction and/or agriculture in economic terms;
iii) that non-wood products have considerable economic potential; and
iv) that new products can in practice significantly affect the financial incentives for land users and governments which currently favour forest conversion.

The body of the work which attests to the value of non-wood forest products in terms of exports, income nutrition, subsistence raw materials and healthcare is increasing (de Beer and McDermott, 1989; Falconer, 1988; FAO, 1989b; Prasad, 1985; Nor, 1987). FAO surveys show that non-wood forest product processing is one of the largest sources of rural employment (Chipeta, 1989). There are also a number of case studies which demonstrate that, at current levels of extraction, the value of marketed non-wood products can exceed that from logging. Examples include rubber and nuts in the State of Acre, Brazil, and honey in the Tabora region, Tanzania (Carneiro, 1988; ODA, 1990). At the very least this work justifies the increased attention now given to non-wood products, and the improvements in economic appraisal designed to ensure that non-wood products are fully taken into account (Winpenny, forthcoming).

Four caveats remain. The first is that the importance of non-wood products is highly variable: the findings of one case study do not necessarily apply elsewhere. Secondly, the statistical database for non-wood products remains patchy and inadequate and, therefore, an uncertain basis for generalizations. Thirdly, although non-wood products are important, the overall traded value of timber and woodfuel is generally far greater. Equally important, the value of timber to governments as a source of foreign exchange and domestic revenue far exceeds that from non-wood products. This is a reality which national TFAPs cannot ignore. Finally, there is an important distinction to be made between current and potential economic importance: the one does not necessarily imply the other.

Debate over the potential superiority of non-wood extractive land-use systems over cattle ranching and/or timber production has been stimulated by research in the Amazonian region (Peters *et al,* 1989; Schwartzman, 1989). Other case studies from Nigeria, Cameroon, Brazil and South-east Asia show that household income from small-scale extraction can be greater than that from agriculture (ODNRI, 1989; Republic of Cameroon, 1989; Hecht *et al.,* 1988; de Beer and McDermott, 1989). There are a number of reasons for arguing that these studies are less significant than has been assumed and that a much wider base of research is required.

Peters *et al.*. (1989) calculated the theoretical returns from a particular area of modified forest with access to a major market. Realizable returns from most of the Amazonian forest would be much lower because of its different species composition, and replication would face major constraints of marketing and transportation (Padoch, 1985). Most importantly, these studies ignore the significance of land tenure and the rationale of existing systems. Agriculture and/or unsustainable logging remain the most rational and profitable use of land for individuals - if not for society - given the short planning horizons associated with the lack of secure long-term land rights. Most non-wood users are also shifting cultivators for whom extraction is just a part of a diverse range of economic activities (Padoch *et al.*, 1988). For them, as it should be for policy makers, the extraction of non-wood products will rarely be a viable alternative land-use system, but merely one of several components. The immediate priority within TFAP is for further research into existing and alternative systems, together with policy reform and action to secure land and use rights of those dependent on non-wood forest products.

The need for further local and product-specific research covering extraction, processing and marketing applies with equal force to the question of which non-wood products have development potential. Social, environmental, and economic conditions are radically different in Latin America, Africa and Asia, and need to be assessed separately (Lewington, 1989). Little research has been carried out to date, but historical experience and current trends unfortunately point to a more limited potential than is often assumed. Viable, equitable and sustainable non-wood extraction systems are extremely rare. The reasons for this include the low productivity and low carrying capacity of extractive systems; an inherent tendency towards destructive over-exploitation associated with open-access common property resources and commercialization; remoteness from markets; the vulnerability of markets to commercially grown or synthesized substitutes; exploitative marketing systems, and insecure land rights (de Beer and McDermott, 1989; Nor, 1987, Prasad, 1985; Verma, 1986). It needs to be recognized that the capacity (or desirability) of government intervention to counteract unfavourable market trends is limited.

The question of the role of government also arises in the context of forest products with international market potential. Much has been written of the unrealized potential of tropical rain forests as sources of new medicines, agrochemicals, and flavourings (Wilson, 1988; Prance, 1990). There are a number of reasons for believing that the potential contribution of these products to forest conservation has been exaggerated. Once a product is found to be valuable, over-exploitation within the forest and/or commercial production outside the forest normally results. Even where sustainable harvesting from the forest is viable and attainable, the potential for channelling significant benefits to land users is uncertain. Many chemical compounds require considerable expenditure on research, development and testing before they can be marketed. It is this research and development, rather than original plant material, which represents the largest part of the value of the product. The market value of undeveloped forest compounds is, therefore, relatively low. However, even where significant financial or economic values can be attached to forest products at source, the institutional problems of translating these values into financial incentives for the individual land users, thereby affecting their economic behaviour in relation to forest resources, are considerable. National TFAPs can play a part in researching these issues, in reviewing the policy and institutional context, and in assessing the case for import substitution. However, the actual development of new products for the international market is best left to the private sector.

The need for realism in assessing the economic potential should not be interpreted as implying that TFAP can justifiably ignore non-wood forest products. These products have been under-valued and under-researched, and some will warrant greater attention on economic grounds. It is also undeniable that many non-wood forest products are of central importance to the poor in remote regions of developing countries. The social issues surrounding non-wood extraction systems, together with the environmental arguments for seeking to link sustainable extraction with conservation, combine to make a strong case. Given the uncertain economic prospects, arguably it is this social and environmental case, coupled with the pressing need for further research, which provides the main justification for attaching a higher priority to non-wood forest products within TFAP.

Recommendations for improving TFAP

Much of the criticism of TFAP has arisen from a failure to communicate what TFAP is and how it operates. Two particular aspects of TFAP need to be stressed in connection with improving the consideration of non-wood products. Firstly, it is crucially important that TFAP addresses the major forestry issues. Given the limits to national absorptive capacity and institutional weaknesses, the setting of priorities is fundamentally important. This may quite justifiably lead to non-wood products being given a low priority in the early stages of TFAP. Furthermore, the economic questions surrounding non-wood products, the lack of data, and the competing national priorities within TFAP mean that it would be unrealistic to expect a major reorientation towards non-wood products within TFAP in the short-term.

Secondly, it needs to be stressed that TFAPs are national exercises. The constraints faced by governments in addressing the underlying causes of deforestation need to be understood. TFAP can assist by securing improved donor co-ordination, and increased access to technical and financial assistance, but these do not by themselves provide the solutions. TFAP and developing countries are seeking to address large and complex problems, for which there is no single or simple answer.

Non-wood forest products have a contribution to make. As the case studies indicate, and the TFAP Co-ordination Unit now accepts, these products have often been given insufficient emphasis within TFAP. Recommendations for improving the TFAP process with respect to non-wood products are given below:

i) increased support for the establishment and operation of national TFAP Co-ordinating Units is needed to guide implementation, and to ensure that the capacity exists to address priority issues. This will require a much greater commitment from national governments and help from lead donor agencies;

ii) higher priority needs to be given early on in the

TFAP process to the collection of data on non-wood forest products, and to research into existing and improved agro-extractive systems;

iii) supplementary guidance notes on non-wood forest products should be produced by the TFAP Co-ordinating Unit, and periodically updated. These could be similar to the annex on 'Conservation' in the most recent TFAP Guidelines (FAO, 1989a), but should also aim to draw out the lessons from different national TFAPs;

iv) there is a need for broader multi-disciplinary representation on TFAP review missions to ensure that non-wood products and livelihoods are adequately addressed. Donors should provide support for the routine involvement of social, economic and rural development expertise in all stages of the TFAP;

v) increased resources for consultations with forest users, and for the involvement of national and international NGOs, should be made available to national TFAPs;

vi) greater attention needs to be paid to the issue of forest-use rights and land tenure. This is a politically sensitive issue but is fundamental to the viability and development of extractive systems.

Concluding remarks

I began this paper by contrasting the enthusiasm now being displayed for non-wood forest products with the criticism that has been directed at TFAP. There is substance in both arguments, but I believe that there is a need to retain a critical perspective. The debate is not advanced by posing simplistic 'either/or' questions, or by ignoring the magnitude and complexity of the challenge faced by developing countries. Non-wood products are only one, albeit important, component of forest utilization, and are only likely to contribute part of a solution in certain situations.

There will be some people who feel that I have overstated the problems and understated the opportunities. My response to that is to point out that most of us here do not have to face these problems - governments of developing countries, and the people in and around the forests, do. If we are truly concerned enough to assist in finding viable and sustainable solutions, we do people no favours by glossing over the problems.

Nor is TFAP fundamentally flawed as some critics have suggested. The review of the eight TFAP case studies has shown that consideration of non-wood forest products within TFAP has been uneven, occasionally extensive, but on balance inadequate, relative to their social and economic importance. National TFAPs have also been very variable in quality. The solution to these problems must lie in reforming TFAP, not abandoning it. TFAPs require greater support from donors, particularly in the early stages of policy review and plan preparation; a stronger commitment to a multi-sectoral, multi-disciplinary approach; and a greater emphasis on understanding forestry issues from the perspective of the people involved and affected.

A comparison of early and later national TFAPs shows that TFAP can be improved. It offers national governments - assisted by international donors and NGOs - an unparalleled opportunity to influence the shape and direction of policies affecting tropical forests. And despite its shortcomings, it remains potentially the most powerful mechanism for ensuring that non-wood forest products, and those dependent on them for their livelihoods, are given the increased attention they deserve.

The TFAP is a partnership between countries with tropical forests, and those without. To suggest that we would be better off without the mechanism of the TFAP - rather than working hard to get it right - would seem to be completely wrong. If we are interested in supporting non-wood extraction, we must support and reform TFAP.

Acknowledgements

Supporting annexes are available from the author at 26 Holly Grove, London SE15 5DF. The author is grateful for the comments and contribution of Gavin McGillivray, and for the assistance of the Tropical Forestry Action Plan (TFAP) Co-ordination Unit, Food and Agriculture Organization (FAO).

This study was supported by the Natural Resources and Environment Department of the Overseas Development Administration (ODA). The ODA bears no responsibility for, and is not in any way committed to, the views and recommendations expressed.

References

de Beer, J H and M J McDermott (1989). *The Economic Value of Non-timber Forest Products in Southeast Asia.* IUCN, The Netherlands

Cameroon, Republic of (1989). *The Korup Project. Plan for Developing the Korup National Park and its Support Zone.* ODNRI/EC/WWF

Carneiro, C M R (1988). *The Development of Integrated Approaches for Sustainable Utilization of Tropical Forests in the Amazon Region.* Report for the International Tropical Timber Organization

Chipeta, M E (1989). *Wood Values, Pricing and Practices in Small-scale Enterprises.* Food and Agriculture Organization paper, Rome

Falconer J (1988). *The Major Significance of Minor Forest Products: Local People's Uses and Values of Forests in the West African Humid Forest Zone.* Food and Agriculture Organization report, Rome

Fearnside, P M (1989). Extractive reserves in Brazilian Amazonia. *Bioscience* 39 (6)

Food and Agriculture Organization (1985). *Tropical Forestry Action Plan.* FAO, Rome

Food and Agriculture Organization (1988). *Tropical Forestry Action Plan; Latin America and Caribbean.* FAO, Rome

Food and Agriculture Organization (1989a). *Guidelines for Implementation of the Tropical Forestry Action Plan at Country Level.* FAO, Rome

Food and Agriculture Organization (1989b). *Household Food Security and Forestry: an Analysis of Socioeconomic Issues.* FAO, Rome

Food and Agriculture Organization (1989c). *Forestry and Food Security.* FAO Forestry Paper No 90, Rome

Hecht, S B, A B Anderson and I May (1988). The subsidy from nature: shifting cultivation, successional palm forests, and rural development. *Human Organization* 47 (1)

Lewington, A (1989). *Report on the Symposium on Extractive Economies in Tropical Forests.* WWF, Washington

Nor, Salleh Modh (1987). *The Potential of Minor Forest Products.* Asian Development Bank report

Overseas Development Administration (1990). *Tanzania Forest Resource Management Project.* ODA, unpublished preparation report, London

Overseas Development Natural Resources Institute (1989). *Cross River National Park, Oban Division. Land Evaluation and Agricultural Recommendations.* ODNRI/WWF

Padoch, C (1985). The economic importance and marketing of forest and fallow products in the Iquitos region. *Advances in Economic Botany,* volume 5, chapter 6

Padoch, C, J Chota Inuma, W de Wong and J Unruh (1988). Amazonian forestry: a market-orientated system in Peru. *Agroforestry Systems* 3: 47-58

Peters, C M, A H Gentry, and R O Mendelsohn (1989). Valuation of an Amazonian rainforest. *Nature,* volume 339, 29th June 1990

Prance, G (1990). Fruits of the rainforest. *New Scientist,* 13th January 1990

Prasad, B N (1985). *Report on Non-wood Forest Product Industries.* Working Paper No 42, Food and Agriculture Organization, Kuala Lumpur

Schwartzman, S (1989). *Tapping the Amazon's Reserves.* WWF Reports October/November 1989

Tropical Forestry Action Plan (1990). *TFAP Update No 16.* TFAP Co-ordinating Unit, Rome

Verma, V P S (1986). *Prospects of Non-wood Forest Products in Developing Countries, Asia-Pacific Region.* Food and Agriculture Organization, consultancy report, Rome

Wilson, E O (1988). *Biodiversity.* National Academy Press

Winpenny, J (forthcoming). *Valuing the Environment: A Guide to Economic Appraisal.* Overseas Development Administration/ Overseas Development Institute

World Rainforest Movement (1990). *Review of TFAP.* WRM/The Ecologist/Friends of the Earth

World Resources Institute (1985). *Tropical Forests: A Call for Action.* WRI/World Bank/UNDP

Editors' notes

1. According to the FAO (TFAP Update No. 21, May 1991), by May 1991, 24 tropical countries had completed the planning phase of a national TFAP, a sector review had been completed in a further 10, with a sector review under way in a further 40 countries.

The Role of the European Commission in the Conservation of the Tropical Forest

Catherine Guibourg
Commission of European Communities, Brussels, Belgium

Summary

The European Commission considers tropical forest conservation and management to be of great importance and the paper outlines how the Commission contributes to the issue. Although strategies for the marketing of rainforest products have not been developed, the Commission wishes to examine their potential and prospects for the future.

The European Commission would like to thank the organizers for inviting a delegate to this international Conference on sustainable strategies for rainforest conservation. The Commission is glad to participate, considering the international importance of such environmental issues where countries from the North and South are required to find solutions together, for coming generations. In particular, the Commission welcomes the presence of delegates from countries with tropical rainforest and hopes that the exchange of information and points of view will improve the knowledge, practices and co-operation of us all.

Why we contribute to tropical forest conservation

Tropical forest conservation and management is an issue which the Commission considers of great importance. According to the United Nations (UN) resolution concerning the sovereignty of states and management of natural resources, tropical forests are national products and therefore their management is the responsibility of the respective government. However, the Brundtland Report adopted by the United Nations stresses the necessity for rapid implementation of strategies for sustainable development and calls for the Northern countries to support and assist the South in this field. In particular, this was because of the extra costs required for national governments to take into account the environment in their policies.

The Commission participates actively in the negotiations relating to global change, the greenhouse effect and the Montreal Protocol. In particular, a resolution on the 'greenhouse effect' adopted by the Council in June 1989 underlines the need for the definition and implementation of a global response to the problem. In order not to jeopardize efforts to diminish the effects of industrial pollution, the Commission also has a general interest in the conservation of tropical forests as a significant reducing factor in man-made emissions of greenhouse gases, particularly carbon dioxide.

Thirdly, the Community remains a major importer of

tropical timber products and consequently has an interest in the sustainable management of tropical forests. Furthermore, the citizens of the Community naturally have concerns about human rights, including the predicament of minority groups and indigenous people which depend on the forest for their economy, way of life and culture.

And last but not least, the tropical forest remains a reservoir of biological diversity which should be given special attention through protection and enhancement for the inhabitants of the forest as well as for the planet as a whole.

How we contribute to tropical forest conservation

In 1987, the Council Resolution relating to the Fourth Environmental Action Programme (1987-1992) lists among the priorities for community action: *"co-operation with developing countries on environmental matters and on protection of natural resources, having particular regard to questions of desertification and water supply, tropical forests and the production and use of dangerous substances."*

Also, since 1987, under article 130R of the Single European Act, environmental protection is to be a component of other policies of the Community, including development aid and co-operation policy. In the mid-1980s, programmes in these sectors that favoured tropical forests were given approximately 20 million European Currency Units (ECU) per year. Considering the necessity and importance of such contributions, recommendations for further action have recently been submitted for consideration by the Council.

The co-operation policy of the Commission is implemented through a dialogue with developing countries at regional or bilateral level, and environmental matters are included within these. (As regards to countries in Africa, the Caribbean and Pacific - or ACP - co-operation is implemented within regional agreements). Nevertheless, environmental matters might not be considered as a first priority by the countries themselves because of economic and employment problems.

For ACP countries, the European Development Fund, in the framework of the Lomé Convention, supported 65 major projects in 1989 concerned with the tropical forest sector. For Asia and Latin America the Financial and Technical Co-operation Fund has financed similar projects in India, the Philippines, Thailand and the Association of South-east Asian (ASEAN) countries. Nevertheless, the Financial and Technical Co-operation is devoted to the least developed countries, and therefore is not set aside for economically advanced countries like Brazil.

A specific budgetary line for *Ecology in Developing Countries* (946) was voted by the European Parliament and created in 1983, permitting the support of a few actions relating to tropical forests, including for instance a project in Colombia on conservation of forest by management by indigenous people. The small size of this line has led the parliament to vote for a line within the line 946 entitled *Fund for the Upkeep of Tropical Forests.* However, no money was available in 1990.

Since 1983, several projects have been initiated that are concerned with tropical forest research.

These have been carried out jointly by laboratories from developing countries and the European Community within the framework of the programme Science and Technology for Development. Finally, assistance has also been given to indigenous people in tropical forests within the Commission's special programme for funding NGOs.

The co-operation of the Commission as it relates to tropical forests considers the forest ecosystem as a whole, including biological and socioeconomic aspects. It gives priority to strengthen national institutions, involvement of international and national NGOs and to indigenous forest dwellers whose traditions and experience should be enhanced for the improvement of international knowledge of tropical forests and sustainable management.

In this aspect, the Commission recognizes the Tropical Forestry Action Plan (TFAP) as the basic framework for co-ordinated funding and action in support of forest activities. It welcomes the TFAP review now underway to improve its strategy. In line with the priorities of TFAP, particular emphasis must be given to the integration of forestry with agriculture, restoration of fuelwood supplies and sustained management of natural resources. Finally, the Commission participates in many of the relevant institutional fora, such as TFAP, the International Tropical Timber Organization (ITTO) and the Convention on International Trade in Endangered Species (CITES).

Conclusion

Enhancing the biodiversity of the tropical forest is of great relevance as a contribution to the sustainable management of the forest.

Up until now, apart from some actions through the Research Programme, the Commission has not specifically developed strategies for the marketing of rainforest products, and wishes to examine their potentialities and the prospects for the future. In particular these include: the kind of products concerned and their characteristics; the interests of all parties concerned; the conditions required to implement sustainable development and trade; and especially the codes and practices that should be applied to assure benefits for all those concerned.

Discussion

Panel
Catherine Guibourg, Michael Flint, Martin von Hildebrand, Dr Otto Soemarwoto

The four speakers were joined on the panel by Manuel Paveri-Anziani (Food and Agriculture Organization, Project Co-ordinator, United Nations Development Programme, Brazil) and Axel Peuker (World Bank).

Oliver Tickell, Oxford Friends of the Earth. My question is about the Tropical Forestry Action Plan (TFAP). I am sure that many people here are familiar with the recent report issued by the World Rainforest Movement (WRM) about the TFAP. Michael Flint said that in order to judge it, you have got to look at what is actually happening on the ground. The conclusion of this report is that what is happening on the ground is an increase in deforestation and that the TFAP has not done anything about the real causes of the degradation that is taking place. I felt that the slightly apologetic, 'but it would all work out in the end', approach taken by Michael Flint was inappropriate to the scale of the criticism. I was wondering if he or maybe some of the other members of the panel that have just joined us could help us on that?

Michael Flint. My reply is twofold. I really think that it is unrealistic to expect deforestation to be reduced by TFAP on the kind of scale that we are looking at. Deforestation, as we have got to keep stressing, is a very complex and deep seated issue. It is not a simple problem that can just be addressed by an international initiative in 5 years and I think that if we expect deforestation to be substantially reduced by anything, let alone the TFAP, then we are not really understanding the magnitude of the problem.

But I would go beyond that and say I think it is wrong to suggest that the TFAP is not improving. I know that the WRM paper included Papua New Guinea and that is a case where the TFAP actually has addressed the real problems. This TFAP and Government are actually saying that they are going to reduce logging. They are going to impose a moratorium on new concessions provided the international community comes up with the difference between what they were going to cut and what they are going to harvest under the World Heritage proposals. So this most recent TFAP shows that, given support from the international community and given commitment from governments - and Brazil showed very promising signs this morning - I believe that TFAP can address the real problems. But, and we come back to it, it is not just a forestry sector problem as the WRM report pointed out. It is a problem that spans all sectors and goes fundamentally not just beyond forestry, but beyond the country's concern. To say that TFAP has failed because it hasn't stopped deforestation, I think, is to really misunderstand how complex and serious the problem is. Of course it is not perfect, of course it is flawed and of course it has got to be reformed. But I really do think that it is much more constructive to say we work within it to make it better and that it can be improved rather than say we should hold back and not get involved.

Chair. Michael, you clearly think it can be improved to the point where it will do some good?

Michael Flint. I think that if you look at the TFAPs you see that there is variation between them. We are dealing with national programmes, we are dealing with countries that have responsibilities and should have commitment to their own forests. The TFAP is a mechanism for the international community to assist developing countries towards this goal. It cannot do more than help the developing countries do that and therefore you are bound to have variation. Some TFAPs have already addressed the problem but some have just promoted 'business as usual'.

Patrick Cunningham, BBC Wildlife. A question for Michael Flint and also for Catherine Guibourg. Neither of you have addressed what I think is a fundamental issue and an important way of addressing the rainforest problem. Demand needs to be reduced in Europe, Japan, the United States and in the so-called 'developed' countries. None of your deliveries have addressed this at all. Have your respective bodies looked into this?

My other point, already raised this morning, is that your deliveries are totally economically based. There is no reference to a moral responsibility, to look at the social aspects of the problem. This is possibly a problem with the original remit of your respective bodies.

Chair. Catherine, let me put this question towards you. The Prince of Wales spoke this morning of being accused of asking for a boycott when in fact he was not. What is the EEC's position on boycotts and controlled imports. Has it got a policy?

Catherine Guibourg. The Commission represents all the European member states and cannot always have the same position as NGOs. Take Brazil for example. They need income from foreign currency which cannot be cut overnight. We must sit down together with the countries concerned and involve all the indigenous peoples and the NGOs. It would be unrealistic to expect to cease imports straight away and it is important to consider the economic aspects as well. I must say that in my introduction I did touch on the necessity to take into account social aspects as well as management of the forest by forest dwellers themselves, so I think this an unfair reproach.

Chair. Not Guilty. Michael do you want to add anything to that?

Michael Flint. A quick response on those two issues. On demand, I think the TFAP is guilty. It has never sought to address the problems of international trade, it was not involved in the GATT negotiations and I think that this is an area where, if not by TFAP, some more attention does need to be given to trade aspects. I think this is a good point. On social and environmental considerations, what I missed out in my presentation but which is in my paper, is the argument that although I believe the economic case for non-wood products would be uncertain, I believe that it is the social and environmental case that provides the main justification for continuing research and support in this area. So, whilst I am saying that the economic case is perhaps weak and needs to be researched, TFAP and other bodies should put more support behind non-wood products because it is for social and environmental reasons that we should be doing this.

Manuel Paveri-Anziani. I think that in the last 10 years, forestry has really changed a great deal in terms of the philosophy of approach to the issue. Traditionally, forestry has dealt only with the problem of timber exploitation for industrial purposes. For years, the Food and Agriculture Organization (FAO), through the Forestry Commission, to which practically all the countries of the world belong or participate, has insisted and promoted that forestry should carefully consider the human and social problem of forestry development. I think that this is something that should be said clearly because forestry in the developing world is beginning to consider this aspect.

Chair. That is a tradition, of course, that has developed in continental Europe far more so than here in Britain. Therefore, you are probably more aware of it.

Manuel Paveri-Anziani. Yes.

Nicholas Guppy, Associate, Centre For Human Ecology, Edinburgh University. I think that there is a very important point that is being missed here which concerns the question of restricting imports of tropical hardwoods and that is the immense waste in harvesting. Between 50 and 94 per cent of the forest is destroyed for a very small portion of timber that is actually harvested. This suggests that instead of a blanket prohibition on the imports of tropical hardwoods, an attempt should be made to assess and pose limitations in rainforests so that exploitation is restricted to a smaller area. That could save up to 90 per cent of the forest.

Chair. Yes, we know logging is very wasteful. Can I get Axel Peuker from the World Bank to say what their policy on this is?

Axel Peuker. Yes, I think a boycott should be judged by its outcome and not by its intention. I am afraid that a boycott, which is not complimented by alternative offers of what the community could do to support those countries who have made an effort to change their policies, is not a very credible threat and could prove a very useful counter-argument. Most governments I have talked to, and I have just recently been in several African countries concerning a conference on rainforests which will take place in Abidjan in November 1990, said that if there was a boycott, they would then know that forests are an asset with zero value on international markets. Our efforts [the World Bank], or the efforts by governments to sustain and protect the forest, would be made less attractive. There would be less incentive, for example, to have tree plantations and to protect pristine rainforest. So I would argue that a boycott might be a useful instrument when it comes to a certain kind of product or species in order to pressure governments to change their policies. But I do not think that as a global statement we should boycott tropical forests. It is counter-productive and for that reason alone I do not think it is a good idea.

In that context I feel the idea brought forward by Prince Charles, and one which has also discussed within the World Bank, concerning the labelling of products is a very helpful one. The question here is one of implementation and we have already discussed this problem with the Ghanaian delegation present today. There seem to be question marks as to how you would implement such labelling schemes. But to sum up, any kind of efforts to induce governments, and the world for that matter, for more sustainable use of forests should be complimented by rewards. It is a matter of incentives.

Mike Lee, University of London. Can I ask Martin von Hildebrand whether he thinks that the Colombian Indians - in the longer term - are likely to retain their spiritual relationship with the forest? Will they continue to use it sustainably? After all, their numbers may well increase the pressure on the forest's resources. They will increasingly come into contact with the influences of the outside world and so on. Are there any safeguards in your strategy against this happening?

Martin von Hildebrand. On the one hand, our experience has told us that retaining tradition is possible. Groups that have already got involved with the market economy have come under very strong pressure. For example, when the coca business came into Colombia the indigenous peoples were harvesting leaves that were then bought at a high price. They got heavily involved by using certain rivers for transport. It was quite interesting to see the young Indians buying tape recorders and outboard motors. Realizing that the authority of the community and knowledge of rituals lay in the hands of the elders, the young Indians started to use the tape recorders to tape traditional songs and rituals and learn about them. When the elders realized this, they started singing in a different way to confuse them, because they wanted them to listen properly and not use modern machines.

To give another example, along one river, 10 or 12 years ago, there were 7 large communal houses used for rituals. Now there are 35. So there is a renaissance in this sense, a revival of their culture. I think that is due to the fact that they have had a chance to say what they think about the issue, to get together and make decisions to strengthen their culture. I think that one of the reasons why we have seen the Indian community moving into our Western society is because the only alternative we offer them is that if they want to reap the benefits from our society, they have to cease to be Indians. They have to become like us. Whereas if their identity is strengthened and maintained, and at the same time they can get medicine and other elements from our society, I think that they would prefer to retain their own culture.

Of course the other aspect which we do hope will work is, from our point of view, our government and development programmes. We need to become more sensitive, to understand them better and to strengthen their culture and come into more productive dialogue. This will not happen on its own, it depends on them, on us, on the dialogue and it depends on how much control they have over the processes at the local level. But I certainly think it is possible that they can retain their culture. Cultures evolve and change but they will retain the essence, yes.

Edward Milner, Film Maker, Acacia Productions. I must say I was rather depressed by what Michael Flint said about the TFAP. I have just been making a film about the destruction of tropical forests in Thailand and it seems to me that there is a contrast between his reaction to the query about the TFAP and Dr Lutzenberger's reaction to the question about FUNAI. It does seem to me that the problem with the TFAP is that it sets the agenda in so many countries for the commercialization of forests. It is all very well for the World Bank and others to say it ought to be changed but unfortunately that is the document you have. It purports to be a plan about forests when it is a plan for the development of forestry. I would honestly ask our paid members, especially the man from the FAO, who admitted that things had changed recently and the World Bank itself is taking more account of the environment, that is it not time to have a complete re-think and to start with a completely new plan which looks at forests and not at forestry? Then it might take account of the people in them, instead of saying something about incorporating social and economic aspects which seems to me to be such a dismissive attitude as to be totally irrelevant in the present circumstances.

Manuel Paveri-Anziani. I think that the situation is changing. A review is being undertaken by an independent group, lead by a former Prime Minister of Sweden, and they will soon be representing their findings. I am sure that many things will change as a result of this study. TFAP is an instrument that the countries should use if they want to. But don't forget, as Michael Flint has said, this is a national exercise and although we do have a responsibility to advise the government about how to deal with the problem of forestry, the ultimate responsibility is in their hands. The problems of solidarity and national security, for example, are influencing these exercises in many countries. The united international system works with the government and it is the responsibility of the government to try to do what we the international community, would like to see in forestry. The TFAP is an instrument that is only 5 years old and I am sure that it will and should be improved. It is difficult to prove that TFAP is increasing deforestation. The FAO are, at the moment, progressing a world inventory programme to ascertain exactly what the forestry situation is in the world in the 1990s, as a follow-up to the 1980 inventory. We will then see if it is true that the problem of deforestation has increased. Obviously in some countries it has, but, for example, in Brazil, in the last 2 years the situation has greatly improved.

Chair. I think it is a matter of language. From the audience's applause, it seems many people would like organizations like the FAO to put other organizations like the International Tropical Timber Organization (ITTO) through the duck test; if it's a duck, call it a duck.

Manuel Paveri-Anziani. Of course, yes.

Chair. But will you ever do something like that?

Manuel Paveri-Anziani. Yes.

Chair. We wait.

Dr Otto Soemarwoto. Can I just say we would like the European Community to do something about its ridiculous agricultural policies and perhaps the Government will step in to do something here. Far more money is wasted every year on the Common Agricultural Policy (CAP) than is wasted on the allocation of resources or inefficiency in forestry. We have had 20 years of reviews on the CAP and absolutely no movement at all.

We could also say that the Japanese agricultural support policy is equally iniquitous. If some of the funds available from the EEC and Japan were in fact allocated directly to saving what remains of the tropical forests, one might believe the representative of the EEC who is here and the representative of Japan who is not and whose absence is noted by us all.

Chair. Come on Catherine, you will have to say something about the CAP. We have had two people criticize it now. Is there going to be a change? Is this considered part of the external affairs directorate's brief or is that some other department?

Catherine Guibourg. I will say that unfortunately I do not come from the agricultural department. I know the arguments concerning this issue and I also know it is a complex situation. My department, the environmental sector within DG1 (External Affairs), was only created one year ago to begin formulating ideas about how to introduce an environmental approach within the Commission with the developing countries. Two or three years ago such an approach had only just been mentioned, so progress has been made.

Helena Paul, Rio Mazan Project, Gaia Foundation, specializing in Ecuador. This morning José Lutzenberger talked about ethics and sin, and Martin von Hildebrand talked about the Indians spiritual values. Patrick Cunningham actually asked a question about morals to members of the panel only very recently. I would like to air this issue again. I am wondering if it is because there is no easy way of putting a price on them that they do not seem to turn up in these arguments. Merely economic factors seem to crop up.

Chair. Is anyone qualified to reply to that? No, right, we will go on.

Geoffrey Willperson, Institute of Cultural Ecology of the Tropics, Veracruz, Mexico. My question or observation is for Martin von Hildebrand. I would like to say first that I speak in total ignorance of Colombian law, so I have no way of evaluating it, but I think that it is commendable that there is recognition of human rights, particularly in relation to forest peoples and also in trying to find alternative methods of land protection. However, I would like to observe that similar schemes, most specifically in the Lacandon forests of southern Mexico and adjoining parts of Guatemala, have failed miserably in their attempts at recognition of Indian right's co-operatives. The Lacandon Indians have resolved it simply in mass lumbering contracts, introduction of new products into the region, clearing on a very broad and rapid scale. In the Lacandon forest we unfortunately reached probably a 90 per cent degradation rate this year. So, these programmes sometimes do not work and you have to be very careful of falling into a certain type of romanticized idealism.

Chair. Why is it going to be different in Colombia?

Martin Von Hildebrand. I think it will be different for

several reasons. Firstly, we are dealing with an area that is not really exposed, there are no roads in the area and it is relatively isolated, so, we have time to work along this line. Secondly, there are laws in Columbia which do not allow the exploitation of timber. Thirdly, these areas are all forest reserve, the laws of which have not been applied effectively. Vast fronts of colonization are difficult to control particularly in areas where Indian communities are interested in maintaining their environment.

Professor Kwabena Tufuor, Ghana Forestry Commission. The TFAP has come under serious criticism. It is not a strait-jacket prescription but can act as a catalyst to enable the tropical countries to see how best they can programme themselves, and see forestry as part of a major development effort in the total programme. In Ghana we took advantage of the international funding from the ODA and the World Bank to see how best we could resuscitate and improve upon forest husbandry. As a result we have the ODA inventory which has gone a long way to help us provide a means for improving upon forest management practices. Also, one of the major outcomes of the TFAP is that we are continuing to review our forest policy. So you can see, at least for us, it has come at a good time when we are almost ready to implement a number of good things for our country, in line with the global requirements for such changes.

Address from the UK Minister for Overseas Development

The Right Honorable Lynda Chalker MP
Minister for Overseas Development, Overseas Development Administration, 94 Victoria Street, London SW1E 5JL United Kingdom

Summary

This presentation provides an update on the Overseas Development Administration's (ODA) forestry initiatives and also discusses the role of other international initiatives, including the Tropical Forestry Action Plan (TFAP), and what needs to be done to make them more effective. The Minister also discusses biological diversity and the role of the ODA in conserving biological resources. Specific activities undertaken by the ODA with respect to non-wood products are also described and the paper suggests some ideas for enhancing the role of non-wood products.

Introduction

I greatly welcome the initiative of Friends of the Earth in organizing this Conference. The subject is a crucial one. And one much older than some people might suspect. One source tells us that *"a large number of drugs and drug plants are derived as forest products....some are extensively used in modern medicine....many of the native medicinal plants, particularly in the tropics, are at present imperfectly known"*.

The message is a modern one even if the language is not. The extract comes from a study carried out 60 years ago and published in 1936 as *"An Index of the Minor Forest Products of the British Empire"*. It does us no harm, I think, to recall that we are not inventing the wheel! I would challenge only the title of that Index for I endorse the recommendation of the Fourth World Forest Conference, made as long ago as 1954, that the term 'minor products' be abandoned in favour of 'economic products other than wood'.

The forestry problem

This audience hardly needs me to describe the crisis we face in tropical forestry. The scale of deforestation, its causes and the value of forests are much debated. I know from my own post-bag the depth of feeling the subject evokes among British people, especially young people.

The tropical forests are concentrated almost exclusively in the developing world. It is those countries which will determine their fate. We cannot debate these issues without the developing countries, and that is why the ODA has sponsored attendance at this Conference by nine representatives. I urge them to put their views forward, and everyone to listen.

It is not for any developed nation of this Conference to question the sovereign rights of developing countries to manage their natural resources. But I do believe that we have something to offer to help developing countries manage their forests in a sustainable way, to their benefit and that of the wider community.

I would like to focus my remarks in four areas: first, an update on ODA's own Forestry Initiative; second, some comments on the Tropical Forestry Action Plan and the other international efforts; third, a new initiative on biological diversity, and finally the particular place of non-timber forest products.

ODA Forestry Initiative

It was in 1988 that we began a major increase in ODA aid to forestry. The Prime Minister announced in Parliament in October of that year that we would spend more on *'the wise and sustainable use of forest resources'.* Then we were supporting 80 forestry projects, at a cost of £45 million.

Just one year later we had 115 projects, costing £65 million. In November last year the Prime Minister announced that we planned to contribute a further £100 million to tropical forestry activities over the next three years. We now have about 50 new projects in preparation. These and more will be financed from the new £100 million. Each project, whatever its scale, must help develop sustainable forestry.

The objectives of our forestry initiative are clear. Above all, we aim to help developing countries maximize the economic and social benefits they enjoy from their forests in a sustainable way. Our aim is to limit deforestation by tackling its causes. We aim to promote reforestation and agroforestry. We must help strengthen forest departments charged with conservation and management. We fund training. And we fund research, designed to increase the productivity of forests.

Many of you will be familiar with the range of our activities. So I do not want to spend long describing them, but there are some important new developments which I want to tell you about.

In Malaysia, we have offered to finance a special £1 million link between the Oxford Forestry Institute (OFI), which is a unique European centre of expertise, and the Forestry Research Institute of Malaysia (FRIM). The OFI and FRIM have signed a Memorandum of Understanding setting up the link, and I hope that the first activities, with visits from scientists at FRIM to Oxford, will take place shortly.

In India, where we have offered £40 million in aid for environmental projects, a team from the OFI are just completing preparatory work on an important forestry conservation project in the Western Ghats Mountains. I met the team and the local forestry experts when I was in India at the beginning of the month and was most encouraged by the way this project is being planned, with the emphasis on managing conservation through the forest communities.

In Nepal, we are looking at a new £5 million phase of our forestry research project. This new phase, which is within the Nepal Forestry Masterplan, will be focused on community forestry for poor people, with special components looking at the social issues (Plate 11).

In Indonesia, we are preparing a package of

assistance worth around £9 million. We are providing a senior management team to advise the Minister of Forests on the introduction and strengthening of sustainable management practices. And we are planning projects in training, research and conservation.

In the conservation project we are proposing to help with the management of two conservation areas, including wetland swamps as well as forest areas, in Kalimantan. Local people there are dependent on the forests and lake fish for their livelihood. The aim of our project is to develop, together with the local people, sustainable management systems for these areas.

In Belize, where the ODA was the lead donor agency for the Tropical Forestry Action Plan (TFAP), we are discussing with the Government a package of five projects worth over £1 million. One is for help with an inventory of mangrove areas. Another involves improving their national legislation on forests.

Finally, forestry research. The ODA finances a major programme of forestry research, currently involving 19 projects managed for us by the OFI. I announced in March an increase of 50 per cent in that allocation for this financial year, bringing it to over £2 million a year.

Tropical Forestry Action Plan

My second theme is the international dimension. Forestry is both a domestic and an international problem. It needs to be tackled in a co-ordinated way, bringing together donors with each developing country and preparing a plan of action to tackle the causes of forest loss. The main international mechanism for doing this is the TFAP. But it is a mechanism and only that.

The TFAP has been the butt of some hefty criticism. We fully agree that it needs reforming. Indeed, I called for this reform when I addressed the United Nations Food and Agriculture Organization's (FAO) General Conference in Rome last November. I said that policies relating to forests need examination and any that encourage deforestation must be changed. Policies should encourage better agricultural practices which help take the pressures off forest lands. They should take account of the knowledge and interests of the people of the forests.

Shortly after the Conference and our representations the FAO set up an independent review to examine the TFAP and make recommendations for reform. The review team visited London in March. They met Douglas Hurd (Minister of State for Foreign Affairs) as well as representatives of the timber trade and the NGOs. They are due to report in the summer.

The TFAP in each country is only as good as the national and donor inputs to it. I believe that Britain has a good record here. Our contributions have been designed to address some of the key issues that the critics of the TFAP have raised. Without our involvement, there would, I believe, be much more to complain about. We have so far helped with the preparation of 11 national plans, and currently expect to help with 9 more. We are now funding 8 projects related to these national plans. We are considering a further 22 projects. We are learning by doing - that seems to be the best way to strike the right balance.

Some say that the TFAP concentrates too much on industrial forestry and plantations. For the ODA I can say that of the 20 cases where we are or will be involved bilaterally in national plans, there is only one where our support is in the industrial sector. And of the 30 projects we are funding or considering, there is only one which is based on industrial forestry. That is not to say we think that industrial forestry and plantations are unimportant. They too have a role to play but only in the right place and with careful planning. That is why I welcome the fact that the Commonwealth Development Corporation is reviewing its forestry portfolio.

Let me give you some examples of the kind of help we have given with TFAPs. In Cameroon we financed a study on edible and medicinal plants. In Guinea we provided an expert to look at mangroves. In Tanzania our expert looked at the small-scale bee-keeping industry, probably the most important non-wood product of the forests of Tanzania. In Ghana we provided experts in forest management, agroforestry and institutional issues.

I agree with those who say that where a TFAP has not addressed the key issues, further work must be done to ensure that these are covered. Here again ODA has played a positive role. In the case of Ecuador, for example, we heard that the on-going TFAP was not looking thoroughly at the role of the private sector, or that of NGOs, or getting the central government fully involved. Our Ambassador took up these points, and we offered the services of Dr Tim Synnott of the OFI. The result? A better TFAP for Ecuador.

It seems to me that the quality of national TFAPs can be greatly enhanced by the lead donor. Lead donor agencies in each country should be tasked with helping governments create TFAP Co-ordinating Units in-country. Those units should involve Ministries of Finance, Planning, Agriculture and others with an interest as well as the Forest Department.

Lead agencies should also be required to help monitor the implementation of the TFAP after it has been prepared, and help the recipient country with problems as they arise. I see a role for a strengthened TFAP Co-ordinating Unit in ensuring the lead agencies carry out these functions. I do not share the total pessimism of some about the TFAP. The exercises completed most recently - for example in Tanzania and Papua New Guinea - have been better.

The Papua New Guinea case is particularly interesting. There the Government has announced a moratorium on new logging concessions. There is a heavy emphasis on conservation. The Government has taken some courageous steps to address the toughest policy issues. And who is the lead agency pushing this? None other than that 'bête noir' of some people, the World Bank!

Papua New Guinea is not a country where we have traditionally had an aid programme. But we did attend the meeting last month to consider the projects arising from the TFAP - and we also paid for British NGOs (The World Wide Fund for Nature [WWF] and the International Institute for

Environment and Development [IIED]) to go. We will be considering how, primarily through the NGOs, we could help further with this. This example shows clearly how NGOs can effectively influence and improve activities of the official agencies. Working with agencies like the World Bank to improve projects is far more productive than blanket criticism from outside.

That the recent exercises have been better tells me that the TFAP can be effective. But it does need reform and I will not let up in the pressure to change it until it is fulfilling the aim we all share for it which is to tackle effectively the causes of forest loss. I hope this Conference will come up with ideas on non-timber products which can be utilized through the TFAP process. The paper by Michael Flint, which you heard this morning, has already given some important food for thought.

Other agencies need to play their part too. The International Tropical Timber Organization (ITTO), meeting now in Indonesia, is discussing guidelines for sustainable forest management. We believe that the ITTO has a lead role here, and we have been pleased to finance work for it. The Council of European Community Development Ministers, which I shall attend in Brussels at the end of the month, will also be considering a Resolution on tropical forestry. I think a major aim there must be to make the management of our effort through the Community more effective.

We are also financing, through ITTO, a study on the feasibility of labelling tropical timber which, as the Prince of Wales said earlier today, might prove one practical way to encourage sustainable management.

Biodiversity

My third theme is biological diversity. It is a fact that we cannot say to within a factor of 10 how many species of plants and animals there are on the planet. Estimates vary between 5 and 50 million.

What we do know is that we are losing them at a frightening rate - we could lose as many as one third of the total in the next 30 or 40 years. We also know that it is the developing countries which house the most species. So safeguarding the number of species must take as its starting point the need to assess and increase the incentives for conservation in developing countries.

I found that one of the most vivid insights into the issue of biological diversity came last year when I attended the Maracá Review Conference held in this august Society. The Royal Geographical Society hosted the Conference as the culmination of the collaborative project which the Prince of Wales, who was its Patron, has already told you about. The Conference involved literally hundreds of British and Brazilian scientists and technicians, to study the rainforest of Maracá Island off Brazil. I well recall how that project identified over 200 new species of insect alone. I am delighted that José Lutzenberger, the Brazilian Environment Secretary, is able to be present and I look forward to discussing Anglo-Brazilian co-operation with him later this afternoon.

We have been looking hard at what ODA's role might be in helping conserve biological diversity. We commissioned a paper from Robin Pellew and his colleagues at the World Conservation Monitoring Centre to help us in that.

ODA already finances a range of projects which have the conservation of biological diversity as a major aim. The World Wide Fund for Nature's Korup project in Cameroon is a well known example. We are also helping with the rehabilitation of the Limbe Botanic Gardens in Cameroon, where rare plants will be conserved and studied. Other examples include assistance with the establishment of a Conservation Monitoring Centre in India and with programmes to help conserve elephants and rhinos in East Africa. And we are the second largest contributor, after Japan, to the core costs of the International Board for Plant Genetic Resources, which has a key role in the *ex situ* conservation of wild relatives of food crops.

We now plan to strengthen these activities. The first requirement is for better information to help set priorities for conservation. The World Conservation Monitoring Centre is planning the production of a Global Biodiversity Status Report. This is a major initiative designed to meet the need for better information. We are offering to help finance the production of the report.

The richest sources of biological diversity are rainforests. Here, we are commissioning from the Oxford Forestry Institute a strategy document to identify possible activities for ODA financing. I am making biological diversity a special focus within the forestry initiative. I expect the OFI document to include outlines for projects for us to consider.

But biodiversity goes wider than forests. We plan similar strategic studies on the biological diversity of rivers, lakes and seas; on wetlands, including swamps and mangroves; and on the so-called wildlands, like the areas of African savannah which house the wild relatives of food crops. These wildland areas contain resources of potentially major economic importance for developing countries. We need to do more to conserve and develop them.

We also support proposals for an International Convention on the Conservation of Biological Diversity. That should set out specific obligations to be undertaken by its parties. Among the areas I have in mind are guidelines on environmental impact assessments, and the establishment and enforcement of appropriate national legislation. Another priority should be agreement on a global list of centres of biological diversity for priority conservation. Discussions on such a Convention have already begun. We hope it will be ready for signature at the 1992 Conference on Environment and Development.

Non-timber forest products

Let me turn now to the focus of this Conference. I am among those who believe that totally insufficient attention has been given to non-wood forest products. The Index of Minor Forest Products of the British Empire which I mentioned earlier listed 140 drugs and spices, 58 essential oils, 63 dyes, 104 gums and resins, 84 oils and oilseeds and over 100 tanning materials. It also gave detailed accounts of the uses of the plants - for example of the 300 species of medicinal plants in use in Nigeria.

The purpose of your Conference is to promote the sustainable economic use of these products. You will have many things to discuss. I would like to highlight just four areas which seem important to me.

We have recently seen the results of a research project in which a biologist and an anthropologist studied the role played by the rainforest environment in the life of communities on the margins of the Gola Forest in eastern Sierra Leone. Special attention has been paid to the forest as a source of hunted and gathered foods, firewood, building materials, raw material for local crafts, and plants used for medicinal and cosmetic purposes. The results emphasize the enormous importance to local communities of non-timber forest resources.

For example, the villagers make regular use of a large number of wild roots and vegetables including wild yams, fungi and sauces and condiments from shrubs and herbs. Forest and farm bush between them supply a huge range of herbal medicines and cosmetics in a region where people are too poor and isolated to be able to obtain manufactured pharmaceutical products. Fortunately in the Gola case the great majority of these products are found abundantly in the farm fallow around the rim of the forest reserve and there has been relatively little need for local people to encroach into the forest itself. This leads me to my first point which is that people living in or near the forest are relying on it for everyday produce. They recognize the value of the forest and are the best allies in conserving it. Negotiating participatory management and buffer zones will ensure the long-term conservation of the forest better than government imposed preservation orders.

Second, I again echo the Prince of Wales in urging that we need to keep a careful eye on the economics, particularly where we are recommending what others should do. In a now famous article, Charles Peters at the New York Botanical Gardens suggested that it made more economic sense to harvest rainforest products than to convert land to agriculture. His findings have however been questioned, notably by a team at Yale University who, like Peters, looked at the Peruvian case. I think we need more economic research to show the conditions under which rainforest products are more profitable. ODA's scientific agency, the Natural Resources Institute, is looking at research possibilities here. The need to use rainforests more economically was given a new dimension at the recent London Drugs Summit. In the Communique a clear link was made between harvesting the natural forest to provide additional income for forest dwellers, and the need to stop the clearing of rainforests to grow drugs crops like coca. So far we have concentrated our efforts on substituting agricultural crops for drugs crops. But we must not overlook the fact that natural rainforests can provide crops too. The London Summit noted that markets are a crucial element.

My third point is that the marketing and distribution of rainforest products is a major constraint. The main role here is for the private sector - and I applaud how Anita Roddick and The Body Shop are leading the way. Some months ago, David Bellamy came to me with a project to identify and market rainforest products in the Solomon Islands, and we have agreed to fund that. The later stages of that project envisage a leading role for the private sector, and I hope they will seize it.

There are also important questions here of intellectual property rights - especially affecting pharmaceuticals. We need practical ideas on how to get to grips with this.

My fourth point is that there are issues of sustainability on non-wood products as there are with timber. Sustainable harvesting means ensuring that the fruit, bark or gum are harvested in a way that does not kill the plant. Most of these plants are minor constituents in the whole forest ecosystem. For them to survive the ecosystem as a whole has to be preserved - including the birds, insects and animals necessary for plant fertilization and regeneration.

These are my four main areas for discussion. I am bold enough also to offer four ways in which your Conference can make a lasting contribution to this debate.

First, by setting up networks or information links among professional colleagues working in the same field in different parts of the world. It is clear from the depth of expertise assembled here that there is a lot of information about - but it needs spreading and sharing.

Second, by developing a basic set of guidelines on what constitutes sustainable management of economic non-wood products.

Third, by promoting greater awareness of the potential markets for products from the forest.

And fourth, by improving our understanding of the value of non-wood products to local communities in and around the forests and how these communities manage their own resources and thus conserve the forest.

I must draw my remarks to a close. Tom Stoppard tells a story about an eminent Nobel prize winning physicist who keeps a horseshoe on his wall. His friends are amazed that a rational-thinking scientist should keep an object of superstition. One of them puts it to him: "Surely you do not believe that a horseshoe brings you good luck?". "No," he replies, "but they tell me it works even if you don't believe it".

Sustainable forest management gives us the opposite problem. We do believe in it, but we don't yet know enough about how it works. That is the forestry challenge for the 1990s. I hope that by the end of your Conference we will know more. And I hope your Conference comes up with constructive recommendations and ideas for all those involved, including governments, aid agencies and the private sector. I can guarantee that the ODA will be studying them keenly.

Discussion

Panel
The Rt Hon Lynda Chalker MP

Jeff Burley, Oxford Forestry Institute. Minister, can I thank you for that wide ranging but very concise presentation. Perhaps there are other people who do not know that the ODA is widely respected because of its moderate approach to things such as the TFAP, ITTO and others which we know have been subject to some considerable criticism. I would like to ask a question which refers to something Dr Lutzenberger said this morning which itself provoked a lot of support from this audience. He admitted that there is a much to be done in developing countries and that they themselves have a lot to do, but he did point out that the development agencies of the developed world have a lot of problems of their own and perhaps should clean up their own act. The question is, can you have ethics without ideology? And can a pot really call a kettle black?

Lynda Chalker. I have a lot of sympathy for what I believe Dr Lutzenberger said this morning. I do think the development agencies have got to get their act together and of course daily we hear pots calling kettles black, though we know that there is a certain tendency to try and shift blame. I think we have got to get at the root causes and solve those rather than bandying words about. It is fine to have an ideology and it is fine to have ethics, but if you are not going to be practical about conserving the forests and about halting forest loss, you are not going to be much use to anyone and that is where I rest my case - we have to be practical in maintaining sustainable forest management.

Aubrey Meyer, Willesden Green. For the purposes of this question I think I should associate myself with FEVORD which is an umbrella group of NGOs, environmentalists and local people in Karnataka [in India]. I want to bring to your attention here a petition directed to Mrs Thatcher on the subject of your intended expenditure. You did make an observation in your remarks that £40 million was destined to be spent there on a conservation project with an emphasis on conservation through management by the local people themselves and you seemed to celebrate the observation by the way you said it. In fact, this petition from FEVORD is asking you not to spend that money. The reason for that appears to be that, of the money from the ODA over the past 10 years, amounting to possibly something like £25 million, £10 million has gone to the Mysore Paper Company, and subsequently £15 million to the Karnataka Forestry Department to basically resource-feed the Mysore Paper Company with raw materials. It now seems that £30 or £40 million is destined for a 3 to 5 year project in the Western Ghats for what has been described by an ODA official as 'an integrated environment and forestry project', mainly through the Karnataka Forestry Department.

Chair. Well, I'm sure the minister will now recognize the project.

Aubrey Meyer. Let me also say that they are specifically asking on account of the 'anti-people' quality of these previous activities there, that this money not be spent. There is considerable loss of faith in what has actually happened in the past and they are obviously in need of reassurance that they will be involved. On the strength of this petition it sounds as though you are obliged by their request that this intended expenditure does not go ahead!

Lynda Chalker. Well, first of all, one of the limbs of our work in Karnataka is 'social forestry' and has constituted some of the initial work we have already been doing. I will look into what the petition says and I do agree that in years gone by, mistakes were made and nobody is saying that has not happened. What I did say when I was talking was that we have to learn from the past and I will be seeing the OFI team when they get back. They have been asked particularly to go into the Western Ghats in order to talk to the people and those I spoke with from the Karnataka Forestry Department can have no doubts we were not asking them to be involved in paper mill projects or anything of that sort at all. Therefore, let us look into this and what they have said. I will deal with it in the way that I outlined in my speech - that is to give the people a chance to benefit from their own forests as well as to conserve them.

Shyam Sunder, Karnataka Forestry Department. Madam Minister, firstly I would also like to mention that there has been a tremendous amount of criticism regarding the fact that a lot of support was given to planting eucalyptus. I submit that this is unjustified because within the entire social forestry programme there are seven or eight components of which only one component is making seedlings available, and even there, eucalyptus happens to be only one species. Unfortunately some of the areas which were thought to be suitable are so bad that no other species can really succeed.

On the Mysore Paper Company programme, I think the confusion is because of an earlier project taken up in support of the industry. This has nothing to do with the social forestry programme. The present programme is purely conservation orientated and, as the Minister explained, the involvement of the people is necessary in order to see that it goes through in the proper manner. It seeks to develop resources so that the present biotic pressure on the forest is lifted by developing firewood resources in the outer fringes of the forest which are totally degraded. So, this component seeks to provide the strength for taking up conservation measures in the forest.

Lynda Chalker. Thank you very much. Well, I can add nothing to the voice from Karnataka!

Chair. It is a reminder to us all that things are more complicated than they seem.

than 380 housewives across the UK on a variety of issues relating to the 'Rainforest Food Project' during late April/May 1990.

A limited analysis of initial returns indicates the following:

- There is significant positive support, but with some qualifications.

- As expected, a limited understanding of the issues and a high level of cynicism as to the 'gimmickyness' of products such as 'Fruits of the Rainforest' ice-cream and their value in genuinely helping preserve the forest.

- As always, ultimately their purchasing decision will be governed by the tough market-place criteria of taste, enjoyment and value for money.

Conclusions

For this project to work on a long-term basis, we believe it essential for the relevant institutions and the 'green' establishment to work with the broad sweep of industry in a way not yet seen. Such a partnership will be essential to provide the practical and emotional support necessary to ensure success - if indeed this approach is considered to be the right one.

We propose to devise some form of logo as a focus for our efforts under 'The Rainforest Food Project'; to proceed it will be important to secure the endorsement of an appropriate body.

We are already in active discussion with The Royal Botanic Gardens, Kew. Their support has provided invaluable practical direction and guidance and we hope to be able to fund further, original research by them in the longer term.

The rainforest harvest is a sensitive area; 'guarded' support from those of you within the relevant institutions and pressure groups can become whole-hearted through active participation in the process. You have the knowledge and can influence attitudes in the media and amongst the general population; we, in industry, can provide the energy and skills to take the idea to a broader audience and promote the objective of controlled long-term demand for foods from the rainforest.

Summary of the rainforest food research

This paper represents a summary of consumer research undertaken by Cambridge Market Research using their Fast Foodfax Service. They investigated attitudes to the idea of using rainforest foods through an illustrated example of an ice-cream product using rainforest harvested fruits.

Methodology

The research took the form of a supervised self completion questionnaire. In order to explain the nature of the rainforest project, respondents were shown an introduction and a colour picture of an ice-cream product 'Fruits of the Rainforest' before completing the questionnaire.

All questions in the questionnaire were closed but there was opportunity for discussion following completion which provided a greater depth of understanding of their underlying attitudes.

Sample

Fieldwork was undertaken between 25th April and 4th May amongst a nationally representative sample of 380 housewives drawn from 18 sampling points. They were selected on a balanced quota to provide:

North/South AB1/C2DE 15-34/35-64

Results

All figures are presented as percentages of housewives responding to each question.

1. Generally, how appealing do you find the idea of products containing foods from the rainforest?

Very Appealing	Fairly Appealing	Rather Appealing	Very Unappealing
32%	56%	10%	2%

Whilst the majority were in broad agreement with the idea, further analysis indicates both a surprisingly high level of awareness of the problems and a quite heated discussion of the principle not normally seen in research of this type.

Under 25s were more positive, more environmentally conscious generally, there was also a slightly more positive response in the south compared with the north of Great Britain.

Many were highly cynical that such ideas are just 'jumping on the green bandwagon', with others concerned that this was just another problem of 'money and politics in underdeveloped countries'.

Support from a recognized body such as Greenpeace or Friends of the Earth was extremely important in offering reassurance of the authenticity and value of the process.

2. Please indicate whether you agree or disagree with the following statements:

a) Using wild harvested foods in new products is a good way of trying to save the rainforest.[1]

Agree Strongly	Agree Slightly	Neither Agree or Disagree	Disagree Slightly	Disagree Strongly
32%	40%	21%	4%	2%

b) The best way of saving the rainforest would be to turn it into a national park.

Agree Strongly	Agree Slightly	Neither Agree or Disagree	Disagree Slightly	Disagree Strongly
20%	28%	31%	10%	11%

c) Britain should be involved in trying to save the rainforest by contributing funds.[1]

Agree Strongly	Agree Slightly	Neither Agree or Disagree	Disagree Slightly	Disagree Strongly
19%	34%	28%	9%	9%

In general, people were positive in their reactions and to the principle of helping in some way.

Nevertheless, this did not stop the majority believing the UK could do more in directly contributing funds.

We were left with the overall impression that many simply did not appreciate the scale of the problem. Almost half felt the answer was to turn all rainforests into a national park.

3. How likely would you be to buy a product like the ice-cream depicted on the photograph?[1]

Very Likely	Fairly Likely	Neither Likely nor Unlikely	Rather Unlikely	Very Unlikely
24%	48%	20%	6%	1%

When offered a specific product idea the generally positive response was sustained. The idea of purchasing rainforest foods was a good compromise: *"we are giving and getting something in return".*

Almost three quarters would consider buying a product of the type illustrated, although many would need to know more about the product and the rainforest connection before going further.

4. How important would the following factors be in encouraging you to try this ice-cream product?

Now please tick the one feature which would be most important to you.[1]

	Very Important (%)	Quite Important (%)	Not Very Important (%)	Not at all Important (%)	Don't Know (%)	Most Important (%)
New Taste	32	58	8	2	1	29
Pack Design/ Presentation	9	43	34	12	2	1
Contribution to Saving the Rainforest	44	42	9	2	1	34
Wild Harvested Fruit Content	19	47	26	4	2	3
Presence of Biriba and Cupuaco	9	29	40	12	10	2
Price	29	52	13	2	1	24

When pressed as to the important motives behind purchasing, rainforest connections were important, but more traditional considerations such as taste and value for money became of increased relevance. Certainly to ensure sustained demand and 'repeat purchasing' these factors would be of great importance.

5. If a litre tub of Walls Italian ice-cream cost £1.69, how much would you be prepared to pay for a litre tub of ice-cream containing rainforest fruits?[1]

£1.49 or less	£1.59	£1.69	£1.79	£1.89	£1.99	£2.00 or more
4%	4%	15%	29%	26%	16%	5%

Consumers would certainly be willing to pay a small price premium, but such a premium would have to be seen to be justified and not seen as profit taking over normally available, equivalent products.

Editors' footnote

1. The Cambridge Market Research figures, as submitted to Friends of the Earth, do not add up to 100 per cent.

First Experiences: Trading in Sustainable Rainforest Timbers

Chris Cox
Ecological Trading Company, 1 Lesbury Road, Newcastle-upon-Tyne NE6 5LB United Kingdom

Summary

Timber, because of its poor environmental and social track record, is often discounted as a useful component from primary forests. The Ecological Trading Company (ETC), by trading directly with forest communities, seeks to address this problem by making premium prices available for sustainably produced timber. Higher prices mean that good forest management can be afforded, implemented and enforced. The availability of high quality, highly portable and affordable sawmilling equipment makes sensitive timber harvesting a realistic option. All ETC timber has a full sourcing history.

My name is Chris Cox and I am one of the two directors of the Ecological Trading Company (ETC). I would like to talk about the background to this company and some of our experiences to date.

This Conference is looking at the possibilities of a rainforest harvest consisting mainly of non-timber products, and rightly so. Much attention has previously been paid to the effect of the timber trade on rainforests and here is not the place to cover this ground again. However, as we are in fact importing tropical timber, I feel there are certain points that do need mentioning.

Firstly, even though at present most tropical timber entering the trade is from unsustainable sources, this does not mean that in the future the situation could not be greatly improved. To do so would miss an important opportunity to increase rainforest value.

Secondly, some economic studies of secondary products consistently undervalue timber in monetary terms as a harvestable commodity. Using the criminally low local market prices for timber as a basis for comparison can give misleading figures. It is little wonder that secondary products can be made out to be a more attractive option. I believe that timber should and will play an important role in the rainforest harvest for many years to come.

Whereas different types of rainforest produce different types of 'secondary' products, all rainforests grow trees, and grow them in great abundance. Their potential to produce timber to improve the economic well-being of those who live in and around them is to me not in question. Rainforests are furiously dynamic places with a constant cycle of death and rebirth of trees. Anyone here who has tried to manoeuvre their way through a primary forest will testify to this, the path is constantly blocked by huge trunks in various states of decay, surrounded by a vigorous regrowth of young trees trying to reach the light. The annual incremental growth per unit area far exceeds that of temperate forests, particularly when stimulated by the formation of 'gaps' which let in sunlight to stimulate germination of dormant seeds and if one thinks of the ideal growing conditions in rainforests it is easy to understand why. Plant life thrives in warm wet places and this above all characterizes the climate in the moist tropics.

So, on a purely biological level, rainforests have everything going for them, especially for timber production. What is in serious question is the methods by which tropical forests are being exploited for timber, and I am sure most of this audience would agree that the current methods are not right. Large scale wasteful 'mining' operations with big machines and low timber prices need to be replaced by smaller community based projects, with high quality portable machinery, higher prices, smaller numbers of trees being felled, but those trees used more efficiently. Such a scenario could and should be part of any extractive reserves.

I believe that the challenge now for anyone involved in the tropical timber trade, like the Ecological Trading Company, is to redesign that trade and act now as if our particular forest source was the last such source on Earth - and we were not allowed to change our occupation! This would surely concentrate the mind and stimulate the immediate adoption of truly sustainable practices, whatever that means in each particular case!

My colleague Hubert Kwisthout and myself have been professional timber users for ten years. I make furniture and joinery, he, musical instruments, Northumbrian pipes in fact. We both used tropical timbers for various reasons, the same reasons that most people use them: they have excellent qualities and they appear to be very good value for money (though stolen goods share the same characteristic!).

As timber users and environmentalists, we sought to follow the advice of Friends of the Earth and only purchase our timber from sustainable sources. I do not know if anyone here has tried to obtain African Blackwood, or Far Eastern plywood from sustainable sources: I promise you it is not easy. Even if you can find a timber merchant who knows what you are talking about, the chances are he will not have any real information.

Faced with such lack of information, and being unhappy with the inevitable conclusion that a lack of sustainable tropical alternatives amounts to recommending a boycott in all but name, we decided to set up a new importing company that would only sell tropical timber from sustainable sources. We would provide all the information about the origins and production methods of the timber to our customers that we as consumers had been unable to find. We gambled that there would be enough fellow wood-users of like mind for us to sell to.

Our brief was to be able to assure our customers that any timber they bought from us would directly contribute to the safe future of the rainforest from which it came. By now, as the various rainforest campaigns had done a pretty good job in raising public awareness, we felt that the risk of setting up this new venture was a risk worth taking. More importantly we felt it needed to be taken because nobody else seemed to be doing anything along those lines.

Having gambled that we would be able to sell the timber, our task was to find some from sustainable sources which would stand up to considerable scrutiny.

Starting up any new business involves chance contacts and the occasional strokes of luck. One simply does not have the resources to be systematic. Hubert previously spent some time as a volunteer at Friends of the Earth International and during a conference in Berlin he heard about the Yanesha Indian co-operative in the Amazonian part of Peru who were apparently adopting an innovative approach to natural forest management. This seemed as good a place as any to start looking for timber so in April 1989, I went to Peru to visit the co-operative to have a look for myself.

Their strip-shelterbelt system, using a 40 year harvesting cycle was set up with a lot of technical input and advice from USAID and the Tropical Science Centre in Costa Rica. It is an attempt to provide an ecologically viable alternative to the ecologically unviable options in the region which largely consist of cattle ranching and timber poaching.

Unfortunately there is not time here to describe their system, but I will be happy to supply further details afterwards. Suffice to say that it meets what we consider the essential requirements of a sustainable system:

1) secure land ownership;
2) participation by, and benefits for, the local communities in the forest;
3) appropriate technology that respects the fragility of the forest ecosystem;
4) forward planning management;
5) pride and determination to make the project succeed.

Some environmentalists might take issue with the biological aspects of the system and claim that it is unproven. How do we know, they say, that a 40 year rotation is long enough? Suppose that there is a steady loss of trace elements over the years by taking timber out even in a very careful way? Will they be sufficiently replenished by dissolved minerals in rainfall?

Technically such critics have a point. But I believe they are missing a wider one. Of course the only way to be completely certain is to climb into some tropical tardis and go 40 years into the future to make sure the system works. But the Yanesha do not have 40 years to experiment with. They have to make decisions now about their way of life and the future of their forest.

Cattle ranching and most plantation cash cropping is unsuitable for poor rainforest soils. That has been proven time and again. The Yanesha's forestry system is likely to last a great deal longer than any currently available. We felt it deserved our support, which is why we are importing timber from them, at premium prices, to give their project a chance to survive. Our first container arrived in February 1990, the timber is now available from our main agents in this country, who are Milland Fine Timber in Hampshire.

Now we come to a point of crucial importance, and

I believe it applies to this Conference as a whole. It is not enough simply to design systems of production that are sustainable only from a biological viewpoint. Any forestry enterprise must be able to pay its way in the real commercial world. In Peru, the main problem was a lack of good markets for the hardwoods they were so carefully producing. Such projects fail time and time again because the marketing aspect is not sufficiently well thought out. They cannot rely on being propped up by charitable foundations forever, however vital their role has been initially. Any project has to cover its operating costs and provide its participants a decent standard of living from the sale of its produce.

In other words, a truly sustainable system also has to be socially and economically sustainable. It is the whole package or nothing. The bottom line for this is that they have to be able to sell their timber at a high enough price to compete with ecologically unsound alternatives. If they cannot, then in the long run they will fail. And if they fail, the forest will fail too, as short-term options involving unsustainable forest use become more attractive. So as with nearly all things, it comes down to money.

In Peru, and I believe almost everywhere else in the tropics, the problem is that the local timber companies do not pay sufficient prices on the forest floor, if indeed they pay anything at all. In Peru, the local price per board foot varies from 3 to 10 cents. They should be getting ten times that to cover costs and be viable. (The ETC pays them a dollar per board foot). In Ecuador, a tree whose timber can sell for $4000 retail in the UK is sold locally for as little as $6. In Papua New Guinea, native peoples make more from selling half a dozen wild eggs than they do from selling a large tree to the logging companies.

The fundamental inequality in such trade means that any talk of sustainable harvesting of forests for timber is complete nonsense, unless the value we all know timber has, is adequately reflected in the price paid for it at source.

It is a basic policy of the ETC to pay the highest possible price for timber directly to producers. This is in stark contrast to most trading companies who seek to get away with paying as little as possible. These high prices are highly conditional: they are in exchange for proper long-term management of the forests being implemented. On the other hand, good prices mean that the money to carry out such management is available on a rolling basis through the sale of timber.

High prices on the forest floor mean in most cases the final consumer will be required to pay a little more. A recent poll commissioned by World Wide Fund for Nature (WWF) and conducted by MORI determined that consumers of finished wood products would be prepared to pay around 13 per cent more for sustainably sourced timber (source: WWF/MORI Survey, 1990). By trading directly with forest producers, the ETC intends to be able to pay significantly more at source while keeping prices under control at home.

We have been greatly encouraged by the response to our first container in spite of the unfamiliar names and the somewhat higher prices. We and our agents at Milland have had several hundred enquiries already and have sold most of the timber before it is even out of the kilns. This is encouraging us to look at other sources of timber and indeed other forest products. I would be pleased to talk to anyone at this Conference who would be able to supply us with sustainable timber from a community-based forestry project.

Financial aspects of setting up ETC

To conclude, a brief word about the financial aspects of setting up a company like the ETC. Being a commercial venture with strong environmental considerations as a bottom line does not exactly open many doors to financial institutions. Neither does being a commercial venture open doors to environmental funding to us. In fact, we neatly fall between two stalls: we are seen as too commercial to access conservation funding and not commercial enough by banks and other lending bodies. Financially speaking, we have been damned for what we are and damned for what we are not.

However, we are setting up a trust which will enable us to access funding to carry out research and development work. Perhaps the most exciting aspect of the ETC, so far, is that simply by offering the prospect of a good market, we have been able to catalyse the creation of a brand new forestry project in an indigenous reserve in the north of Ecuador. Via the trust, we are pleased to announce that both the Flora and Fauna Preservation Society, and also the World Wide Fund for Nature, will be able to support us in this project.

A key feature of this will be the use of a highly portable sawmill called the Trekkasaw (Plate 12): this has the capacity to produce export quality lumber deep in the forest without the need for roads and big yellow machinery which have proved so disastrous for rainforests in the past. The idea is that the lumber will be carried out in manageable pieces, by hand or by mules, down existing transport avenues, forest tracks or by canoe down the rivers. This kind of scheme could provide a blueprint for future, small scale and sustainable rainforest timber extraction methods.

Conclusion

If we are truly concerned about the future of tropical rainforests from a wider global perspective, as I am sure everybody here is, it is now essential that we as representatives of the green consumer movement support such initiatives. We have to be prepared to try out new products and pay the right price for more familiar ones. This means supporting a new breed of companies who are sticking their necks out by adopting fair and transparent trading practices, and trying to get it right. I hope that the Ecological Trading Company, amongst many others, will be able to play its part in this exciting and important process.

Sustainable Marketing and Development of Rainforest Products: The Path Taken by the Body Shop

Robert Forster
(for Dr Jason Clay, Cultural Survival) The Body Shop International, Watersmead, Littlehampton, West Sussex BN17 6LS United Kingdom

Summary

The Body Shop aims to provide a market which gives preference to those land use options which empower forest people and serve to maximize the conservation of the forest environment. In developing such markets, companies must bear in mind two important aspects; control and fair compensation for the forest people. If these are not brought into play immediately, market forces will continue to bring about the degradation of the tropical forests, the increasing misery of its people and the ruination of their livelihoods.

Tropical forest marketing campaigns, including the ones run by The Body Shop, are concerned with making better use of rainforests by providing an economic alternative to the wholesale removal of trees and the conversion of forest into farms and ranches.

How can the economic productivity of forests be increased, whilst allowing them to remain intact, and the lives of the forest dwellers be protected? That is the question before us.

All tropical forest countries have run up huge debts and they all have exploding populations. The forests will not be able to stay intact unless they can pay their way and support more people.

In the event that little is done to relieve these countries of their overseas debts, or to help them control population growth, it will be a choice of using forests, or losing them.

It seems likely that with the prevailing stranglehold which the economic powers have over the fate of the world's resources, the value of the forests will have to be proven in the market place if they are to be conserved.

However, The Body Shop does not believe that the world can afford to turn capitalism loose in the rainforest, either through their company or any other. Nowhere in the world does monopoly capitalism exist in a more pure form than at the mouth of each tributary to the Amazon. It has been a major cause of environmental destruction, cultural degradation and genocide. The market-place for forest products has got to change and companies will have to change their practices if they are to work constructively in the rainforests.

The work which The Body Shop is doing to develop a market for forest products and to establish equitable trading links with the poor nations is guided by a number of underlying principles which come under a general policy termed 'Trade-not-Aid'. Put simply, this means creating trade for long-term employment rather than giving cash hand-outs. More specifically, these principles are listed as follows:

- respect for all cultures, religions and the environment;

- utilize traditional skills and materials;

- trade in replenishable, naturally-occurring materials;

- raw materials should be procured from sustainable sources both at the macro-environmental level (global climate and/or pollution) and at the micro-environmental level (in this case, the rainforest);

- post-harvest activities, such as processing and transport, should not degrade the environment;

- the demand for raw materials should not be driven by profits and growth, but by the real needs of individuals and groups. In this way, economic activities should help to eradicate inequality, not create it. The aim is to make a reasonable profit, not to make a killing;

- as societies we should move away from accumulation to more equitable exchange;

- the long-term impact of trade must be assessed right from the start of project identification and regularly monitored thereafter. (All such dealings in the Amazonian forest, therefore, would be handled by Cultural Survival - an academic-based human rights group with decades of experience in this area. Cultural Survival identifies suitable projects and products and monitors or hires other competent individuals to monitor both);

- there should be just rewards for the primary producers. These are the people who have traditionally lived in the forest maintaining natural diversity and ecological stability. Their knowledge and labour must be given full recognition and compensation. (Various mechanisms can be used to achieve this - patents, royalties, higher commodity prices, profit sharing);

- businesses must return part of their profits to local communities. These should go back to the producer groups for them to use rather than for the aggrandizement of individuals in the West or local élites;

- businesses must take it upon themselves to serve as models in their own transactions so that others, too, will change;

- businesses must take an active role in educating the public about the environmental problems confronting the planet and the role of consumers in it.

Since April 1989, The Body Shop has been gathering samples of potential products from the Brazilian Amazon and learning about the social, economic and political factors that affect the livelihood of forest people. While research and development continues on product formulations, availability of raw materials and exposing previous records of toxicity, The Body Shop has given financial assistance to a number of projects aimed to support the forest people of Amazonia. The key areas of support are in strengthening organizations that are co-ordinating campaigns for land rights, developing sustainable methods of production that involve forest people, and creating and/or modifying markets.

Such projects include:

■ core support to forest dwellers' programmes such as the Indian Research Centre at Goiania run by the Union of Indigenous Nations (UNI). Here, training is given to Indians in resource management and law;

■ support has been given to the Nucleus for Indigenous Rights (NDI) to fund test cases such as the one that resulted in federal judges declaring the gold miners' invasion of Yanomami Indian land to be illegal. This has set a precedent in the state of Roraima as well as in other areas;

■ core support to the Ecumenical Centre of Documentation and Information (CEDI). The collation and broadcasting of information regarding the situation confronting indigenous people is vital for the lobbying and legal work carried out by the NDI. Support has also been given to purchase computer hardware and software to interpret satellite imagery that will enable the boundaries of Indian areas in Brazil to be demarcated and monitored for invasion;

■ funds have been given to the Co-ordinating Body for the Indigenous Peoples' Organizations in the Amazon Basin (COICA). To be effective, COICA needs an efficient communication system, and funds will be used to purchase telephones, computers for electronic mail and fax machines;

■ research has been funded on botanical and cultural issues that will help to clarify the sustainability of harvesting certain products;

The Body Shop's strategy in locating products worthy of attention has been to focus initially on those that exist in the market already. Some 250 samples have been received and out of those which have gone through a preliminary set of tests, about 10 to 15 raw materials look extremely promising and perhaps another 10 to 15 have serious potential.

The basic conditions for selection, however, are useful properties and no toxicity complications. If these are not satisfied, no matter how abundant or easily processed the raw materials are, it is unlikely there will be any commercial potential.

With a short-list of useful products, the next stage is to turn to those who live in the forest to see if and where supplies might be available, in what quantities, at what price, etc, or work with those who want to produce for this new market. We ask both the forest residents and the botanists what the potential problems and risks are with creating or increasing markets for these raw materials.

In summary, The Body Shop's aim is to provide a market which will give preference to those land use options which empower forest people and serve to maximize the conservation of the forest environment. The two most important things that companies have to bear in mind in developing such markets are control and fair compensation for the forest people. If these are not brought into play immediately, market forces will continue to bring about the degradation of the tropical forests, the increasing misery of its residents and the ruination of their livelihoods.

Quantitative Ethnobotany and The Case for Conservation in Amazonia

Professor Ghillean Prance, W Balée and Dr Brian Boom
Institute of Economic Botany, New York Botanical Garden, Bronx, New York 10458 USA

R L Carneiro
Department of Anthropology, American Museum of Natural History, Central Park West at 79th Street, New York 10024 USA

This paper formed the basis of the presentation at this Conference by Dr Brian Boom. The bulk of the paper, with the above title and authors, was reprinted by permission of the Society for Conservation Biology and Blackwell Scientific Publications Inc. This version omits the complete table of results which can be found in the original reference: *Conservation Biology*, Volume 1, No 4, December 1987, pp 296-310.

Summary

Quantitative data are presented on the use of trees in terra firma *dense forest by four indigenous Amazonian groups: the Ka'apor and Tembé, both Tupi-Guarani-speaking groups of Brazil; the Panare, a Cariban-speaking group of Venezuela; and the Chácobo, a Panoan-speaking group of Bolivia. In each case, an ethnoecological forest inventory was conducted of a 1 hectare parcel of forest. All trees at least 10 centimetres diameter at breast height (DBH) were marked and botanical specimens were collected. They were then presented to indigenous informants to gather data on use.*

From these interviews and the identification of specimens collected, it was possible to calculate the percentage of tree species on each hectare that was useful to each group: Ka'apor, 76.8 per cent; Tembé, 61.3 per cent; Panare, 48.6 per cent; Chácobo, 78.7 per cent. Furthermore, by dividing the trees into various use categories (food, construction technology, remedy, commerce and other), and designating the cultural importance of each species as 'major' or 'minor', it was possible to devise a 'use value' for each species, and by summation, for each plant family. Based on these calculations, it was determined that the Palmae was the most useful family for all four indigenous groups. Our data support the assertion that the terra firma *rainforests of Amazonia contain an exceptionally large number of useful species and that certain plant families (for example Palmae) deserve special consideration in terms of conservation. The fact that each indigenous group has different suites of most useful species is, in fact, more a reflection of plant endemism within Amazonia than intercultural differences* per se. *High indigenous plant use combined with high endemism has important implications for conservation policy: many reserves are needed throughout Amazonia.*

Introduction

The usefulness of Amazonian forests as demonstrated by indigenous peoples who depend on them has often been cited as one reason, among others, for their conservation (for example Myers, 1982; Fearnside, 1985). Upon searching the literature, however, we found little quantitative data to support this claim. We designed, therefore, a quantitative study to show how useful Amazonian forests are to indigenous Amazonian peoples in terms of the number and proportion of useful species and families therein. The purpose of this article is to present our quantitative data on the use of trees in four 1 hectare plots of *terra firma* dense forest by four indigenous Amazonian groups, and to show the value of this data to the field of conservation. We have also attempted to quantify the usefulness of the principal species and plant families involved in our study.

Forest inventories of one hectare were taken in the habitats of the Ka'apor, Tembé, Chácobo, and Panare Indians. Here we report the utility of trees greater than or equal to 10 centimetres diameter at breast height (DBH) from these plots to each of the four groups. Some of these results have been discussed elsewhere (Balée, 1986, 1987; Boom, 1985, 1986a, 1986b, 1987), emphasizing extraordinarily high percentages of tree species and individual trees from the plots that are useful in one or more ways to the Indians concerned.

In these earlier studies, uses were very broadly defined, such that any species that could be used for firewood and any species that bore parts edible for game animals, if useful for nothing else (such as supplying edible parts for people, construction material, technological items, and medicine) were also considered to be useful, at least in one or both of these ways. Thus, Balée (1986, 1987) found 100 per cent use for both *terra firma* plots by the Ka'apor and Tembé, and Boom (1987, personal communication) found 82 per cent use for the Chácobo and 49 per cent for the Panare, using these categories. We define 'use' more narrowly here.

In this paper we do not discuss plants that supply only fuel and/or attract game animals, upon which indigenous diets depend, not because these are not useful *a priori,* but rather because the vast majority of trees fall into one or both of these categories anyway. Instead, we attempt to calculate the value of tree species and families in terms of indigenously recognized uses less regularly distributed throughout the corpus of our ethnographic data and botanical collections. The objective is to evaluate the tree species and families that seem to be most useful to all four indigenous groups and to recommend measures to protect these species and their associated habitats.

Materials and methods

The four groups on which this paper focuses speak languages of three different linguistic families: Tupi-Guarani (Ka'apor and Tembé), Panoan (Chácobo), and Cariban (Panare). They reside within the frontiers of three different Amazonian countries: Brazil (Ka'apor and Tembé), Bolivia (Chácobo), and Venezuela (Panare). Their contact histories and populations are all different. The Ka'apor were pacified in 1928 (Ribeiro, 1970), and the Tembé in the 1850s (Wagley & Galvão, 1949). The Summer Institute of Linguistics first effectively contacted the

Chácobo in 1955 (Prost, 1970). The Panare have been more or less in contact with non-Indians since the first Spanish explorers entered the middle Orinoco region in the 1600s (Henley, 1982).

Group populations are: Ka'apor (*ca* 500), Tembé (*ca* 156), Chácobo (*ca* 400), and Panare (*ca* 2000). With the exception of the Ka'apor and Tembé, who live in adjacent territories, these groups occupy different types of forest in terms of species composition and dominance. Despite these differences, we believe that there are broad similarities in terms of the ways these people use the forest and the families, if not genera and species, of trees that are most useful to them.

The method common to all these studies was the hectare forest inventory (*cf* Boom, 1986b). Kroeber (1920), in a critique of ethnobotanical studies of his time, suggested that such studies become more quantitative. Carneiro (1978) was the first to estimate the percentage of useful trees per plot of land to the Cariban-speaking Kuikuru of the upper Xingu River basin, in Brazilian Amazonia. One can infer that the percentage of useful trees named by the Kuikuru from this plot was 76 per cent, according to Carneiro's data (Carneiro, 1978). Since Carneiro did not, however, obtain herbarium specimens, one cannot determine the actual percentage of useful species to the Kuikuru. The current project originated as an attempt to combine ethnological data on plant utility with the botanical documentation of herbarium vouchers.

Categories of plant use

The data on plant utility reflect declarations made by indigenous informants combined with our own observations of the cultural deployment of plants in each ethnographic case. In no case, incidentally, do informants' accounts disagree with such observations.

To compare the results of these studies, we divide uses of trees from the inventory plots into these categories:

a) 'edible' (including parts, such as fruits, seeds, and latex, which people consume);

b) 'construction material' (such as wood used in post-and-beam construction, canoes, bridges and leaves used for roofing thatch);

c) 'technology' (a very broad category, which includes lashing material, glue, pottery temper, dye, soap, pipe stem, arrow point);

d) 'remedy' (for sinusitis, congestion, diarrhoea, headache, vomiting, fever, unwanted pregnancy, bleeding wounds, snakebite, cradle-cap, canker sores, insect repellant);

e) 'commerce' (boat caulking, rubber, souvenirs);and

f) 'other' (magic, toys, dog-fatteners, fermentation aids, and perfume).

These categories do not necessarily reflect the indigenous classification of uses, if such classification was reflected in lexicons of these languages, as we believe it is (*cf* Berlin *et al.*, 1974).

In fact, only one category may be considered to be readily recognized by the Indians themselves, as demonstrated in the indigenous lexicons. This category is 'edible'. The Ka'apor and Tembé, for example, readily identify this category as *ma'e u'u awa* ('what people eat') or *awa mi'u* ('people's food') and distinguish it from, for example, *so'o mi'u* ('game animal food' in Ka'apor) and *miyar mi'u* ('game animal food' in Tembé). The other categories may be considered to be artificial constructs based on our own collapsing of indigenous use categories, since these categories are not readily named in any of the four languages except by circumlocutions (see Berlin *et al.*, 1974).

No single or short set of terms covers the semantic range of 'construction material', as here defined, in any of these languages. Rather, house beams, posts, ridge-pole, thatching material, canoe-building material, and the like, are all individually named. No indigenous term in any of the four languages approximates what we term 'technology'. Rather, arrow points, lashing material from the bark of trees, glues, dyes, soaps and so on are individually named. One of the most difficult categories to define is that of 'remedy'. The most common American English sense of the term 'remedy' is "something, such as medication or therapy, that relieves pain, cures disease or corrects a disorder" (Morris, 1973). Such is not the case with the range of meaning of terms such as *puhan* (Ka'apor) and *pohang* (Tembé), which cover not only the most common American English sense of 'remedy', but much more. The best gloss for these terms is, in fact, 'catalyst' (*ie* that which induces change). Thus, for example, the wood of *Tetragastris altissima* is believed by the Ka'apor to be a Kawii-*puhan* ('beer catalyst'), insofar as when it is added to the ceremonial beer (*kawi*), it is believed to effect a stronger, more potent brew. This use of the term *puhan* seems to go beyond the American English sense of the noun 'remedy'. At the same time, however, *puhan* refers to 'remedy' in a conventional sense. Drinking a decoction of the bark of *Fusaea longifolia*, for example, is believed by the Ka'apor to be a 'diarrhoea remedy' (*marikahipuhan*). We include under the category 'remedy' only those species for which informants state a testable application to a human illness; that is, the culturally prescribed application, treatment, and effects of the plant on a given illness are stated by informants in such a way as to be falsifiable. Plant uses that are untestable in terms of the indigenous formulation of their application, given limitations in the present tools of ethnobotanical science, are placed in the category 'magic' or 'other'.

The category 'commerce' is not lexically distinguished in these languages from economic reciprocity. In Ka'apor, for example, the word for 'giving' (*me'e*) is the same as that for 'selling'.

Having defined the range of meaning of these use categories, both in terms of indigenous perceptions (Alcorn, 1981) and our own observations, we would distinguish quantitatively the relative utility of specific plants in given situations in the same terms. Some plants are clearly more useful than others for specific purposes, that is, they are explicitly preferred by the Indians themselves for a given purpose over other plants that can also fulfil that purpose, but to a less desirable degree. For example, the Ka'apor distinguish between 'quite edible' (*u'u-ate-awa*) and 'less edible' (*u'u-we-awa*). Thus, it seems illogical to weigh equally, for example, the small, insignificant yet sweet fruits of *Protium* spp. (Burseraceae), which in Ka'apor society are generally eaten only by children and are never the objects of intensive gathering and economic exchange and the substantial fruits of *Theobroma grandiflorum* (Sterculiaceae, Plate 3), which are much sought after items of food distribution among the Ka'apor. In other words,

Theobroma grandiflorum fruits are more important to the Ka'apor than *Protium* spp. fruits in an indigenous and objective sense, that is, in terms of their edibility. The same distinction - more important versus less important - can be applied to plants in each of the other categories of use, according to indigenous accounts and our own observations of the extent to which people seek out certain plants as opposed to others which are nevertheless useful for approximately the same ends.

Therefore, in evaluating and comparing the utility of species, each major use of a plant is counted as 1.0 and each minor use as 0.5. We would define the use value of a species as the sum of the values corresponding to its major and/or minor use(s) in each culture. Thus, if a species (*ie* some of its parts) can be used as a major technological item and at the same time serves as a minor remedy, possessing no other uses to the culture in question, then the use value of the species is 1.5 (1 + 0.5). To calculate the familial use value per hectare plot, we add together the use values of each species in a family, whether useful or not, occurring on the plot (although species with no use value, as here defined, are excluded from our species list). This is divided to counter the high familial use values that would accrue to families that contain many species useful only in minor ways (as with Burseraceae to the Ka'apor).

Results and discussions

Most species of tree occurring on the Ka'apor and Tembé plots were useful, as here defined, in some way. Of the 99 species occurring on the Ka'apor plot, 76 (76.8 per cent) were useful; of the 119 species on the Tembé plot, 73 (61.3 per cent); of the 94 species on the Chácobo plot, 74 (78.7 per cent) and of the 70 species on the Panare plot, 34 (48.6 per cent). The specific uses of species from the four plots are now discussed.

a) Food

Of the 99 species on the Ka'apor plot, 34 (34.3 per cent) are major or minor food plants; the more important species include *Euterpe oleracea* (Palmae, Plate 1) and *Theobroma grandiflorum* (Sterculiaceae). Of the 119 species occurring on the Tembé plot, 26 (21.8 per cent) are major or minor food plants; the more important species include *Oenocarpus distichus* (Palmae) and *Pourouma guianensis* (Moraceae). Of the 94 species on the Chácobo plot, 38 (40.4 per cent) are major or minor food plants; the more important species are five palms, *Astrocaryum aculeatum, Jessenia bataua, Maximiliana maripa, Oenocarpus mapora, and Scheelea princeps,* and four Moraceae, *Pourouma cecropii folia, P. guianensis, Pseudolmedia laevis,* and *P. macrophylla.* Of the 70 species occurring on the Panare plot, 24 (34.3 per cent) are major or minor food plants; the more important are *Mauritia flexuosa* (Palmae, Plate 5), *Parinari excelsa* (Chrysobalanaceae), and an as-yet-unidentified Sapotaceae species.

b) Construction Material

Species useful in major and minor ways for construction account for 20.2 per cent (20/99) of the species from the Ka'apor plot; the more important species include *Fusea longifolia* (Annonaceae) and *Licania* spp. (Chrysobalanaceae), which are used as rafters and tie-beams. *Licania* spp. is used because it is rot-resistant partly because of the abundance of silica found in the rays of its wood (Prance, 1972; ter Welle, 1976), which discourages termite infestations. In the Tembé plot, 30.3 per cent (36/119) of the species are useful for construction; the more important species are *Minquartia guianensis* (Olacaceae), which is one of only two species used for house posts and *Xylopia nitida* (Annonaceae), commonly used for ridge-pole. The Tembé so value *Minquartia guianensis* for house posts that there is a taboo on its use as firewood: if burned, it is believed that numerous village deaths would ensue. On the Chácobo plot, 17.0 per cent (16/94) of the species are sources of construction materials. The more important Chácobo species for house posts are *Lindackeria paludosa* (Flacourtiaceae), *Amaioua guianensis* (Rubiaceae), *Mezilaurus itauba* (Lauraceae), and three species of *Sclerolobium* (Leguminosae); *Vochysia vismiifolia* (Vochysiaceae) and *Diplotropis purpurea* (Leguminosae) provide durable wood for the construction of simple bridges over small streams. In the Panare plot, only 2.9 per cent (2/70) of the species are used in construction; *Mauritia flexuosa* (Palmae) furnishes leaves for roof thatch on houses, and *Amaioua corymbosa* (Rubiaceae) is a preferred species for house framework construction because of its durable wood.

c) Technology

Species used in major or minor ways for technology account for 19.2 per cent (19/99) of the species in Ka'apor plot; the more important species include *Licania membranacea* (Chrysobalanaceae), the ashes of which are used in making pottery temper, and *Lecythis idatimon* (Lecythidaceae), from the bark of which is made high quality lashing material. On the Tembé plot, 21.0 per cent (25/119) of the species are used in technology; the more important species are *Inga alba* (Leguminosae), from the bark of which is produced a black dye for painting the shaman's gourd rattler, and *Lacmellea aculeata* (Apocynaceae), the wood of which is used for making spoons and ladles. Types used for technology in the Chácobo plot account for 18.1 per cent (17/94) of species. The more important technological species of the Chácobo include *Astrocaryum aculeatum* (Palmae), the 'wood' of which is carved into hunting bows and arrow points; *Brosimum utile* (Moraceae), the inner bark of which is made into barkcloth, and several species that supply a fibrous inner bark for lashing material: *Guatteria discolor, G. hyposericea, Xylopia polyantha* (Annonaceae), *Cecropia ficifolia* and *C. sciadophylla* (Moraceae). In the Panare plot, 4.3 per cent (3/70) of the species are useful for technology; *Cochlospermum orinocense* (Bixaceae) and *Lecythis corrugata* (Lecythidaceae) provide a fibrous inner bark that is used to make tumplines for burden baskets, and the leaves of *Maximiliana maripa* (Palmae) are woven into the burden baskets themselves.

d) Remedy

Species useful in major or minor ways in the preparation of remedies account for 21.2 per cent (21/99) of the species on the Ka'apor plot; important remedies come from species such as *Parahancornia amapa* (Apocynaceae), the latex of which is taken orally to treat stomach ailments, and *Virola michelii* (Myristicaceae), the sap of which is used to treat canker sores. On the Tembé plot, 10.9 per cent (13/119) of types have medicinal application; important species include *Dipteryx odorata* (Leguminosae), the oil of which is used to alleviate earache, and *Carapa guianensis* (Meliaceae), the oil of which is rubbed on the body to repel blackflies (*Simulium* spp.). The Chácobo indicate that 35.1 per cent (33/94) of the species on the plot are useful as remedies; examples include two species of Rubiaceae, *Calycophyllum acreanum* and *Capirona decorticans*, the barks of which are dried, powdered, mixed with water to form a paste, and applied to skin wounds to prevent or cure infections. In the Panare plot, 7.1 per cent (5/70) of the species are used medicinally; important species in this category include *Tabebuia serratifolia* (Bignoniaceae), the bark of which is used as a remedy for stomach ailments, and *Simarouba amara* (Simaroubaceae), which is employed to treat snakebite.

e) Commerce

Relatively few species of plants are commercialized from the forest plots of any of the four indigenous groups studied, because of their relatively isolated situations. In the cases of the Ka'apor and Tembé, these species are used in minor commercial ways, while for the Chácobo and Panare, the commercialization of some species is a major part of their present culture.

From the Ka'apor plot, 2.0 per cent (2/99) of the species are in this category. These are *Licania heteromorpha* (Chrysobalanaceae), the dye obtained is used to paint *Crescentia cujete* (Bignoniaceae) bowls, which in turn are sold as souvenirs on a very small scale, and *Symphonia globulifera* (Guttiferae), the latex of which is used to glue and blacken parts of arrows, which are also sold on a very small scale as souvenirs. In the Tembé plot, 5.0 per cent (6/119) of the species are commercialized; examples include *Protium* spp. (Burseraceae), the resins of which are sold on a small scale for boat caulking, and *Licania* sp. 3 (Chrysobalanaceae), from which the dye is used to decorate *Crescentia cujete* bowls sold as souvenirs. In no case does commercialization of these tree species involve destruction of the tree itself. Collection of latex from *Symphonia globulifera* involves nonlethal scoring of the tree; resin from *Protium* spp. is collected from the ground after it is naturally exuded from the tree. Obtaining bark from *Licania* spp. to be used in the preparation of dye does not involve the girdling of the tree; the Indians affirm that their practice of stripping off bark pieces on one side of the tree does not kill it. In the case of the Chácobo, only 1.1 per cent (1/94) of the species are commercialized; the latex from *Hevea brasiliensis* (Euphorbiaceae, Plates 24 and 26) is collected and, after curing and coagulating the liquid rubber over fire and forming it into large, oblong balls (Plate 25), it is taken to market for sale. This rubber is the Chácobo's principal source of cash; Brazil nuts (*Bertholletia excelsa*, Plates 27 and 28) are also collected for sale but because no trees of this species occurred in the inventory plot, these are not considered here. From the Panare plot, 4.3 per cent (3/70) of the species are in the commercial category; the most important of these is *Dipteryx punctata* (Leguminosae), whose seeds are collected and sold for the extraction of coumarin. The other two Panare commercial tree species are less important: the red exudate from *Swartzia laevicarpa* (Leguminosae) is used to paint decorative baskets that are sold as souvenirs, while the bark of *Casearia sylvestris* (Flacourtiaceae) is burned to produce a black paint that is likewise applied to decorative baskets.

f) Other

Species in the 'other' category of use account for 8.5 per cent (9/99) of the species on the Ka'apor plot; an example is *Tetragastris altissima* (Burseraceae), the wood of which is used as a fermentation catalyst (see above). On the Tembé plot 4.2 per cent (5/119) of the species are in this category; an example is *Sagotia racemosa* (Eurphorbiaceae), the fragrant roots of which the hunter rubs on his body to become lucky in the hunt. On the Chácobo plot 1.1 per cent (1/94) of the species are in the 'other' category; the spathe of *Maximiliana maripa* (Palmae) is used as a toy by children. In the case of the Panare there were no useful tree species in the plot that were not included in the categories already discussed above.

Tables 1 to 4 list the most useful species (with values of 2 or more) for each group. Those species that are not substitutable, insofar as no other plant species can be used in place of them for a given purpose in a given culture, are indicated, as are those among the nonsubstitutable found only in *terra firma* dense forest.

Of the 9 species listed in Table 1, which are those with a use value of 2.0 or more to the Ka'apor, 5 (55.5 per cent) seem to be exclusively of *terra firma* dense forest (ie they are not encountered in old swiddens, swidden fallows or swamp forest). Of the 10 species listed in Table 2, which are those with a use value of 2.0 or more to the Tembé, 5 (50 per cent) seem to be exclusively of *terra firma* dense forest. Tables 5-8 list the families with the highest familial use values (with values of 1 or more).

Examples of nonsubstitutable species include *Euterpe oleracea* (Palmae), used for bench making by the Ka'apor; *Symphonia globulifera* (Guttiferae), which serves as a contraceptive; and *Carapa guianensis* (Meliaceae), which is used as an insect repellent. To the Tembé, only *Dipteryx odorata* (Leguminosae) is used to relieve earache, and only *Carapa guianensis* is used as a useful insect repellant. Of the most important species to the Ka'apor, 8 (88.8 per cent) are exclusively of *terra firma* dense forest and/or nonsubstitutable; of the most important species to the Tembé, 7 (70 per cent) are exclusively of *terra firma* dense forest and/or nonsubstitutable. The total number of nonsubstitutable tree species from the Ka'apor plot is 6 (6 per cent of all species), and the total number of nonsubstitutable species from the Tembé plot is 2 (1.7 per cent of all species).

The overall results of our analysis are summarized in Tables 9 and 10. Table 9 shows the percentages of useful tree species, arranged by category of use, in each of the four inventory plots. Table 10 shows the percentage of total useful tree species, irrespective of category of use, in each of the four inventory plots.

Conclusions

Our data definitely confirm the assertion that the *terra firma* rainforests of Amazonia contain an exceptionally large number of useful species. The majority of tree species from four *terra firma* plots of 1 hectare each are useful to four respective indigenous groups, at least in the use categories we have defined here. Our data further show that some of the tree species of *terra firma* forest are useful to the Indians in nonsubstitutional ways. Some species, in other words, are irreplaceable insofar as

Table 1. Most important species to the Ka'apor (with use values of 2 or more). (*) nonsubstitutable species; (+) species exclusively of *terra firma* dense forest.

Species and Family	Use Value
Euterpe oleracea (Palmae)*	3.5
Licania heteromorpha (Chrysobalanaceae)+	3.0
Oenocarpus distichus (Palmae)	2.5
Fusaea longifolia (Annonaceae)+	2.5
Lacmellea aculeata (Apocynaceae)+	2.5
Tetragastris altissima (Burseraceae)+	2.0
Symphonia globulifera (Guttiferae)*	2.0
Eschweilera coriacea (Lecythidaceae)+	2.0
Carapa guianensis (Meliaceae)*	2.0

Table 2. Most important species to the Tembé (with use values of 2 or more). (*) nonsubstitutable species; (+) species exclusively of *terra firma* dense forest.

Species and Family	Use Value
Dipteryx odorata (Leguminosae)*	3.0
Carapa guianensis (Meliaceae)*	3.0
Couepia guianensis (Chrysobalanaceae)+	3.0
Licania sp 3 (Chrysobalanaceae)+	3.0
Inga alba (Leguminosae)	2.5
Oenocarpus distichus (Palmae)	2.5
Anaxagorea brevipes (Annonaceae)+	2.0
Fusaea longifolia (Annonaceae)+	2.0
Tetragastris altissima (Buseraceae)+	2.0
Radlkoferella macrocarpa (Sapotaceae)	2.0

Table 3. Most important species to the Chácobo (with use values of 2 or more). (*) nonsubstitutable species.

Species and Families	Use Value
Euterpe precatoria (Palmae, Plate 13)	3.0
Scheelea princeps (Palmae)	3.0
Socratea exorrhiza (Palmae)	2.5
Astrocaryum aculeatum (Palmae)	2.0
Maximiliana maripa (Palmae)*	2.0
Oenocarpus mapora (Palmae)	2.0
Licania octandra (Chrysobalanaceae)	2.0
Brosimum utile (Moraceae)	2.0
Ficus nymphaeifolia (Moraceae)	2.0
Micropholis guyanensis (Sapotaceae)*	2.0
Vochysia vismiifolia (Vochysiaceae)	2.0

Table 4. Most important species to the Panare (with use values of 2 or more). (*) nonsubstitutable species.

Species and Family	Use Value
Mauritia flexuosa (Palmae)*	2.0
Maximiliana maripa (Palmae)*	2.0

they are the sole species employed to achieve culturally desirable ends.

The notion of 'useful' species varies, of course, from culture to culture: for example, numerous species in our data are also high-quality timber species (such as *Mezilaurus itauba, Carapa guianensis,* and *Tabebuia serratifolia*), which outside of indigenous

Table 5. Most important families to the Ka'apor (with familial use values of 1 or more).

Family	Familial Use Values
Palmae	3.00
Apocynaceae	1.75
Guttiferae	1.50
Chrysobalanaceae	1.29
Malpighiaceae	1.00
Lecythidaceae	1.00

Table 6. Most important families to the Tembé (with familial use values of 1 or more).

Family	Familial Use Values
Palmae	1.50
Chrysobalanaceae	1.39
Annonaceae	1.25
Lauraceae	1.08
Malpighiaceae	1.00
Meliaceae	1.00

contexts are used on an industrial basis. Our data deal only with the non-industrial uses indigenous Amazonians have for these species, which are far more diverse than the uses to which these species are put in Western society. Although we have not discussed trees for firewood and trees that attract game, which account for the vast majority of the species on the Ka'apor and Tembé plots (Balée, 1986, 1987), the extent to which all four plots of forest are useful to all groups in ways that are less

Table 7. Most important families to the Chácobo (with familial use values of 1 or more).

Family	Familial Use Value
Palmae	2.29
Sapotaceae	2.00
Sterculiaceae	1.50
Vochysiaceae	1.25

Table 8. Most important families to the Panare (with familial use values of 1 or more).

Family	Familial Use Value
Palmae	1.25
Bignoniaceae	1.00
Bixaceae	1.00
Lecythidaceae	1.00

commonly represented is interesting.

Species useful for identical purposes among different groups certainly vary, partly as a function of phytogeographic differences. For example, the Ka'apor use species of *Tabebuia* and *Brosimum* in making their bows, while the Chácobo use *Astrocaryum aculeatum* for this purpose (see above). *Astrocaryum aculeatum* has not yet been collected in the Ka'apor region, if indeed it exists there. In other words, different suites of species (ie endemism) within given Amazonian forests do not affect the utility of these forests *per se,* to comparable indigenous cultures. Rather,

Table 9. Percentage of useful tree species of all species on plots for each indigenous group by use categories.

Use Category	Ka'apor	Tembé	Chácobo	Panare
food	34.3	21.8	40.4	34.3
construction	20.2	30.3	17.0	2.9
technology	19.2	21.0	18.1	4.3
remedy	21.2	10.9	35.1	7.1
commerce	2.0	5.0	1.1	4.3
other	8.1	4.2	1.1	0.0

Table 10. Percentage of useful species (in all categories specified) per hectare plot to the indigenous groups studied.

Indigenous Group	Percentage of Useful Tree Species from Inventory Sites
Ka'apor	76.8
Tembé	61.3
Chácobo	78.7
Panare	48.6

endemism, combined with the high indigenous utility of all forest in this survey, suggests that the conservation of only one or a few blocks of forest would preserve, in fact, many useful Amazonian species of trees. The implications for conservation policy are inescapable: many reserves are needed throughout Amazonia.

Finally, our results suggest that certain plant families and *terra firma* dense forest should be of high priority for conservation. It is interesting that the palm ranks consistently among those families with the highest use values for all four groups. Palms have often been described as the 'grasses of the tropics', because they are so useful to those who depend on them. We have offered here a positive quantitative test of this intuitive statement. Other families that rank among the highest in terms of familial use values for at least two of the four groups include Lecythidaceae (Ka'apor and Panare), Chrysobalanaceae (Ka'apor and Tembé), and Malpighiaceae (Ka'apor and Tembé). Some of the most important plant families are distributed mostly in *terra firma* forest, meaning that this forest type should be a priority for conservation. These important families contain many outstanding useful species which, in addition to other useful species with high use values and nonsubstitutable species not of these families, should be carefully studied, with the aim of managing and perhaps domesticating them.

References

Alcorn, J B (1981). Some factors influencing botanical resources perception among the Haustec. *Journal of Ethnobiology* 1: 221-230

Balée, W (1986). Análise preliminar de inventário florestal e a etnobotânica Ka'apor (Maranhão). *Boletim do Museu Paraense Emílio Goeldi* 2 (2): 141-167

Balée, W (1987). A etnobotânica quantitativa dos índios Tembé (Rio Gurupi, Pará). *Boletim do Museu Paraense Emílio Goeldi, Botânica,* 3 (1): 29-50

Berlin, B, D E Breedlove and P H Raven (1974). *Principles of Tzeltal Plant Classification.* Academic Press, New York, USA

Boom, B M (1985). Amazonian Indians and the forest environment. *Nature* 314: 324

Boom, B M (1986a). The Chácobo Indians and their palms. *Principes* 30: 63-70

Boom, B M (1986b). A forest inventory in Amazonian Bolivia. *Biotropica* 18: 287-294

Boom, B M (1987). Ethnobotany of the Chácobo Indians, Beni, Bolivia. *Advances in Economic Botany* 4: 1-68

Carneiro, R L (1978). The knowledge and use of rainforest trees by the Kuikuru Indians of Central Brazil. In R I Ford (ed), *The Nature and Status of Ethnobotany.* University of Michigan Press, Ann Arbor, Michigan, USA, pp 201-216

Fearnside, P M (1985). Environmental change and deforestation in the Brazilian Amazon. In J Hemming (ed), *Change in the Amazon Basin.* Volume 1, Manchester University Press, Manchester, UK, pp 70-89

Henley, P (1982). *The Panare, Tradition and Change on the Amazonian Frontier.* Yale University Press, New Haven, Connecticut, USA

Kroeber, A L (1920). Review of uses of plants by the Indians of the Missouri river region, by Melvin Randolph Gilmore. *American Anthropologist* 22: 384-385

Morris, W (ed) (1973). *The American Heritage Dictionary of the English Language.* Houghton Mifflin Co, Boston, Massachusetts, USA

Myers, N (1982). Deforestation in the tropics: who wins, who loses. In V H Sutlive *et al.* (eds), *Where have all the Flowers Gone? Deforestation in the Third World.* Studies in Third World Societies, No 13, College of William and Mary, Williamsburg, Virginia, USA, pp 1-24

Prance, G T (1972). An ethnobotanical comparison of four tribes of Amazonian Indians. *Acta*

Amazonica 2 (2): 7-27

Prost, M D (1970). *Costumbres, Habilidades, y Cuadro de la Vida Humana Entre los Chácobos.* Instituto Lingu-ístico del Verano, Riberalta, Bolivia

Ribeiro, D (1970). *Os Ìndios e a Civilizaçao: A Integração das Populações Indigenas no Brasil Moderno.* Editora Civilização Brasileira, Rio de Janeiro, Brasil

ter Welle, B J H (1976). On the occurrence of silica grains in the secondary xylem of Chrysobalanaceae. *IAWA Bulletin* 2: 19-29

Wagley, C and E Glavão (1949). *The Tenetehara Indians of Brazil: A Culture in Transition.* Columbia University Press, New York, USA

Tropical Forest Products and Extractive Resources in Xishuangbanna, China

Xie Jiwu
Kunming Institute of Ecology, Academia Sinica, 25 East Jiaochang Road, Kunming, Yunnan, China

Summary

Xishuangbanna is located in the south-west of China and is famous for its rich forests. There are several kinds of tropical monsoon forests, seasonal rainforests, secondary forests and artificial communities, providing a total forest cover of 28.8 per cent.

The region is one of the richest sources of tropical forest products in China. There are over 1000 plant species to be found which can be used for economic profit. The artificial forests are multi-storey polycultures; an excellent example of the rational utilization of land in the tropical regions and conducive to the development of a diversified economy.

There is an abundance of useful plants in Xishuangbanna, including 500 species with medicinal uses, plants from which industrial, edible and essential oils are extracted, tropical fruits, beverages and flowers, rubber plants, fibres and timbers.

We have long recognized the importance of extracting products from the tropical rainforests without long-term harm to either the forests or the people living there. Extracting items which provide sustained income for local people makes economic sense, whereas exclusive reliance on timber does not.

This paper also discusses the relationships between conservation and exploitation, ecology and economics with regard to the tropical forests in Xishuangbanna.

Introduction

Xishuangbanna is well-known in China for its numerous national minorities and tropical biotic resources. Its location is centred on 22 degrees N and 101 degrees E, with a total area of about 19,220 square kilometres, an altitude range from 477 metres to 2429 metres and a total population of about 650,000.

The climate is categorized as tropical monsoon with an annual mean rainfall of 1200 millimetres and annual mean air temperature of 21.8 degrees Celsius. Different types of tropical forest are distributed throughout the area including tropical monsoon forest, seasonal rainforest, tropical secondary forest and many kinds of artificial communities. The forests in this region have been devastated. They have been reduced from 69 per cent in 1950 to 28.8 per cent in 1986. This represents an annual mean decrease of about 1.1 per cent. These deforested areas have been replanted with rubber and other tropical plants or crops.

Investigation has shown that the region has more than 3500 species of tropical plant, making it the richest region of plant germplasm resources in China. Xishuangbanna has a large number of endemic, relic and original species of cultivated crops and more than 1000 species can be used for economic products.

Tropical forest resources and products

There are 3 kinds of tropical vegetation in Xishuangbanna, with a characteristically complex flora and high bio-productivity:

a) primary forests which includes evergreen forest, seasonal rainforest and rainforest;

b) tropical secondary forests including wild banana communities, bamboo forest, *Prodophytium* and others;

c) man-made forests including multi-storey and multi-species communities and monocultural economic forests.

As a result of a study of tropical flora in Xishuangbanna, we found that the rainforest has five main layers. A 1.57 hectare plot had 364 species belonging to 121 families and 291 genera, dominated by *Parashorea, Antiaris, Pometia, Pouteria, Knema, Horsfieldia, Terminalia,* and *Toona.* The tropical secondary forests were shown to be floristically simpler than the primary forest, being dominated by bamboo (*Dendrocalamus strictus*), wild banana (*Musa* sp.), *Trema orientalis* and *Mallotus paniculatus.*

Man-made forests are composed mainly of artificial communities and economic forests. They consist largely of rubber trees, tea trees, *Homalomena occulta, Cinnamomun glanduliferum, Baccaurea ramiflora* and *Cassia siamea.*

One of the multi-storey and multi-species artificial communities is the rubber-tea community. It was created by Chinese scientists with the selection of the rubber tree *Hevea brasiliensis* (Plates 24, 25 and 26) and the tea tree *Camellia sinensis* var. *assamica*, both being of high economic value. These were then planted in a manner which would simulate the structure and function of multi-storey tropical rainforest to create a new type of artificial economic ecosystem. This research, the result of about thirty years study, is now internationally renowned. Because rubber and tea are the most economically significant plants in tropical areas of China, it is important to develop more efficient and productive methods for cultivating these crops. Our research demonstrated that a natural community that contains more species and a more elaborate storey formation is more productive, more stable, and more capable of environmental protection than other communities. Rubber and tea were therefore planted together to create an artificial community and improve the above-mentioned functions. The economic productivity of the rubber-tea community was 178 per cent higher than that of a monocultural rubber plantation, and 58 per cent higher than that of a monocultural tea plantation.

Tropical forest products and useful plants in Xishuangbanna include the following:

a) 500 species of medicinal plant including the dragon-blood tree (*Dracaena cambodiana*), long pepper (*Piper longum*), wild siamese cardamon (*Amomum villosum* var. *xanthoides*), glorylily *(Gloriosa superba), Amomum kravanh, Areca cathecu, Cinnamomum cassia, Cinchona succirubra* and *Caesalpinia sappan.* A product from the maytenus tree (*Maytenus hookeri)* can prevent cancer cells from dividing continuously, ultimately breaking the tumour down, and yunnan devilpepper (*Rauwolfia yunnanensis*) is used to treat high blood pressure.

b) There are approximately 100 plant species from which industrial or edible oil can be extracted. Important oil plants include lard-fruit (*Hodgsonia macrocarpa*), malabar chestnut (*Pachira macrocarpa*), horsfieldia (*Horsfieldia tetratepala*), *Nesua nagassarium, Celtis wightii, Litsea glutinosa, Styrax tonkinensis* and *Ostodes paniculata.*

c) There are about 200 species that contain essential oils including ylan (*Cannanga odorata*), yunnan camphor (*Cinnamomum glanduliferum*), cassia oil (*Cinnamomum cassia*), *Vanilla pierrei, Cymbopogon citratus, Paramichelia baillonii, Litsea cubeba, Acronychia pedunculata* and *Aglaia odorata.*

d) There are 64 species of tropical fruits and beverages including shaddock (*Citrus grandis*), mango (*Mangifera inddica*), rambutan (*Nephelium lappaceum*), eggfruit (*Lucuma nervosa*), cacao (*Theobroma cacao*), cola (*Cola acuminata*), *Litchi chinensis, Psidium guajava, Artocarpus ptheerohylla* and *Carica papaya* (Plate 23). Some wild fruits are *Nephelium chryseum, Garcinia xanthochymus, Ficus auriculata, Pedilanthus emblica* and *Pouteria grandifolia.*

e) There are many kinds of useful wood products. Some of them are from fast-growing and precious trees including the larant tree (*Anthocephalus chinensis*), balsa (*Ochroma lagopus*), bushbeech (*Gmelina arborea*), brown rosewood (*Dalbergia fusca*) and yunnan white seraya (*Parashorea chinensis*). Those yielding fibres include bamboo (*Schizostachyum chinense*) and orchids (*Dendrobium* sp., *Vanda* sp.).

Conservation and rational exploitation of tropical resources

The rational utilization of the forests and lands in tropical regions improves conservation value and helps restore the ecological balance. Traditional agricultural methods in Xishuangbanna cause a high degree of erosion and a rapid decline in productivity, and are therefore not sustainable. They also promote rapid weed growth and loss of valuable forest cover. This is a significant problem in tropical areas. The exploitation of resources in Xishuangbanna is not rational and already the tropical forest has been destroyed over a large area; about 13,300 hectares are destroyed each year.

The development and use of tropical forests for humanity is an important issue. If we harvest tropical forests sustainably, we minimize the damage and provide a continuous income for the local people. Some nature conservation areas should be kept, but we could improve the tropical and secondary forests by reforming their structure to increase their productivity. Planting *Amomum villosum* and *Homalomena occulta,* for example, can improve each hectare of forest in a 'scientific' way and increase the income for humans; the basic functions of the forests remain intact, contributing to their conservation over large areas.

In our recent experiments we replaced the lower storey of rainforest or secondary forest with *Amomum* sp. which has a high economic value. Following this disturbance, most plant species remained, the primeval protective function of the forest was unaffected and the productive function increased a great deal. By underplanting with *Amomum villosum,* 75 kilogrammes of this plant can be harvested from one hectare. Such cultivation should be widely welcomed in Xishuangbanna.

Another method of conserving tropical forests is to set up different kinds of artificial, multi-storey, multi-species communities. Experiments have shown that some economic crops such as *Camellia sinensis* var. *assamica, Coffea arabica, Cinchon ledgeriana* and *Rauwolfia yunnanensis* require a specific amount of shade during their growth period. Both the quantity and quality of these products can therefore be improved. Planting them in the shade of certain rubber trees to build artificial multi-storey communities is a way of improving the sunlight utilization ratio, reducing water loss and increasing the amount of soil water. In tropical areas especially, the soil fertility depends largely upon the status of the vegetation, because it not only continuously returns nutrients to the soil but also itself stores a large amount of nutrients. These communities therefore reduce erosion and maintain soil fertility. Clearly, artificial or semi-artificial multi-storey and multi-species forest ecosystems have good productive and protective functions.

Conclusion

The tropical zones of China are rich in plant resources, which gives them a great advantage over other regions of the country. The ultimate goal is to meet the local peoples' demands and that is why we should study tropical forest products and put them to good use. It is imperative that we exploit these resources in a rational way on the basis of environmental protection and ecological balance.

Thanks to its climate and tropical forests, Xishuangbanna is rich in resources. There are currently 242,667 hectares of forest reserve, comprising rainforest, seasonal rainforest, montane rainforest and evergreen forest. We suggest that the preservation of 30 per cent of the natural tropical forest within Xishuangbanna is better than the *ex situ* conservation of tropical forest germplasm. The results of the above work suggest a need for the enlargement of the area of forest reserve. Man-made tropical phytocommunities are taking shape in China and play an important role in economic development and the enhancement of the peoples' living standards.

Strategies to forestall the removal of remaining tropical forest must be linked to economic development. Sustainable use seems to be the key, but current efforts appear too diffuse. We have provided some ideas about protecting the rainforest through the development of non-wood products. Planting economic species under the forest canopy and adapting the rainforest to make artificial multi-storey and multi-species communities can be very useful methods of conservation and utilization in Xishuangbanna. They have been identified as key factors for improving the productivity of tropical forests.

To optimize the use of tropical forest resources in Xishuangbanna, we need to maintain a proper balance between their utilization and conservation.

References

Feng Yaozong (1986). Ecological study of an artificial rubber-tea community. *INTECOL Bulletin* 1986: 13

Xie Jiwu (1986). *Experimental Study of the Ecological Characters of Amomum Villosum at Different Altitudes*

Xu Zaifu (1982). *Research on Reservation of Germplasm Resources of Tropical Plants in Xishuangbanna*

Pei Shengji (1982). *A Preliminary Study of the Ethnobotany in Xishuangbanna*

Zhang Keying (1986). The influence of deforestation of tropical rainforest on local climate and disasters in the Xishuangbanna region of China. *Climatological Notes.* No 35

Xie Jiwu (1989). *Study of the System Productivity of an Artificial Rubber-tea Community in Tropical China*

A Study of the Non-timber Forest Products of Ghana's Forest Zone

Julia Falconer
Technical Co-operation Officer, UK Overseas Development Administration, Forest Management Project, Ghana

Summary

This paper describes the study of non-timber forest products undertaken as part of a project in the high forest zone in southern Ghana. This focuses on how products are used, the role they play in the rural household economy and also assesses the supply of non-timber forest products in forest reserves. The study will help identify ways in which local peoples' knowledge and priorities can be incorporated into forest management planning and indicate marketable products for which forest management will be designed.

We are conducting a study on the uses and markets for non-timber forest products in the southern forest regions of Ghana. This programme is just one component of a larger ODA-funded Forest Resources Management Project (FRMP). The FRMP is jointly supported by the Government of Ghana and the Overseas Development Administration (ODA). It in turn is part of a larger forestry sector programme being managed by the World Bank. The overall objective of the FRMP is to develop and support sustained yield forest management and strengthen the Forestry Department in this area. As my time is limited and as we are currently in the middle of our field research, I will limit this talk to a description of our research on non-timber forest products (NTFPs).

To begin with I must try to put our project in context. At this Conference we have largely heard about the problems and potentials of forest management in Amazonia. There is a danger that the issues discussed and conclusions drawn about problems in this region will be considered pan-tropical. In West Africa, and more specifically in Ghana, forest resources, forestry issues, problems and potentials are very different to those in Amazonia. We should not forget that there are many different types of tropical forest, with very different resource problems and potentials. More importantly, the social, economic and political systems which have and will continue to dictate how these resources are used, differ from one region to another and one country to another.

Ghana's forests

Ghana is situated along the West African coast. It has two main vegetation zones; forest in the southern third of the country and savannah in the north. Ghana's forest zone stretches across approximately 82,000 square kilometres. Within this forest area there are distinct ecological zones ranging from wet evergreen in the south-western most corner of the country to dry semi-deciduous forest in the northern and eastern savannah/forest boundary areas.

In the last 40 years much of the forest has been cleared, largely for expanding agricultural production (notably cocoa) and mining. At present, with the exception of the south-western area, virtually all remaining intact forests are found in sharply defined forest reserves. The area of forest reserve is approximately 18,000 square kilometres or slightly more than 20 per cent of the land area of the forest zone. There are small patches of forest outside reserves which are generally sacred groves. Otherwise, the vegetation outside forest reserves is largely a patchwork of different secondary vegetation types. Furthermore, in comparison to Amazonian and Asian forests these forests are relatively species poor. There are about 2100 plant species of which 680 are tree species.

Non-Timber Forest Product Programme

The NTFP programme consists of two parts geared to identifying ways of incorporating NTFPs into both traditional and participatory forest management planning. In the first, we examine the demand for NTFPs; in the second part we assess their supply in the forest reserves.

By non-timber forest products I mean all products which are not processed by large industries, such as timber. I include wild animals as well as plants.

Part 1: Assessment of the demand for NTFPs: household uses, markets and small-scale enterprises

The objectives of this research programme are to examine the uses of NTFPs, the role they play in rural household economies and the impact of increasing commercialization and forest degradation on these uses. The research programme has two main components:

(1) to examine people's use of NTFPs through a series of village level household studies; and
(2) to examine the trade of NTFPs through a series of market and consumer studies.

We are comparing the household uses and trade of NTFPs in two different forest regions; the Ashante and Western regions. In comparison to Western region, Ashante is more developed and more densely populated. Consequently, there are greater land pressures, more economic opportunities and less forested land. The Western region has considerable forest both inside and outside forest reserves, is less developed in terms of infrastructure and basic services, has fewer economic opportunities, and is less densely populated. Transportation is a major problem in this region especially at the height of the rainy season. It is an area undergoing rapid change; recently-built roads are improving access to forest areas, and the degradation of cocoa lands in more eastern regions is pushing cocoa farmers into this region. In addition, the forests in Western region are important supply sources for several of the widely traded NTFPs.

The project is based in Kumasi, the historic capital

of the Ashante kingdom and location of the largest market in the forest zone. It is therefore the site of our most intensive market research. While Kumasi provides a focal point, we are examining markets and uses of NTFPs throughout Ashante and Western regions.

The NTFP village studies

We are conducting intensive studies in villages to examine the household uses of NTFPs including resources used for house construction, household and farming equipment, animal fodder, transportation, fuel, food and medicines. We are also studying NTFP gathering and processing enterprises in these communities; our inter-disciplinary research team includes foresters, a nutritionist, an anthropologist and a sociologist.

Examples of household uses of NTFPs

NTFPs have many household uses, from housing poles and roofing material to materials for stuffing pillows. Examples of some of these uses are described below.

Most people rely on forests for building material. The majority of houses are a type of mud switch construction. The frames are built with tree stems as standing poles, the leaf petioles of the raphia palm are used as cross slats, and canes or other forest climbers are used to bind the structure together. The resulting frame is filled with mud. Roofing materials vary from region to region. However, raphia palm leaves are the most popular and are woven into tiles. Another popular roofing material is bamboo, which is split and used much like Roman terracotta tiles.

Food storage barns (Plate 14), livestock pens and other farm buildings are invariably made from a variety of forest trees, palms and bamboo. Essential household items made from NTFPs include: pestles and mortar, spoons, grinders and food storage containers. Agricultural equipment such as hoe handles and fishing equipment such as crab traps are also made using NTFPs.

Within a single community there is a great range of exploited species. Some have multiple uses. For example the fruit of *Ceiba pentandra* or silk cotton tree has several domestic uses: the seed floss is used in making pillows; it has several medicinal uses; the fruit is used to cork holes in canoes; and the leaves are ingredients for several popular soups. Another multi-purpose plant is the climbing palm (commonly known as cane) which is used in house construction, as fishing lines, and in the production of fish traps and cane baskets which are the main storage containers used by most households (Plate 19).

The gathering and processing of NTFPs earns a certain amount of cash income and although few people rely on it solely, it does provide a critical supplement. In several of the study villages for example, women collect several different species of woody climber and the roots of a forest tree (*Parkia bicolor*) to produce a sponge (Plates 16 and 17). Everyday, women soak the stems of climbers then beat them to break them down into fibres. These fibres are then teased and pulled, washed and sundried. The resulting sponges are molded into bundles and packaged into bales for sale at rural and urban markets.

In our study we are only looking at a few villages so that we will be able to return to them several times and compare the uses of NTFPs in different seasons. The villages were selected to reflect varying access to forests and regional markets. Some villages were also selected because they are in key supply areas for particular NTFPs of commerce.

There are four study villages in Ashante, two of which are far from any forest area. The other two are in close proximity to forest reserves. They have varying degrees of accessibility; in some cases they have good laterite roads with lorries plying them throughout the day. At the other extreme, the roads are terrible, and generally impassable during the rains; few vehicles ply these routes. Farming is the main activity in all villages either for food crops such as plantain and cassava or cash crops, especially cocoa. In several villages NTFP gathering provides an important source of income.

In Western region four villages are under study. They were selected for their proximity to important supply sources of widely traded NTFPs, as well as for varying access to markets. In all cases the villages are close to forested areas while three are close to forest outside forest reserves. Two villages have relatively good access to markets although in all cases, transportation is a much greater problem than in Ashante; all roads are impassable during the rains. In two villages, the collection of raw cane and chewstick logs (*Garcinia epunctata*), and cane basket weaving are major economic activities. In the other two villages, NTFPs are widely used, but less frequently traded, as transportation is too costly. The region as a whole is noted for its traditional healers; plant medicines gathered from the forest provide the main source of medicine.

The NTFP market research

The second component in this section examines the trade of NTFPs within Ashante and Western region. There are several aspects to this research on NTFP trade. The overall objective is to get an idea of the range of NTFPs sold in the study region as well as a more thorough understanding of the trade and of a few selected products.

We are conducting market censuses for NTFPs in all markets in Ashante and selected markets in Western region. The census records the NTFP products traded and the number and types of traders selling them (Plate 18). For each market we conduct the census in both the dry and rainy seasons in order to examine seasonal dimensions of NTFP trade. More than 100 markets have been visited so far.

In addition to the NTFP census in all regional markets, we are conducting several studies to assess the quantities of NTFPs entering Kumasi. This includes a road survey recording NTFPs entering Kumasi on major roads, as well as in the lorry parks recording the NTFPs off-loaded at different market sites.

From early results of the market census we have selected several NTFP items, which are heavily traded throughout the region, as subjects for in-depth study. These are canes, chewsticks, food wrapping leaves, plant medicines and bushmeat. For these items we are examining all aspects of the trade, tracing the product and the people involved in the trade from central market sites to the forest supply areas.

Chewsticks are similar to toothpicks and are widely used for dental care in both rural and urban settings. The forests in Western region are the main supply source of this NTFP and the species of the forest tree *Garcinia,* in particular *Garcinia epunctata* are used to produce chewsticks. The gathering, processing and trade of chewsticks involves many hundreds of people in both Ashante and Western regions - the splitting of logs into chewsticks is undertaken by hundreds of women in Kumasi's central market.

As indicated earlier, cane, of which several species exist in Ghana, is an important non-timber product. Commercially, they are used by the basket-making industry, as well as the expanding cane furniture industry. Canes are generally collected in headloads, are split into long strands, woven into baskets and eventually taken to the market. These baskets have a widespread use in the coastal fish trade and for goods containers in farming.

The large leaves of several species of the Marantaceae family are gathered from forests and used in much the same way that we would use plastic wraps, carrier bags and even foil for cooking. These leaves have a large market and their collection and trade provides a livelihood for many women in rural Ashante.

Bushmeat, an important source of protein and even a luxury food in urban centres, is widely consumed and traded in both rural and urban areas. The most commonly hunted species include snails, grasscutters (a species of giant rat) and several species of duiker.

Plants are also exploited for their medicinal properties and appear to be widely traded throughout the study region in both urban and rural households. A vast number of species in the forests, fallow and farmlands are used to produce a large range of medicines, for example the fruit of the *Piper guineesis*, a climber, is used in many treatments. However the variety of plant medicine species traded is more limited. Often those selling medicines are healers and can thus provide advice, as well as sell medicines.

Finally we are examining consumer demand for these products in both rural and urban areas. This has been achieved through the several surveys and studies listed below:

■ In village studies, consumption of bushmeat, use of chewsticks, plant medicine and cane baskets;

■ Consumer surveys: Kumasi and other urban centres on consumption of bushmeat, chewsticks and use of plant medicines;

■ Trader surveys at Kumasi central market on use of food wrappers, and cane baskets; and

■ Interviews with chop bar owners and customers (Ghanaian equivalent of Burger King) who are large consumers of bushmeat.

In the end we hope to estimate the size of the trade (the quantities traded, the numbers of traders and gatherers involved), the source of the products, the profitability of the trade (in relation to other activities), and the sustainability of the trade in terms of consumer demand, resource availability, and marketing problems.

Part 2: Assessing the supply of NTFPs: an inventory of selected NTFPs

In addition to research examining the uses or demand for NTFPs we are now trying to assess the supply of selected NTFPs in forest reserves. Thus, a special NTFP inventory team has been formed to work alongside the on-going project inventory. We have restricted the inventory to a core group of NTFPs which are heavily traded, or which are known to be under increasing exploitation.

The objective of the inventory is to assess the existing stock of selected NTFPs, including canes and several other climbers (especially ones used as medicines or sponges), bamboo, several species of herbaceous plants (Marantaceae and Zingerbaceae), snails and edible mushrooms.

In addition, the inventory's usual tree sampling methods are being slightly modified for a few tree species of NTFP importance. For example *Garcinia epunctata* is harvested when small (5-10 centimetres diameter at breast height [DBH]) for chewsticks.

As the NTFP component is being incorporated into on-going inventory work we are forced for logistic reasons to use the same sampling design. The sample plots are one hectare in size (20 metres x 500 metres) and are stratified systematically. Over the past three months a NTFP inventory team has been working in one of the reserves in Western region. There they have established 49 temporary sample plots (TSPs); 24 plots in forest logged within the last three years and 25 in un-logged forest (lightly felled more than 15 years ago or never felled).

We hope therefore to be able to assess the effects of logging on selected NTFPs. There are two distinct areas of logging in the reserve, operated by two different concessionaires. In one case the intensity of logging is greater; they are removing a greater number of tree species and in smaller size classes. In the other case they have been more selective. In both cases, however, the intensity of current logging is much greater than in the past harvest.

Currently, the NTFP inventory is designed to assess the existing stock, by counting the number of mature and immature stems per plot in the case of canes, and for herbaceous plants, by recording the presence or absence in the plot. The NTFPs currently under study include the following.

- Cane: five species (we are recording immature, mature and cut canes per plot).
- Climbers: nine species which are used as medicines and sponges;
    - Sponges: *Acacia kamarunensis* (a liana whose stem is beaten to produce a chewing sponge), *Momordica angustisepala, Mellettis chrysophella, Cyphostemma adenopodum, Psophocarpus palustris, Landolphia* sp.;
    - Medicines: *Piper guineensis* (fruit harvested for medicine), *Spiropetalum hetrophyllum* (stem used as a medicine and a sponge), *Paullinia pinnata* (whose leaves and roots are used as medicines);
- A further three species which provide

foods: *Dioscorea* sp. (wild yam), *Telfairea occidentalis* (seeds), *Manniophyton fulva* (leaves and fruit);

- Two families of perennial herbaceous plants (clumping): recording presence or absence of clumps in the plot;

  - Marantaceae leaves (various different species whose identity is still under investigation). Includes *Thaumatococcus danielli* which in addition to being used as a food wrapping leaf is exported to Tate and Lyle as a sweetener;

  - *Afromomum* sp. used in many medicinal preparations and an important item of trade.

Additionally we are measuring bamboos, edible mushrooms and snails (individuals per plot).

The core group of NTFPs represent a first step in our inventory. The species incorporated into future NTFP inventories will vary slightly from reserve to reserve in order to incorporate products of local importance.

In addition to the TSP inventory, the project is also establishing permanent sample plots (PSPs) which are intended to provide information on the growing stock; to measure the growth of individual trees in different forest types.

These plots are 100 metres x 100 metres. It is estimated that 629 PSPs will be established over Ghana's high forest zone. In the next year it is hoped that we will be able to incorporate selected NTFPs into PSP sampling so as to get some basic information on their growth habits and productivity.

In the meanwhile, the design of the PSP has already been modified so as to improve the quality of the data on NTFP trees which are harvested at small sizes. In two sub-plots of each PSP, trees will be measured down to 1 centimetre DBH (instead of the usual 10 centimetres DBH). In addition, in some reserves, these plots are the subject of a detailed botanical inventory which records all plants found on the plot. This was the case for two of the four PSPs in the Fure River, the site of the on-going NTFP inventory. There is, therefore, great scope within the inventory, and especially PSPs, for more detailed and in-depth NTFP study.

Conclusion

In conclusion, the information from the NTFP inventory along with that from trade and household studies will provide much needed information for on-going forest management planning. It will allow us to incorporate products of local importance into forest management, thus helping to sustain the forest resource. In addition, this information will be of great importance for the FRMP's developing programme for participatory management of forests outside reserves.

Community Versus Company-based Rattan Industry in Indonesia

Yance de Fretes
Yale School of Forestry, 409 Prospect Street, Newhaven, Connecticut 06511 USA

Summary

This presentation outlines Indonesia's policy regarding non-timber products such as rubber, rattan and resins. Rattan potential for the country is discussed, which includes an assessment of traditional silviculture and its possible role in rainforest conservation. It is argued that community-based plantations, as opposed to company-managed, are preferred but that a number of preconditions need to be set before such plantations are established.

Introduction

After surviving the communist rebellion in 1965, Indonesia was faced with unhealthy economic conditions and a number of social problems, such as high unemployment and slow economic growth. The new Government immediately established new policies to stabilize the economic and sociopolitical situation. These policies relaxed strict regulations on foreign enterprise and economic development. For example, the 1966 Investor Act gave timber industries five years income tax exemption, and reduced taxes on timber companies and log exports (Repetto, 1988; Myers, 1980).

As a result, Indonesian economic growth increased significantly from $10 million annually before 1966 to $573 million in 1975 (Gillis, 1987). The new policies also attracted many local and foreign companies to invest in timber industries. In only six years the number of planned plywood mills increased from approximately 16 in 1977 to 182 in 1983 (Repetto, 1988). The new policies, however, led to an estimated annual rate of deforestation of 700,000 hectares by 1985 (Repetto, 1988). However, despite forest degradation and other environmental problems created by the new timber policies, the revenue from the timber industries increased between 1971-1981. Yet only a small proportion of the revenue was collected by way of taxes and royalties.

Unfortunately, the policies are no better for non-timber forest products, such as resin, rattan (Plate 8), rubber and tengkawang, which can significantly contribute to the Indonesian economy.

It is not clear why the governments of many tropical countries such as Indonesia are not interested in non-timber forest products. The possibilities are, firstly, that governments do not fully appreciate such products. The Indonesian Forestry Department, for instance, classified non-timber products such as rattan, resin and honey as by-products (*hasil ikutan*). This term reflects their impression of the importance of non-timber products. Secondly, since the main emphasis of the timber policies was to earn foreign currency, policies were therefore established to promote and increase exports; many non-timber forest products are collected, harvested and marketed locally by large numbers of rural people and families. It is also difficult for the Government to deal with these people, with regards to tax and rent collection (Fearnside, 1989). Thirdly, non-timber products are difficult to assess monetarily and are often under-estimated. Furthermore, there is not enough institutional support to represent the local people's need for non-timber products.

Recent studies of the economic revenue from non-timber forest products such as fruits, latex, and taxe have shown that non-timber products have the potential to generate significant revenue at sustainable levels (Peters *et al.*, 1989; Fearnside, 1989; Heinzman *et al.*, 1989). However, these studies only considered market goods from the forests. If somehow non-market goods such as oxygen, climate and hydrological functions of the forests could be counted, then the value of non-timber forest products and services would far exceed total revenue from timber extraction.

Rubber and rattan are among other non-timber forest products which have made a significant contribution to the Indonesian economy. Despite a poor economy in the mid 1980s, export earnings from the rattan trade constantly increased (see Figure 1). In 1971, rattan exports earned only $782,000, but reached $81 million in 1981 and as much as $89 million in 1985 (Alun, 1987). Unfortu-

Figure 1. Rattan Exports from Indonesia 1969-1985 ($ million)

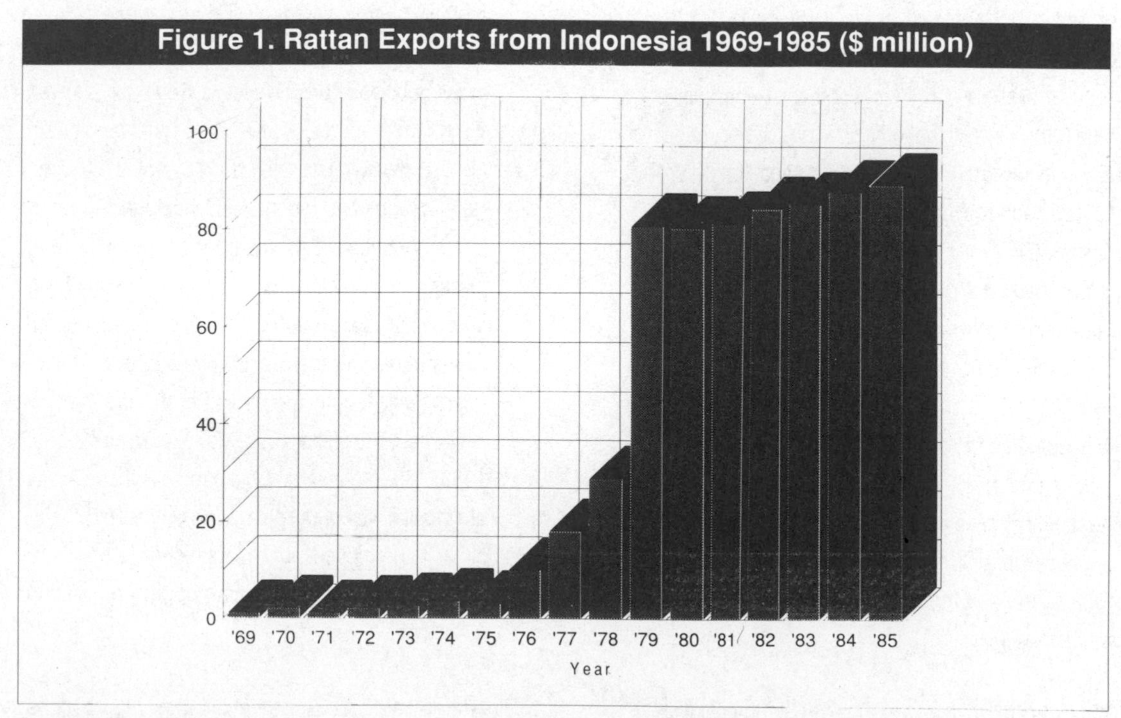

Source: Alun (1987)

nately, there is no data on the local rattan trade to enable the total value of Indonesia's rattan industry to be calculated.

Compared with other non-timber forest products, Indonesia's rattan trade has a great advantage because 80 to 90 per cent of world demand has been produced from the country (Alun, 1987; Peluso, 1983). Alun (1987) states that current exports are actually only a small proportion (41.1 per cent) of the rattan production potential. Furthermore, his reasoning for minimal rattan production is due to the lack of adequate programmes for data recording; the fact that rattan collection is not the primary income for local people; poor transportation to local markets; and the destruction of rattan habitat due to logging and other agricultural activities.

Rattans are palms that climb other vascular plants or lay on the forest floor. Dransfield (1979) estimates that about 50 per cent of the 600 rattan species are found only in South-east Asia, while Alun (1987) states that of 516 rattan species, about 330 species grow in Indonesia. Approximately 4 million hectares of rattan grow in the forest in Kalimantan Timur (East Kalimantan), and about 1 million hectares grow in the forests of Sulawesi Utara and Sulawesi Tengah (North and Central Sulawesi) (Alun, 1987). Of the total number of species, about ten have commercial value (Manokaran and Wong, 1983). These include rotan manau (*Calamus manan*) distributed throughout the Malay Peninsula and Sumatra; rotan sega (*C. caesius*) found in the Malay Peninsula, Sumatra, Kalimantan, and the Philippines; and rotan irit (*C. trachycoleus*).

Rattan has been used by people in South-east Asia for centuries, particularly for building materials, hunting tools (strings of bows and traps), baskets (anjat), for fires, and for a number of different medical purposes.

Company or community-based non-timber forest product industries

A number of research projects on rattan silviculture have been carried out by the Forest Research Institute in Kepong, Dehra Dun (India), the Philippines, Thailand and Bogor (Indonesia), by BIOTROP (Manokaran and Wong, 1983; Manokaran, 1983; Ahmad, 1983; Dransfield, 1979). Results vary with each species responding differently with regards to growth rates and mortality (Manokaran, 1983; Manokaran and Wong, 1983). Many studies show that rattan cultivation has a high mortality. For instance, a silviculture project which tried to plant rotan semambu (*Calamus scipionum*) in Sungei Bulog Forest Reserve, Selangor, showed 66 per cent mortality after 7 years (Manokaran, 1983). However, Dransfield (1988) states that large rattan plantations (about 4068 hectares) in Kinabatung had just 15 per cent mortality. Aside from existing trials, rattan cultivation has been practised successfully for years in central Kalimantan (with the commercial species *C. caesius* and *C. trachycoleus*), south Borneo, Perak and central Sulawesi (Dransfield, 1979; Manokaran and Wong, 1983). This means that local people in those areas are familiar with rattan cultivation, so it would not be difficult to introduce rattan plantations or silviculture to them as an alternative to logging or shifting cultivation.

With regards to conservation, new approaches

have been taken to conserve biological diversity. The Man and Biosphere Programme (MAB), for instance, tries to combine preservation of species, natural habitat and sustainable use of natural resources by utilization and development of buffer zone areas. Conceptually, buffer zone management generates income for local people. However, still unclear is what kind of management can be conducted in reserves without disturbing the fauna and flora. Ideas about promoting small-scale agriculture or agroforestry techniques in buffer zones are perhaps more economic and social forms of development rather than biological and ecological. They will eventually change the vegetation (structure and canopy), influence food condition and increase edge effects (Diamond, 1986; Lovejoy *et al.,* 1986).

Rattan silviculture, however, can minimize these effects in buffer zone management because rattan can grow in the under-storey requiring no land preparation, and thereby allowing the forest canopy to remain intact. Habitat disturbance perhaps only occurs during harvesting, 7 to 10 years after planting, but it is safe to say that such changes are small compared to permanent habitat change ('disturbance') when a farmer uses cash crops. Therefore, rattan silviculture promises to be a great hope in meeting the biological, ecological and economic considerations in buffer zone management and forest conservation of tropical forests.

Dransfield (1979), and Manokaran and Wong (1983) suggest that commercial rattan species can be harvested 7 to 10 years (*C. trachycoleus* and *C. caesius*) and 12 to 15 years (*C. manan*) after planting. Of importance, these species can be harvested at least more than once. It was not clear from where the Indonesian Forestry Department's estimation was based, but they have suggested that sustainable yield for Indonesian rattan is about 615,500 tons annually (Alun, 1987).

An important question arises from this: should rattan plantations be managed by companies or be community-based? Both types of management have advantages and disadvantages. Community-based plantations are perhaps the preferred choice, but there are a number of preconditions that need to be set before plantation establishment.

First, even though the local farmers are familiar with rattan cultivation, they do not have experience of the marketing or exporting of rattan products. Farmers will need to be educated or trained in the marketing of their products. Without 'neat' organization it would be harder to obtain uniform quality products or to maintain rattan supplies.

Second, many if not all villagers in Kalimantan are shifting cultivators. They cultivate their crops such as rice, cassava and taro, and harvest in 3 to 6 months. Thus, it will not be easy for them to switch to long-term investments such as rattan plantations which are harvested after 7 to 12 years. In other words, they will have to wait for a return on their investment. Another problem is that cash is spent quickly, so somehow they will have to manage their incomes wisely over a longer period of time. There are many cases from timber operations or agricultural plantations that show that labourers' families live well just after monthly payment but that they are in extreme poverty by the end of the month. Many family members face malnutrition due to inappropriate monthly spending (de Fretes, 1985).

Land and hunting territories have been claimed by villagers, usually by planting perennial crops during fallow periods. A study by Universitas Mulawarman of Kalimantan Barat in 1983 concluded that rattan cultivation was not a silvicultural practice, but one that had been driven by economic motivation, free labour from family members, and as an effort to claim land (Alun, 1987). Therefore, in promoting community-based rattan plantations, improvement of the silvicultural aspects should be considered. Nevertheless, land claiming incentives can be used to encourage community participation in rattan plantations.

Despite the agro-cultural difficulties with community organization and land-ownership in community-based rattan plantations, company-based ownership does not offer good solutions. Rattan plantations differ from timber or agriculture plantations. Many rattan species naturally need forests, and the shade that they provide, for growing and climbing. Therefore, mechanized management as practised in tree plantations would possibly be inappropriate. Machines can not move freely in dense forests without causing destruction to habitats or damage to potential regeneration. Thus, manual or human labour is more likely to be compatible than machinery, and perhaps more economically sound as there will not be a need to invest in machinery which will only be used periodically.

One issue concerning the deforestation of tropical rainforests is the low income of the people. The issue has led to a new approach in current forest conservation policies such as the Man and Biosphere Programme, where forest conservation should also provide income alternatives (direct benefit) for local people and farmers. McNeely (1988) of the International Union for Conservation of Nature and Natural Resources (IUCN) suggests that economic incentives should be inccrporated when promoting conservation of biological diversity. High species diversity and endemism are found in tropical countries where most of their populations are 'economically' poor. This often puts biological diversity under the greatest threat from direct harvesting or habitat destruction through shifting cultivation. Therefore, the economic incentives approach should be considered as a way to encourage more ecologically sound natural resource utilization. This approach has been widely adopted in reserve management in other parts of Indonesia (Craven and de Fretes, 1987; Craven, 1988; Wells, 1989; Waken, 1990).

Unemployment is one major target of the current Government's development policies for the timber industry. In fact the idea behind the Government ban on log exports in 1985 was to push the private sector into investment in timber factories and manufacturing inside the country. They hoped this would absorb part of the labour force and decrease unemployment.

For the rattan industry, community-based plantations are probably more appropriate for the following reasons. There are many examples that show that large companies' approach to forest and agricultural industries do little to assist absorption of local labour. Sen (1978), for instance, states that multinational corporations do not reduce unemployment but raise it by increasing wage costs. Rattan plantations do not require the big capital and technical investments needed for logging or other agricultural industries. To some extent, local people are already familiar with rattan cultivation. The fact that large corporations, both national and international, fail to recruit local people is due to the realization that it is difficult to obtain capital return from the human investment (*ie* training or education). In addition, many, if not all, local people or farmers are not used to this kind of work or to binding contractual agreements.

Even if companies could promise training for their staff, they could not guarantee a permanent change from a traditional agricultural way of life, as corporate employment is controlled by various regulations and bureaucracy.

Conclusion: our homework

If community-based plantations are recommended, there are a number of conditions, in the first instance, that have to be met. They are: continuity of supplies of both raw and semi-processed materials; quality and quantity of supplies of finished products (furniture); and the industry's reliability and creditability. Certainly, the rattan farmers need to be organized to meet these requirements. Investment in rattan factories, shops or transport can be wasted if there is no continuity in supplies or in the reliability of the product.

Organization can be based on regions, tribes, or clans. In this way, dissemination of information and knowledge regarding the rattan trade can be conducted more easily. It also gives the farmer more power to bargain with both middlemen and the furniture industry, as well as the Government. Perhaps farmers should build up their own production chain without involving middlemen (*ie* straight from the rattan plantation to furniture factories and shops). With assistance from international and national interest groups, farmers can set up networks to monitor national or world rattan demands and prices, so they can 'control' rattan price by maintaining rattan supply. However, as we have seen with many export commodities, world demand does not always grow constantly over time. Farmers should be conscious of this fact.

An essential factor in 'traditional' rattan cultivation is land claims. Many, if not all, farmers and hunters always cultivate perennial plants in their garden when they abandon the area as an indication of their territory. Land status needs to be clarified before the plantations start, *ie* whether land is communally or privately owned, belongs to a group of farmers or a tribe. Each title has advantages and disadvantages, and may vary from location to location. If present or historical cultural bonds are strong (*eg* in Kalimantan and Irian Jaya) then the land should be managed communally or privately when these bonds are loose.

Putting values on non-timber forest products from tropical rainforests hopefully can change current Government policies on the timber industry, which is destructive and captures only a small part of the potential revenue. Large-scale industries and timber policies change the life of local people where logging takes place. Therefore, new policies are essential that try to maximize the utilization of tropical forest products at sustainable levels by involving local people. This should be a part of the effort to conserve tropical rainforests and to reward local people for their participation in their conservation. Nevertheless, we should remember that tagging dollars to tropical forest product use by local people and their Government is not a miracle solution, but it is not a bad concept to utilize economic value in conservation efforts, particularly conservation of tropical rainforests. However, we should remember that these efforts should not be to maintain economic control over the fate of rainforests, but slowly to remove economic dominancy.

We should also consider the values and beliefs of local people, and their interaction and relation with the forest itself. They need to be conveyed to those people that make decisions and policies affecting tropical forests, and to those who consume (and enjoy) products from these forsets. The willingness by indigenous people to sacrifice and share what they have with the entire village has allowed communal-based resource management to be practised harmoniously for centuries. This way of life, I believe, should go side by side in our effort to conserve part of our planet's natural resources, the tropical rainforests.

Acknowledgements

I would like to thank The Ford Foundation for the invitation to the conference; Emma O'Bryen and Heather Cannon of Media Natura for their generous help. My special thanks to Peter Palmiato of Yale's School of Forestry and Environmental Studies for English correction.

References

Ahmad, D H (1983). The effect of sowing media on the germination of *Calamus manan* and *Calamus caesius. Malaysian Forester,* 46 (1): 77-79

Alun, T (1987). Substitusi eksport komoditi traditional: kasus pengembangan ekspor rotan hasil industri Indonesia: (Translated - Export substitution of traditional commodities: development of the rattan exports from Indonesian industries case). *Ekonomi dan Keuangan Indonesia,* XXXV (1): 74-103

Craven, I and Y de Fretes (1987). *Arfak Mountain Nature Conservation Area, Irian Jaya. Management Plan 1988-1992.* A Report for the Directorate General of Forest Protection and Nature Conservation, Bogor

Craven, I (1989). The Arfak mountains nature, birds head region, Irian Jaya, Indonesia. *Science in New Guinea,* 15 (2): 47-56

de Fretes, Y (1985). Penduduk Arso binggung: memilih dusun sagu dan terus berburu atau menjadi petani kelapa sawit (Arso People Are confused: owner of sago fields and hunters or oil palm farmers). *Kabar dari Kampung,* 18

Diamond, J M (1986). The design of a nature reserve system for Indonesian New Guinea. In M E Soule (ed), *Conservation Biology,* Sinuaer Ass, Inc Massachusetts, pp 485-503

Dransfield, J (1979). Manual of the rattans of the Malay Peninsula. *Malayan Forest Records 29,* Forest Department, Ministry of Primary Industries Malaysia

Dransfield, J (1988). Prospects for rattan cultivation. *Advances in Economic Botany,* 6: 190-200

Fearnside, P M (1983). Development alternatives

in the Brazilian Amazon: an ecological evaluation. *Inerciernia,* 8 (2): 65-78

Fearnside, P M (1989). Extractive reserves in Brazilian Amazonia: an opportunity to maintain tropical rainforest under sustainable use. *BioScience,* 39 (6): 387-393

Gillis, M (1987). Multinational enterprises and environmental and resources management issues in the Indonesian tropical forest sector. In C S Pearson (ed), *Multinational Corporations, Environment, and Third World Business Matters.* World Resources Institute, Duke University Press, Durham

Heinzman, R M, C C S Reining, J J Castilo, J D Nations and R O Mendelsohn (1989). *Valuation and Sustainability of Non-timber Forest Products in the Maya Biosphere Reserve, Guatemala.* Draft Manuscript, pp 1-14

Lovejoy, T E *et al.* (1986). Edge and other effects of isolation on Amazon forest fragments. In M E Soule (ed), *Conservation Biology,* Sinauer Ass, Inc Massachusetts, pp 257-285

Manokaran, N (1983). Survival and growth of rotan semambu (*Calamus scipionum*) seedlings at 7 years after planting. *Malaysian Forester,* 46: 81-85

Manokaran, N and K M Wong (1983). The silviculture of rattans - an overview with emphasis on experiences from Malaysia. *The Malaysian Forester,* 46 (3): 298-315

McNeely, J A (1988). *Economic and Biological Diversity: Developing and Using Economic Incentives to Conserve Biological Resources.* IUCN, Switzerland

Myers, N (1980). *Conversion of Tropical Moist Forests.* National Academy of Sciences, Washington DC

Peluso, N L (1983). Networking in the commons: a tragedy for rattan? *Indonesia,* 35: 95-100. Cornell University, Ithaca

Peters, C M, A H Gentry and R O Mendelsohn (1989). Valuation of an Amazonian rainforest. *Nature,* 339 (29): 655-656

Repetto, R (1988). *The Forest for the Trees? Government Policies and the Misuse of Forest Resources.* World Resources Institute, Washington DC

Repetto, R and M Gillis (1988). *Public Policies and the Misuse of Forest Resources.* A World Resources Institute Book, Cambridge University Press

Sen, S C (1978). *Multinational Corporations in the Developing Countries.* Eastern Law House, Calcutta

Waken, V (1990). *Social Forestry in Irian Jaya: Prespectives*

Wells, M P (1989). *Can Indonesia's Biological Diversity be Protected by Linking Economic Development with National Park Management? Three Case Studies from Outer Island.* A report for the World Bank. Unpublished

Game Harvesting in Tropical Forests

Dr Kent Redford
Centre for Latin American Studies and Department of Wildlife and Range Studies, University of Florida, 319 Grinter Hall, Gainesville, Florida 32611 USA

Summary

For centuries tropical forests have been a source of wildlife for human consumption. This paper focuses on Amazonian forests where the extent of faunal exploitation for commercial purposes has been well documented. However, the previous and current extent of subsistence exploitation is less well known. Taken together these forms of wildlife exploitation have accounted for the removal of tens of millions of large-bodied vertebrates such as deer, peccaries, spotted cats, macaws, currasows and caiman. Patterns of wildlife exploitation in other tropical forests are similar to those in Amazonia. Some of the possible ecological effects of the removal of these animals are discussed along with the potential use of wildlife as an extracted product from tropical forests.

At this Conference, we have heard a lot about the impending extinction of all sorts of tropical organisms - animal and plant. That is not the purpose of my talk or, in fact, of this meeting as a whole. Instead, I have been asked to address the question of bushmeat. This subject is often-ignored and I feel very honoured to be invited to speak on this because it proves to me that the Royal Geographical Society and Friends of the Earth have, in fact, more wisdom than the World Bank. In a publication in the early 1980s, in which the World Bank listed the benefits to be gained from tropical forests, there was not one single mention of bushmeat.

The theme of this paper, however, is not just about bushmeat extraction in tropical forests but also about the importance of considering the interactions between humans and tropical forest animals - past, present and future. I shall concentrate on the Neotropical forests and, within that, on the Amazon basin.

In the past, many people have considered human action in tropical forests as incidental and not something of major importance to ecological processes. The interaction between humans and animals has, of course, a very long historical perspective.

Evidence for this has been accumulating from many different disciplines including archeologists, ethnobotanists and ecologists themselves. I interpret their findings in a rather radical fashion by saying that there is no such thing as virgin forest anywhere in the tropics. It is probably impossible, for example, to find any 100 square kilometres of the Amazon where there has been no human influence on its structure.

The present conservation climate puts tremendous

emphasis on multiple-use areas and extractive reserves. There is a very interesting and complicated relationship between the conservation of biodiversity and the creation of extractive reserves, but by no means will they go hand in hand into the future as happily married partners.

Part of the reason for the importance of this consideration is something that Martin von Hildebrand pointed out in a previous presentation. Consider these facts: in Brazil, there are 74 million hectares of Indian land but only 13 million hectares of national park; in Columbia, there are 18 million versus two and a half million. Those of us interested in animals, and the harvesting of animals must, therefore, begin a dialogue with those interested in the rights of tropical forest peoples. This is a very fertile and important area for consideration and not one that we can simply dismiss.

This paper will be divided into four sections. The first looks at the history and types of faunal exploitation and shows that there has been an incredible amount of this kind of exploitation by humans. The second asks whether this exploitation has been selective and compares, just very briefly, the situation in the Amazon with other tropical areas. The third considers the potential effects of removal of large numbers of individuals of these species and, finally, there are some thoughts on the general advisability of game harvesting.

There are several ways in which humans have been involved in the process of 'defaunation' (or the removal of fauna), and these can be divided into two major categories: indirect and direct. Amongst the indirect ways, you have the extraction of Brazil nuts. Such extractive activities have enormous impacts on the animals which would have, for example, consumed these nuts had they not been removed to satisfy our craving at cocktail time. In addition, indirect defaunation occurs by the human removal of animals which are potential prey for other animals. There has been some very nice work done on vultures, for example, showing that in areas of high subsistence hunting pressure you have far fewer individuals and species of vultures.

Another indirect method in which humans are involved in defaunation is the destruction of habitat. A perfectly good patch of forest might not be able to host the most important game animal in the Neotropics, the white-lipped peccary (*Tayassu pecari*). This species has very wide traditional patterns of movement and if these are disrupted you will end up with few, if any, white-lipped peccaries. Another obvious example is river turtles. If you destroy a nesting beach, eventually you will lose the population in that river basin. More subtle effects that we must start considering are, for example, mercury from mining and its downstream effects and fire within the forest canopy which people have suggested decreases pollination of Brazil nut trees.

The direct removal of fauna by humans can be put into several different classifications: wildlife for food, non-edible products and sport hunting.

The commercial exploitation of some Amazon animals has been going on since the arrival of Europeans. Here are just a few examples. In the late 1860s, at least 48 million giant river turtle eggs were used annually for oil. There was a tremendous trade in the feathers of birds at the turn of the century. In the 1960s, '70s and '80s there was extensive exploitation of Neotropical forest animals for their skins and leather.

Many animals were exported from the Peruvian Amazon including live monkeys for the biomedical trade and the skins of caimans (mostly for leather purses and shoes). In the six years between 1962 and 1967, a total of over one and a half million individual animals were removed. But what does that mean? How do you interpret such a figure?

Let us look at *Felis pardalis,* the ocelot. Now, I'm not an economist; I'm an ecologist. I don't care how many are exported; I care how many are killed. This is a very important distinction that hasn't adequately been made in the past. It is estimated that three animals are killed for every one that makes a tick on an export statistic. So, if you multiply the export figures for ocelots by three, within that six year period, you get almost 200,000 ocelots that were killed. If you then look at the average ocelot density, and assume that you have removed every single ocelot in that forest, you have exploited 230,000 square kilometres of forest. This is one-third of the Peruvian Amazon which, in six years, has been cleared of ocelots. The point is that the effects of market involvement on fauna are tremendous.

As well as commercial interaction with fauna, there are obviously subsistence reasons for defaunation as well. Game is an extremely important contribution, in terms of nutritional levels, to many human groups in the Amazon and in fact in many tropical areas where the forest has not been seriously degraded. A wide range of mammal taxa are taken for meat, ranging from tapirs through lesser anteaters to monkeys and squirrels. You get a similarly broad range for birds, from Amazon parrots through trumpeters to macaws and, most commonly, guans and currasows. Not only is a wide range of animal taken but also a great number of individuals of each species.

The animals that are most frequently taken represent an important element of the ecological community. At one study site, Manu in Amazonian Peru, there were 319 bird species. Of these, the game birds represented only 9 per cent in terms of numbers of species. They, however, represented over 50 per cent of the bird biomass. The pattern was even more dramatic for commonly hunted mammals; 80 per cent of the biomass was represented by 18 per cent of the species. Neither is this an anomaly of Manu: work from several different sites in the Neotropics showed that game animals are very important in terms of biomass, comprising 75 to 85 per cent of the biomass in unhunted areas.

The effects of hunting on these game animals is considerable. We have combined a wide range of studies and it is possible to show, albeit roughly, that at moderate hunting levels there are decreases of between 60 and 80 per cent in the density of game animals. At high hunting levels original densities of game animals drop 93 per cent, which translates into substantial community and ecological effects.

In terms of body size, with the exception of large raptors, it is the large birds that are taken. Of the mammals taken for food, it is the large ungulates, the large primates and the large rodents that are preferred; for skins, it is either large ungulates or carnivores.

With reference to the food habits of game animals, in Manu, fruit-eaters comprise 84 per cent of the game mammal biomass. The equivalent figure for birds is 70 per cent. The hunted species are therefore mainly fruit-eaters. Interestingly - and frequently ignored - the fish species most heavily taken are also large fruit-eaters or large carnivores. If you look at the most commonly taken animals within the Brazilian Amazon, they fit this pattern whether they are fish, birds, mammals or reptiles. And if you compare this with other tropical areas like Zaire, Cameroon and Sarawak, you have the same pattern with large frugivores being the principal game species for subsistence hunters.

There are a few cases that suggest that the loss of fauna significantly affects the ecological system. On Barro Colorado island in Panama, the loss of large carnivores has been shown to increase the populations of agoutis which results in increased predation on certain plants with, most probably, a consequent effect on the forest canopy structure. In another study, from tropical Mexico, areas without the usual large mammalian herbivores have very different patterns of recruitment into the seedling class with ensuing effects on forest structure. Large frugivores also may play important seed dispersal roles and their loss may also affect forest structure.

We now reach the crucial question: what are we going to do about hunting in tropical forests? Are we going to continue this sort of extraction from the rainforest? Now, game meat is not honey. Ecologically, honey is more like fruit and latex than it is game. You cannot capture a deer, slice off a prime cut and release it to regrow! You'll kill that animal. Yet for the purpose of these discussions, sustainability has been defined in terms of the individual reproductive unit. However, sustainability can also be defined in terms of population levels and it is within this definition that we need to discuss the harvesting of game.

Game is very important in many areas of tropical forests. But in these forests you have many people who make their livelihood from extractive activities, and in all of these cases bushmeat represents a necessary supplement without which their way of life would not be possible. Julian Caldecott has put this so eloquently: *"When game stocks remain adequate, monetary poverty need not be associated with dietary poverty."*

The question remains: what should we do about this exploitation? There has been little work done on this issue, but the indications are that markets of game meat severely affect local patterns of consumption and, also, the abundance of game. We have two choices when considering the harvesting of game meat - leave it at subsistence levels (and prohibit commercialization), or allow commercialized production. By following the second option, we must anticipate that the animal population will collapse because the ecological and life-history characteristics of the most important game species are such that they are being harvested at non-sustainable rates. For example, woolly monkeys (*Lagothrix lagothricha*) produce maybe one offspring every one or two years and take 12 years to reach reproductive maturity, and yet it is the most frequently taken game animal in many forest areas in the Amazon. This animal will not survive at current exploitation levels.

My conclusion is even more drastic than this. For the first option, not only must we insist that only subsistence harvesting takes place, we must also insist that there is no logging in the area and that no roads enter the area. These factors have severe repercussions on game animals.

The case is very different if you are talking about what I might call 'display fauna', which is produced for a luxury market (wildlife for the pet trade, for example). I am confining myself in this discussion to tropical game, and the people that cannot live without the protein that it represents.

Even if it is decided to proceed with extraction at a subsistence level, ecological effects must be considered. A species may not have become demographically extinct (you may, for example, still be able to find giant river otters in tributaries of the Amazon) but these animals have become ecologically extinct. Ecological extinction has been defined as the reduction of a species' abundance, so although it is still present in the community, it no longer interacts significantly with other species. We must stop thinking about minimum viable population sizes in the simple, demographic sense and now start thinking in an ecological sense - in terms of the interactions involved. In areas where there has been extensive hunting, even though it is for subsistence purposes, some of the major animal taxa have been driven to ecological extinction.

We must consider not only the plants in tropical forests but also the animals. For, without the animals, the tropical forests may collapse from within.

References

Caldecott, J (1988). *Hunting and Wildlife Management in Sarawak.* IUCN, Gland, Switzerland and Cambridge, UK

Colyn, M M, A Dudu and M Mankoto ma Mbaelele (1987). Donnees sur l'exploitation du "petit et moyen gibier" des forets ombrophiles du Zaire. In, *Gestation de la Faune en Afrique sub-Saharienne.* IGF, Paris, pp 109-141

Infield, M (1988). *Hunting, Trapping and Fishing in Villages Within and on the Periphery of the Korup National Park.* WWF Publication 3206/A9.6, Gland, Switzerland

Redford, K H and J G Robinson (In Press). Subsistence and commercial uses of wildlife. In, J G Robinson and K H Redford (eds), *Neotropical Wildlife Use and Conservation.* University of Chicago Press

Robinson, J G and K H Redford (eds) (In Press). *Neotropical Wildlife Use and Conservation.* University of Chicago Press

Public Awareness and Extractive Economies

Anna Lewington
Consultant to the World Wide Fund for Nature (UK), Panda House
Weyside Park, Godalming, Surrey United Kingdom

Summary

This paper introduces some of the more surprising yet widespread uses of rainforest plants and proposes that an awareness of these uses and of our need to safeguard plant resources is important to a wider acceptance of plant products from extractive reserves. Most of the plants that are utilized in the developed world today were first identified and used by rainforest peoples. Yet this aspect has not received the wider recognition it deserves.

To begin my lecture I would like to introduce you to this gentleman (Plate 20). I am sorry that he is not here today in fact, speaking in my place, since what I want to talk about draws on his experience and knowledge and that of thousands of Amazonian people like him. I am very glad that some forest people are at this Conference, since it is their voices which should, I feel, be leading this debate.

In his own language, Don Calazacón is a Tsatchila, but the surrounding society has labelled him and the 1495 other members of his group as Colorado Indians. Though their lands are now very much reduced in size, they once occupied a large area of forest in lowland Ecuador in the vicinity of the town which has taken its name from the people: *Santo Domingo de los Colorados.*

The word *Colorado* refers in this context to the distinctive orange/red colour of Don Calazacón's hair. It is covered with a paste made from the waxy outer coating of the seeds produced by a small tree, native to the forests of tropical America, *Bixa orellana* (Plate 22). Known commonly in South America as achiote or urucu, Amazonian peoples have used this pigment, separated from the seeds by soaking and boiling, since time immemorial for face and body decoration, and for the colouring of fibres, pottery, implements and masks. Though one practical aspect of the paste is its effectiveness as a protection against insects, the pigment has important socio-religious significance.

In Europe and America, annatto, as the pigment is called, has found a completely different use. Many of us eat it every day. Classified in Britain as E160(B), it is the commonest natural food colourant for orange shades and is extensively used to colour confectionery of all kinds, as well as margarine, butter and cheese. *Bixa orellana* is now cultivated commercially in plantations in India, Kenya and Tanzania, but the wild trees are distributed across South and Central America and Amerindian peoples first showed 'Westerners' how the pigment could be used. (The bitter chocolate drink, incidentally, offered to Cortés by the Aztecs, contained ground *Bixa orellana* seeds). Furthermore, as with hundreds of domesticated varieties of rainforest plants - the progeny of which have become important staples in our global diets - the occurrence and characteristics of 'wild' *Bixa orellana* trees are almost certainly the result of selection over millenia by indigenous peoples. But who thinks of *Bixa orellana* or the people who first used it when they eat a sandwich or buy a piece of cheese? Where is the label that informs us of its rainforest origin? And what real benefit has the food colouring industry been to the Colorado Indians or any other Amerindian group? The answer to this question is, it would seem, unfortunately none.

As a further example, I would like to look at another plant product, also from the Amazon. Without it, none of those who travelled to this conference by plane would have made it, neither would those of us who travelled here by car. Natural rubber latex accounts for 100 per cent of the rubber used to make the world's jet aircraft tyres - this includes, of course, Concorde and the Space Shuttle - and up to 50 per cent of that used to make an average radial car tyre.

No synthetic rubber yet produced has been able to match the amazing qualities of natural rubber - its low heat generation, for example, when continually flexed, its strength and building tack, and its ability to remain flexible even after long exposure to the sub-zero temperatures encountered during high altitude flying.

Whilst tyre manufacture accounts for around three-quarters of the 5 million tonnes produced each year, natural rubber is still indispensable for numerous industrial products, for example; surgical gloves, car suspension systems and engine mountings, for road and rail bridges, escalator hand rails, Wellington boots, and that darling of the London Rubber Company, the condom - increasingly important because of the spread of AIDS.

As you may already know, the latex used to make these goods comes from trees now grown in commercial plantations in Malaysia, Thailand and Indonesia (having been introduced into Malaysia from Brazil at the end of the last century) but wild rubber trees are widely spread across the Amazon and are used today as a genetic resource to improve, in various ways, those cloned plantation trees grown on the other side of the world. But who actually benefits from this?

Amerindians were the first to discover and use natural rubber. The early travellers to South and Central America were amazed when they were shown a variety of objects made from it, including toys, footwear, pouches and bags, and even syringes. Cortés's men in Mexico used rubber latex to waterproof their clothing, having observed the uses made of it by local people.

The history of our Western interest in natural rubber has however been a very sordid one; a story of unbridled exploitation and abuse. The atrocities carried out against those forest Indians and African slaves who were forced during the rubber boom to tap the latex for merciless overlords almost defy belief. Since then, as we have heard Antonio Macedo describe, those communities of rubber tappers who have continued to work in the Amazon have done so under extreme duress, and have been forced to fight to free themselves from gross exploitation and to protect the forest, on which they and the rubber trees depend, from violent expropriation by cattle ranchers and colonists. The bravery and foresight of Acre's rubber tappers has, as we all know, created the first extractive reserves.

But who thinks of Amazonia when they land safely at Heathrow or JFK airports? What is the real price of a radial tyre in environmental *and* in social terms?

I was interested to discover recently that, rather than invest time and money on conservation activities in Amazonia (but aware of the frightening loss of Amazonian forest where wild rubber trees occur), the International Rubber Research and Development Board (IRRDB) based here in England mounted an expedition to Amazonia in 1981 to collect, and I quote: *"new genotypes, before they disappear".* Some 12,000 'new genotypes' were collected *"which are now growing in the International Rubber Research and Development Board's 'Germplasm Centres' in Malaysia and the Côte d'Ivoire".* The gentleman with whom WWF-UK has corresponded at the IRRDB - and who, I should explain, has said that he is keen to consider co-operating with WWF in conservation-orientated activities - expressed the view that WWF's projections for the loss of species by the year 2000 was *"to overstate the case for conservation". "Surely,"* he writes, *"on a Darwinian view, the continuous disappearance of those species which fail to adapt to the changing environment is an essential part of the evolutionary process?"* But land speculation, cattle ranching, mines, dams, roads and hungry colonists, not to mention the agents of biotechnology and other businesses who have been quietly acquiring plants and genes from Third World countries, only to sell back to them patented super-varieties, is not quite what Charles Darwin had in mind.

A major component of the much-discussed rationale behind the setting up of extractive reserves has been to give a market value to products from rainforest plants and trees and therefore literally prove their market worth. But we already know that the world value of natural rubber runs into billions of dollars every year. And for this business to continue to flourish, the industry needs genes from wild Amazonian trees. So why has this not proved a powerful enough argument in the past to stop the forest from being burned? How much more valuable does natural rubber have to be - forming as it does the basis of transport systems all around the world - before the trees themselves, not just their genes, can actually be saved?

Whilst I am sure that many people, like myself, would much prefer to buy car tyres made from latex tapped by Macedo and his colleagues from wild Amazonian trees, thereby supporting both the forest and its people, than from an anonymous plantation where the trees are grown merely as a profitable crop, will this activity change the governmental policies which have allowed the surrounding forest to be burned, or mined or invaded by colonists?

I whole-heartedly support the initiatives of forest people to use their rainforest as they see fit and to sell surplus products if this is what they really desire.

Surely, it is this expression of self-determination which should be the principal criterion underlying our support for the products entering Western markets from extractive reserves. Forest people have already performed an enormous environmental service as forest guardians - as 'environmental scientists' as His Royal Highness,

Prince Charles, has said.

If forest peoples are excluded from the initial discussion stages or persuaded or pressured into accepting (before they have really assessed its worth) an initiative that is much more a product of our market-orientated thinking than of theirs, what is there to stop the forest, their ancestral lands, from being reduced to an exotic, luxury bazaar, the subject of a fickle market which when bored with one product simply moves on to the next in a gesture of environmental decadence?

In 1988 I completed *Plants for People,* a book in which I have tried to show the ways in which we all use plants around the world, to make everything from face paint to medicines, to manufacture everything from toothpaste to spectacle frames. During the course of my research I was interested to discover not only the extent of our Western dependence on plants, but the scale of our ignorance of this use. Many manufacturers, I found, were surprisingly unaware of the origins of the materials they deal in - traded, as they often are, under code names or hidden behind chemical formulae. In some cases the fact that plants had been used at all was revealed only with a kind of embarrassment, a distinct reticence to discuss something as 'backward' as a plant.

When it comes to the consumer, in most cases an even greater ignorance has existed of the origin of the products we use - hardly surprising when this information is not divulged. Who thinks, for example, of the Brazilian wax palm or its product carnauba wax when they apply lipstick (the wax is used widely by lipstick manufacturers to stiffen the product), when they eat Smarties or 'M & Ms' (it coats the outside shell), or when they polish the car?

Who thinks of balata latex when they send a golf ball flying - the best golf balls are coated with this latex since it increases back-spin - or of the rainforests of Central America when they chew gum? Latex from *Manilkara sapota* trees is still used in vast quantities to make this universal symbol of insouciance.

Before we rush headlong to create and furnish markets with the products from forest areas and extractive reserves, three things seem to me to be important:

1) to create a greater public awareness of our dependence on plants - rainforest plants included - in almost every aspect of our daily lives, not for esoteric entertainment, but as the basis of the foods, clothing, building and furnishing materials, medicines and forms of transport that we use today;

2) to create an understanding of the fact that these plants actually come from geographical regions of the world - that they were not just plucked from nowhere by an invisible industrial hand (though, for generations, plant resources from the Third World have been stealthily removed to the First, where patents and greater profit margins were made); and,

3) most importantly, to create an understanding of the social context of these plants - recognition of the fact that they come to us courtesy not just of other people's land but of their knowledge and culture - and are, therefore, the subjects of Intellectual Property Rights. As Darrell Posey has written, *"Any new ethic [of Green*

Consumerism] that is to work must start with the guarantee of Intellectual Property Rights of native peoples and provide for just compensation for their knowledge".

We tend not to think of the Colorado Indians when we eat a piece of cheese coloured with annatto or when we wash our hands but vast plantations of African oil palm - grown for the oil used extensively to make margarine, toilet soap and shampoo - are raised on what was once their forest home.

The general public wants to help save the rainforest but what it also needs is information as to the best way it can help. As has happened with organic foods and free-range meat and eggs, when provided with information which enables them to assess these products in ethical and environmental terms, a growing proportion of consumers in the affluent West are no longer choosing products solely because of the price. What we have not yet supplied the public with is the social context of the products they buy. It is important now to build on the greatly increased concern for our environment by raising awareness of this issue and of products which can be harvested by local people in accordance with their needs.

Almost all forest peoples are already part of the money economy - whether through a system of barter or direct trade - and require money to enable them both to represent themselves and buy many of the goods they need. But having from the outset been treated as implicitly inferior by those who have foisted themselves upon them and monopolized them from a spiritual, cultural and environmental point of view, they have always got the rawest of raw deals.

Whilst I understand that many forest people welcome initiatives to set up extractive reserves, they need to be allowed the time and space and liberty to produce at their own pace what they themselves perceive as appropriate for their environment and themselves. They need to be in control.

The irony of their situation has been voiced by COICA (The Co-ordinating Body for the Indigenous Peoples' Organizations of the Amazon Basin) thus:

"Faced with a continuous dispossession of our resources, an on-going invasion and loss of our territories, the growing pillage of our forests and the systematic and intentional disintegration of our cultures and ways of life, we are now asked to provide the industrial world which has colonized us with development alternatives. Under these conditions, our obligation to our people, to our children, as well as to our land, rivers and forest, is to struggle to halt this destruction. We have had little spare time during the past 500 years to think about development.

If you want to know what development means to us, you must be willing to accept that our mode of development is not the same as yours...it is not based on the accumulation of material goods nor on the greatest rates of profit, obtained at the expense of our territories and future generations...For development must take into account the well-being of our entire community or group, it must take into account the future.

The key to development for us is an extensive, diversified and integral territory where all its occupants, people, animals, trees and rivers will share the benefits. With the peace of mind that would come from an end to hostilities against us and our territories, we could begin to concentrate on our development. We could begin to teach you about development."

An essential prerequisite then, for any such development is, as Mario de Lima (of the Poyanawa Association) told us yesterday, the recognition and demarcation of traditional lands. Alongside this, forest peoples are asking that they be given the opportunity to represent themselves in matters which concern their own ancestral home and the myriad plants and animals that their own wise stewardship has allowed to flourish for thousands of years.

In this context, and to conclude, it is pertinent to ask again, I think, what the real rationale for our marketing of rainforest products might be. If it is to promote conservation, then we would do well to listen once more to what COICA has to say:

"We want the environmental community to recognize that the most effective defence of the Amazonian biosphere is the recognition and defence of the region's indigenous peoples and the promotion of their models of living within that biosphere and for managing its resources in a sustainable way. The international funders of Amazonian development should educate themselves about the indigenous peoples' relationship with their environment and formulate new concepts of Amazonian development...

We the indigenous peoples, have been an integral part of the Amazon biosphere for millenia. We used and cared for the resources of that biosphere with respect because it is our home and because we know that our survival and that of future generations depend upon it. Our accumulated knowledge about the ecology of our home, our models for living within [it], our reverence and respect for the tropical forest and its other inhabitants, both plant and animal, are the keys to guaranteeing the future of the Amazon Basin, not only for our peoples, but for all of humanity."

Plate 1 Açaí palm fruit *(Euterpeoleracea)*

Plate 2 Kayapo woman preparing açaí

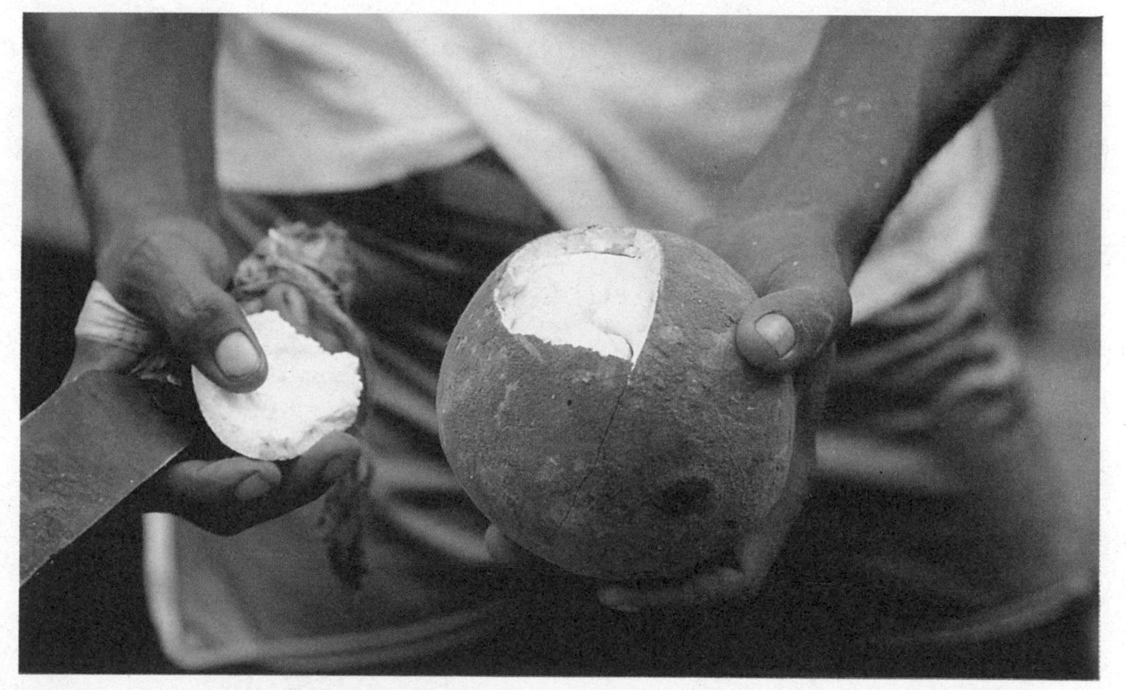

Plate 3 Cupuaçu fruit *(Theobrama grandiflora)*

Plate 4 Guaraná fruit *(Paullinia cupana)*

Plate 5 Aguaje or buriti fruit *(Mauritia flexuosa)*

Plate 6 Rosy periwinkle *(Catharanthus roseus)*

Plate 7 Zambian bee-keepers extracting honey from artificial hives

Plate 8 Rattan in Sumatra, Indonesia

Plate 9 Lauraceae (*Neolitsea* sp). Potential producer of essential oils for the pharmaceutical industry

Plate 10 Herbal remedies in South American market

Plate 11 A Nepali woman tells a British aid worker about preferred fodder species

Plate 12 The Ecological Trading Company in operation with the Trekkasaw, El Pan Project, Esmeraldas province, Ecuador

Plate 13 'Heart of Palm' *(Euterpe precatoria)*

Plate 14 A maize storage barn. Walls are constructed from split bamboo. The roof is made from leaves of the raphia palm which have been woven into tiles

Plate 15 Tree bark (mahogany) used in medicinal preparations sold at Kumasi's Central Market, Ghana

Plate 16 West African women processing the roots of the forest tree *Parkia bicolor* to make a sponge. The roots are soaked, pounded and teased

Plate 17 Several types of sponge made from the processed fibres of several forest climbers sold at Central Market, Kumasi, Ghana

Plate 18 A plant medicine trader in Central Market, Kumasi, Ghana

Plate 19 Weaving a large cane basket of the climbing palm *Erythmospatha hookeri.* It will be used by fishmongers who trade fish in northern Ghanaian markets

Plate 20 Don Calazacón - Colorado Indian from lowland Ecuador (with achiote paste on his head)

Plate 21 Caju (cashew) nut *(Anacardium occidentale)*

Plate 22 Achiote or urucu flower *(Bixa orellana)*

Plate 23 Papaya tree *(Carica papaya)* used for treating stomach disorders

Plate 24 Rubber tapper in the Alto Juruá Extractive Reserve, Acre, Brazil, scoring the bark of a rubber tree *(Hevea brasiliensis)*

Plate 25 Pouring the rubber latex over a mould prior to smoking

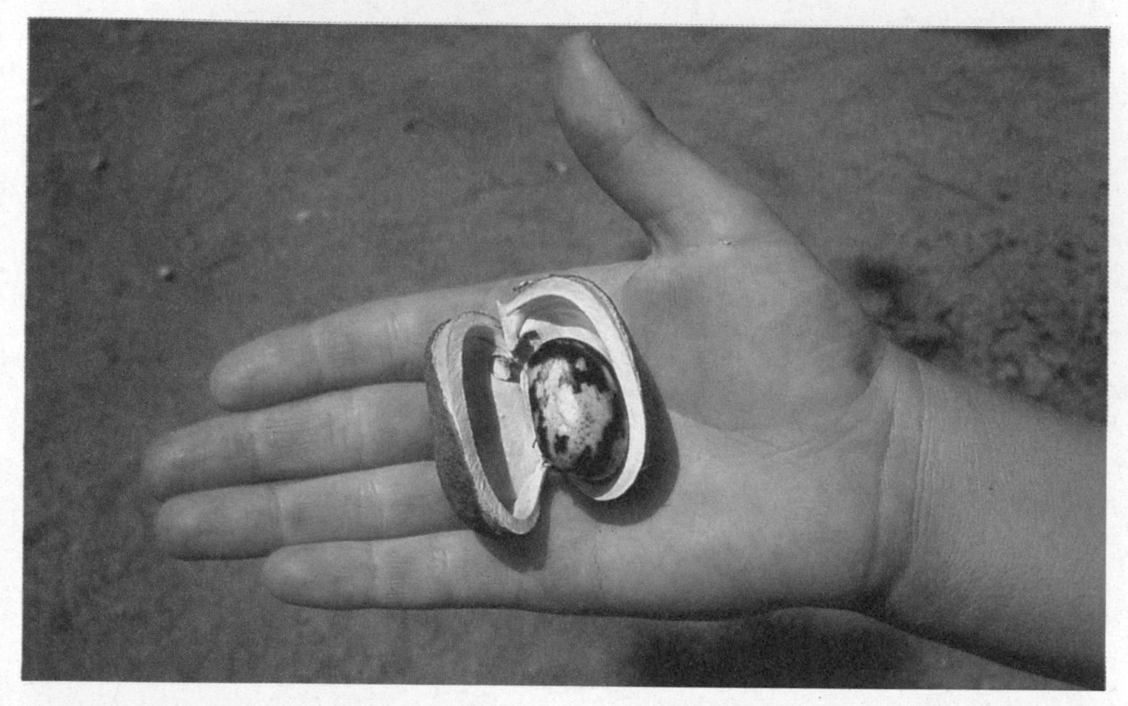

Plate 26 'Pearl of the Amazon' - the seed of *Hevea brasiliensis,* the rubber tree

Plate 27 Brazil nut tree *(Bertholletia excelsa)*

Plate 28 Brazil nut oil extraction equipment in situ (Kayapo village)

Plate 29 Fruit of the Peach palm *(Bactris gasipaes)*

Plate 30 Jatoba seed and seedling (*Hyme naea spp*). Some species of this genus are known to produce a viscous resin which is used to produce varnishes, paints and lacquers.

The Economic Importance and Marketing of Forest and Fallow Products in the Iquitos Region

Dr Christine Padoch
The New York Botanical Garden, Bronx, New York USA

The paper presented at the Conference by Dr Brian Boom, on behalf of Dr Christine Padoch, could not be published in these proceedings since it had previously been committed to another journal on the basis that the data included had not been published elsewhere. Unfortunately, its publication has been delayed and therefore the author's abbreviated version could not be printed in this volume.

Dr Christine Padoch has submitted the following paper relating to her work carried out in the Iquitos region in Peru. This paper has been reprinted here with the kind permission of the Scientific Publications Office of The New York Botanical Garden from the original reference, 'Swidden-Fallow Agroforestry in the Peruvian Amazon', Volume 5, *Advances in Economic Botany*, 1988.

Summary

Although minor (non-timber) forest products have traditionally played a significant role in the economy of the Peruvian Amazon and in the lives of its peoples, their importance has yet to be adequately examined. This paper identifies the important minor forest products that enter the market economy of the Iquitos region, assesses their relative importance in providing cash income for villages in the area and evaluates the contribution of minor forest products to the national and regional economies.

Introduction

The marketing of minor forest products has, in the past and the present, played an important role in the economic life of the north-eastern Peruvian Amazon. A large variety of products are extracted and marketed. While both villages and households in the area of Iquitos differ considerably in their reliance on forest products as a source of income, in most villages, extraction or production of forest and fallow products is nonetheless a significant economic activity. Commercial arrangements for collection and marketing are also highly variable and many goods pass through a complex chain of middlemen before reaching the final consumer. Difficulty of transport and lack of processing facilities are among the important constraints on the expansion and development of the minor forest products trade.

Minor forest products (those other than timber) have long played an important role in the economy of the Peruvian Amazon and in the lives of its peoples. Whether classed as predominantly hunter-gatherers or as agriculturalists, all native groups have relied extensively on plant and animal species of the forest for their food, fibre, medicines, ritual objects, and other needs. Immigrants now sharing the Amazonian environment have likewise adopted many forest products as important household items.

The use of forest products by Amazonian populations has been the subject of a number of studies by anthropologists, geographers, economic botanists, and others. However, the importance of all but a handful of minor forest products in the monetary economy of the region has yet to be examined. The economic impact of some products, notably rubber, has merited and received considerable attention. But rubber, though justly famous, is far from the only economically important forest product of the Peruvian Amazon. It was our purpose in this sub-project (1) to identify the important minor forest and fallow products that enter the market economy of the Iquitos region; (2) to assess their relative importance in providing cash income for the residents of the Bora community at Brillo Nuevo and other villages of the Iquitos area; and (3) to assess the contribution of the trade in minor forest and fallow products to the national and regional economies. While we have focused primarily on the present market situation, we also looked into the history of change in forest products trade and have suggested desirable changes for the future.

Within the class of minor forest and fallow products, we considered materials derived from a broad range of plant and animal species. Included were all products, other than commercially harvested timber, taken from species that occur naturally in both young and old forests. The classification also comprises non-annual agricultural crops that continue to be found in swidden fields after they cease to be intensively managed. Also included as minor forest and fallow products are materials from species that are neither strictly agricultural nor wholly naturally occurring, but are to various degrees 'managed' or 'manipulated'. The specific products we examined included: gums, resins, seeds, essential oils, natural insecticides, fibres, tannins, dyes, edible fruits and tubers, medicinal plants, ornamentals, and animal products such as skins, bones, meat, teeth and claws, plumes, and live animals. Although not usually classified among minor forest products, we also included in our investigations wood products such as firewood and charcoal, wood and other natural materials used for handicrafts, and timber when harvested by local villagers or native communities. We, however, excluded research into the commercial timber trade since, in contrast to the trade in the products outlined above, the timber trade has been the subject of a considerable amount of study by government and other entities.

We recognize that a large volume and variety of forest and fallow products are indispensable locally; these include many of the plants which were found in Bora swidden-fallow fields. However, we concentrated specifically on those products that have been or are bought, sold, or bartered in local or regional markets of the Iquitos area. The residents of Brillo Nuevo and our other study sites, as almost all residents of the Peruvian Amazon, have economically and culturally significant ties with regional, national, and even international markets.

As defined above, our study included, but was not limited to, products harvested from fallow fields, and as such constitutes an integral part of the larger interdisciplinary effort to investigate swidden-fallow agroforestry systems. Our data gathering efforts both built upon and extended information gathered by other researchers working on the fallow fields at Brillo Nuevo. We attempted an approximation of the present and potential market importance of the forest products harvested by Bora households at Brillo Nuevo. Comparable data collected in several other communities in the area allow comparisons of the relative economic importance and potential for trade in minor forest and fallow products in different types of Amazonian settlements. We chose to include products collected from older forest as well as from swidden fallows because at this point it is not always possible to determine whether a given species can be successfully propagated in fallow fields.

Our task of adding an economic dimension to the essentially ecological investigations carried out by other project participants had as its aim the integration of the two general foci of the larger project: ie to study existent Amazonian agroforestry systems and to recommend desirable changes for the future. We hope that the production and market data that we collected allow our recommendations to be based not only on sound ecological understanding but also on a realistic assessment of market conditions and problems.

Historical overview

In order to realistically assess the present and future situation and future prospects of minor forest products trade in the Iquitos area, it is instructive to briefly consider its history. A considerable number of forest products have figured in the economy of the region. Most of them were exploited and fetched good prices for a brief period, only to be replaced on world markets by other, cheaper materials more accessible to North American and European importers.

Long before the founding of Iquitos, in the 17th and 18th centuries, commercial exploitation and export of medicinal plants such as copaiba (*Copaifera reticulata*), naval stores such as copal (*Dacryodes* sp.), condiments such as sarsaparilla (*Smilax* spp.) and vanilla (*Vanilla planifolia*), and other products such as waxes, honey, and turtle eggs were important to the region (Villarejo, 1979:128-129). Sarsaparilla in particular was shipped in large quantities to North American ports. In 1851 a US investigator, presaging the later rubber boom inquiries, commented on the enormous discrepancies between the very high prices sarsaparilla commanded in New York City and the miserable payment the Amazonian collector received, about 1/200th of the eventual price (ORDELORETO, 1980:41).

In the mid and late 19th century, the coincidence of a number of developments dramatically changed the minor forest products trade as well as the character of the Peruvian Amazon. In late October 1853, the first steamship arrived in the Peruvian ports of Loreto and Nauta, and by 1864 the town of Iquitos was established to accommodate the new form of transportation and to serve as a government centre. The possibility of faster and surer transport of men and materials spurred the export of products from the upper Amazon, especially that of rubber (*Hevea brasiliensis,* Plates 24, 25 and 26). While some export of various types of rubber was known earlier, the invention of the process of vulcanization in 1839, as well as the growing needs of the new electrical and automotive industries of late 19th century North America and Europe, greatly stimulated rubber exports. In the last years of the 19th century and the first decade of the 20th, a tremendous economic boom enveloped the Amazon, including the Iquitos region. In 1907 rubber constituted over 20 per cent of all of Peru's exports (ORDELORETO, 1980). After that peak year, as Asian plantations began to produce, prices paid for rubber began to decline, and by 1915 the boom was over.

The rubber boom left its legacy in the region: new towns (among them Iquitos), an increased population of immigrants, and in many cases a reduced, brutalized, and dispossessed population of indigenous peoples. It left little else that could be viewed as development in the region. The latex had been extracted and sent out of the area, and the riches flowing from the trade, in many cases controlled by foreign concerns, were largely exported as well.

A number of other booms in extractive products enlivened the local economy for brief periods of time but were all faint echoes of the great rubber boom.

Tagua or 'vegetable ivory', the seed of the yarina palm (*Phytelephas macrocarpa*) used for making buttons and game pieces, enjoyed a period of high prices in the years following the collapse of Amazonian rubber. After 1925 the export market began to decline as artificial materials replaced tagua.

Around 1925 the trade in gums such as balata (*Manilkara bidentata*) and leche caspi (*Couma macrocarpa*) began to gain importance. Again the prices paid were high for a while, but fell within a decade as importers in the developed world found cheaper and more accessible substitutes (Williams, 1962a, 1962b).

The next product to be exported in quantity was barbasco (*Lonchocarpus* spp.), whose root contains rotenone, a natural insecticide (Wille *et al*,. 1939). Barbasco differed from the other products mentioned as it was not only collected from natural forests but was also planted as a crop. Large quantities were exported by the North American Astoria Company located in Iquitos and other concerns. But the outflow was reduced to a mere trickle as DDT and other synthetic insecticides replaced it in the 1940s (Villarejo, 1979).

Other minor forest products exported in significant quantities included bois de rose oil, an essential oil extracted from palo de rosa (*Aniba rosaedora*) used to scent soaps, and ojé (*Ficus insipida*), a natural antihelminthic.

The number of minor forest products that have figured in the economy of the Peruvian Amazon is large and diverse. However, in virtually all cases the products were exported in large quantities and in largely unprocessed form. Little was done to either insure the continued availability of the product, with the exception of barbasco, or to develop local industries based on the product. Physical, social and political factors frequently made supply of the materials uncertain or expensive (Schery, 1949), and foreign importers were quick to find other suppliers of equivalent or comparable materials. Prominent in the extractive industries were foreign firms which departed the area when prices declined, leaving behind little expertise or wealth on which other industries could be developed. The fall in exports of some minor forest products may be attributed to government regulation, such as the recent ban on export of animal products of several species. Some merchants also complain of what they consider to be serious government disincentives to the export of forest products, such as the general lack of government credit and the recent revocation of tax exemptions for extractive industries in Loreto. However, it appears that the local and international market system can be largely blamed for the greatly fluctuating nature of the Amazonian trade.

Also notable as a constant in the history of forest products trade is the position of the collectors. They almost invariably received little for their labours and often were and still are involved in exploitative relationships with merchants and middlemen, placing them in a situation of virtual slavery or debt bondage.

This brief historical sketch has been provided to emphasize our point that the collecting and marketing of minor forest products is neither a new pattern in the Iquitos area nor has it been confined to the most famous Amazonian product, rubber. Recommendations and planning for enhanced use and marketing of such products must take into account the problems and injustices that have plagued the industry in the past.

Present situation

In this paper we cannot give a definitive assessment of the role of minor forest and fallow products trade in the entire Department of Loreto nor in the Peruvian Amazon. Since we were able to obtain information from only a small number of villages in the Iquitos area, we have aimed at outlining the general situation in a rather loosely specified 'Iquitos region'.

This region shares with the entire Department of Loreto a number of characteristics. It is rather sparsely populated (about 1.5 persons per square kilometre), and its population is very young, with close to 60 per cent below the age of 20, promising that the present population growth of 3 per cent per annum will at least be maintained (ORDELORETO, 1981). The residents of the region are generally poor, although their poverty tends sometimes to be overlooked because of the recent boom in petroleum extraction in the area. However, that activity benefits a small proportion of the local inhabitants. In 1974 a socio-economic survey conducted in a large sample of villages on the Upper Amazon and Napo Rivers found the average household income to be only somewhat above $1 per day (IPA, 1974, II: 130). While the income of some villagers whom we interviewed is higher, the monetary budget of rural dwellers is still very low by world standards.

The trade balance for the Department of Loreto is unfavourable and has been rapidly deteriorating. In 1979, exports brought in about $9 million, and imports totalled about $28.8 million. The balance had changed by 1982 to about $8 million in exports and $49 million in imports, and in 1984 to only $3.8 million in exports and $18 million in imports (CORDELOR, 1985:164).

Since the 1950s, extractive industries have ceased

to be the most important income generators in the region (ORDEORIENTE, 1971). Agriculture, including livestock production, is now the area's most important economic activity. However, forest-based activities still play a significant role in the region's economy.

As assessment of the total value of forest and fallow products entering the Iquitos area market and of trends in that market is very difficult to obtain. Among the problems encountered in attempting to find such a measure is the variation in geographic entities for which data were and are reported. Some reports give data for the Iquitos Forestry District, others for the entire Peruvian Amazon. Still others cite the Eastern Region (Oriente), while other reports cover the Department of Loreto which was recently diminished in area when the new Department of Ucayali was created. Another problem in using available data stems from variation in the measures of production that are used. Some information is given in weights of the product, others in the greatly fluctuating Peruvian currency, still others in US dollars.

A larger problem that concerns us is the question of reliability and completeness of data collected by various agencies. In the case of trade in highly restricted but valuable goods such as animal skins, we assume that no reliable data will be available

Table 1. Production of minor forest products for Iquitos in 1980

Product	Production (kg)	Value ($)
Aguaje (*Mauritia flexuosa*, Plate 5)	46,690	2,801
Canela (*Endlicheria* sp.)	500	1,600
Cortezas y picadas (various)	3,907	156
Chanca piedra (*Phyllanthus niruri*)	2,742	219
Rubber (*Hevea brasiliensis*)	308,549	631,081
Ojé (*Ficus insipida*)	218,976	262,771
Palm heart (various)	501,769	50,177
Piassava (*Leopoldina piassaba*)	36,410	106
Peach palm (*Bactris gasipaes*, Plate 29)	32,220	1,993
Sangre de grado (*Croton* spp.)	118	614
Ungurahui (*Jessenia bataua*)	2,500	300
Umarí (*Poraqueiba sericea*)	10,220	1,022
Barbasco (*Lonchocarpus* spp.)	319,408	no information
		Total: $952,780

Source: Ministerio de Agricultura, 1980

since much of the trade is clandestine. Even when other legitimate products are considered, an accurate assessment of production or trade is still very difficult to obtain. The entire trade is a very widely dispersed activity, and data on important goods such as native forest and fallow fruits, charcoal, firewood, medicinal plants, etc, are entirely absent or very sketchy at best. Only a few products, those almost exclusively produced for export, are probably censused accurately by government agencies. Table 1 shows highly incomplete production and value data for Iquitos taken from a 1980 Ministry of Agriculture annual report. The most important products are clearly rubber, ojé, palm heart, and barbasco. (Watson Cisneros, 1964, provides production data for some forest products in eastern Peru for the period 1955-1962).

Community level production

While data on the regional importance of forest and fallow products trade is certainly incomplete, information on the role of forest and fallow products in the household budgets and activities of villagers is virtually non-existent. In considering research into these questions we found that it is first necessary to recognize the diversity of the region.

Villages in the Iquitos area vary considerably in the type of production their residents engage in and in the products they market. The chief determinants of this variation include:

(1) suitability of the area for intensive annual cropping;

(2) opportunities the area offers for activities such as fishing and hunting;

Table 2. Relative importance of transport costs to Iquitos

Village	Percentage of sale price*
San Antonio	8
Aucayo	8
La Unión	10
Tamshiyacu	12
Santa Ana	12
Señor de los Milagros	20
Tarapoto	25
Libertad	25
Shiriara	28
Mishana	28
Yarina	39

* Percentage of sale price of ten sacks of fruit expended in transportation charges from village to Iquitos market.

(3) location of the village in relation to Iquitos or other markets as well as relative ease and costs of transportation;
(4) location in relation to valuable forest resources, patterns of tenure of forest areas and other resources;
(5) village history, including length of settlement, and;
(6) the history of occupational specialization in the region.

Villagers who have access to seasonally flooded areas which receive annual depositions of fertile silt (barreales) often devote much of their time and other resources to the production of rice, a crop that the government is encouraging with special loan programmes. When the opportunity to profitably produce an annual crop such as rice is available, exploitation of forest and fallow products usually becomes relatively less important. Settlements in areas where fishing is exceptionally good, such as on some particularly productive oxbow lakes (cochas), are often important commercial fishing centres. If the residents of such communities also have relatively easy access to Iquitos, then, especially when water levels are low, supply of fresh fish to the urban market becomes a predominant activity and sale of forest and fallow products declines in importance.

Location of villages and their relative access to land and water resources influence not only opportunities to engage in other occupations but also the type and quantity of forest and fallow products that can be collected. Few villagers will exploit stands of fruit-bearing palms such as aguaje (*Mauritia flexuosa*, Plate 5) or ungurahui (*Jessennia bataua*) located more than about two hours' walking distance from their homes or from sites where the heavy fruits can be loaded into boats. Some communities located not far from stands of forest fruits have no access to these resources because residents of other villages claim tenure to these sites and exclusive rights to harvest and sell the products.

Another factor that accounts for variation in production and marketing is the distance or cost of transport of produce from the community to a market (see Table 2). Some items, notably fruits, are perishable and must be sold within a few days after harvest. Only villages with relatively fast, reliable, and inexpensive available transportation can afford to market such products in quantity. In some instances buyers will come from Iquitos to the community if the area is a known centre of production of particular goods.

Yet another determinant of levels of production and marketing appears to be the history of settlement and specialization. Several villages, for instance, specialize in the sale of handicrafts such as bags, baskets, brooms, or hammocks. In many such settlements a pattern of handicraft making apparently developed when a craftsman joined the community and taught his neighbours the skills necessary for manufacture of some forest-product-based artifact. As more villagers learned the craft, the area became known as a production centre, and in many such cases the large volume of production attracted buyers from Iquitos. The length of time an area has been settled, as well as the size of the human population and the intensity of exploitation of particular materials, will of course determine the availability of the raw materials and the success with which such industries can continue.

With these and many other factors affecting the patterns of marketing products, communities of the Iquitos region obviously differ greatly; no 'typical village' or 'typical marketing pattern' exists. In an attempt to obtain some measure of the variation and levels of forest and fallow product exploitation and marketing, 13 communities were surveyed, among them villages with considerably differing access to land and water resources, varying access to markets, and different histories. Included were both communities near Iquitos and others at a considerable distance. In some villages production of rice and other annual crops was overwhelmingly important and in others fruit, forest fibre, and handicraft sales predominated. Not included were settlements located more than a day and a half by boat from Iquitos.

In most of the 13 villages surveyed, between five and ten households were sampled; in each of these an adult male and/or female household member was interviewed. In two communities, Señor de los Milagros and Mishana, a joint interview was conducted at a meeting of most of the male household heads. Such a format was employed in these villages because community authorities deemed it more acceptable, and we followed their wishes. In the instances where individual

Table 3. Major products marketed, by category

1. Intensively managed crops: manioc (*Manihot esculenta*), plantain (*Musa paradisiaca*), rice (*Oryza sativa*), maize (*Zea mays*), pineapple (*Ananas comosus*).
2. Cultivated fruit trees: peach palm, pifuayo (*Bactris gasipaes,* Plate 29), caimito (*Pouteria caimito*), uvilla (*Pourouma cecropiifolia*), guaba (*Inga edulis*), cashew (*Anacardium occidentale,* Plate 21), sapote (*Quararibea* sp.), umarí (*Poraqueiba sericea*), pomarosa (*Syzygium malaccensis*), toronja (*Citrus paradisi*).
3. Forest fruits, leaves, palm heart: aguaje (*Mauritia flexuosa*), ungurahui (*Jessenia bataua*), husasaí, chonta (*Euterpe precatoria,* Plate 13), bijao (*Heliconia cannoidea*).
4. Handicrafts: chambira hammocks (*Astrocaryum chambira*), chambira bags (jicras) (*A chambira*), tamshi fibre baskets (*Heteropsis jenmanii*), bombonaje fibre baskets (*Carludovica palmata*), sesta de tamshi (*Heteropsis jenmanii*), paddle (remo caspi) (*Pithecellobium laetum*), seed necklaces (many species), feather ornaments (fans, necklaces, crowns, many species).
5. Roofing and wall materials: wall panels (esteras) (*Mauritia flexuosa*), thatch (crisnejas) (*Lepidocaryum* sp.), thatch (*Phytelephas macrocarpa*).
6. Animal products: meat (deer, peccary) and skins.
7. Charcoal: many species.
8. Firewood and construction wood: many species.
9. Medicinal plants: chuchuashi (*Maytenus krukovii*), clavohuasca (*Mandevilla scabra*).
10. Fish: many species.

households were surveyed, no attempt was made to collect a random sample, because the limited time available to us and our desire to get as large a sample as we could made selection impossible. We talked with anyone who was willing and not too busy to be interviewed during either day or evening hours. The reliability of our data is also limited by the fact that we had to rely on the recall of our informants for data on the entire past year's (1982) marketing. As both production and prices vary greatly throughout the year, these data are, of course, subject to considerable error.

Questions were limited to 1982 production and were designed to elicit the name of all goods marketed, the income realized from sales, and the cost of transporting those goods to market. We attempted to determine the relative importance of forest and fallow products as income generators to rural households.

The types of products marketed by villagers who were interviewed were divided into ten categories. Table 3 lists the important products subsumed under each of these categories. It should be noted that all categories other than 1 and 10 comprise products that we have referred to in this report as 'forest and fallow products'.

The listing of market products shown in Table 3 is by no means exhaustive. There are, for instance, numerous species of medicinal plants that are

Table 4. Per cent of household incomes derived from crops and forest products

	Category*									
Village	**1**	**2**	**3**	**4**	**5**	**6**	**7**	**8**	**9**	**10**
San Antonio	56	0	8	0	0	0	0	0	0	36
Aucayo	61	2	0	0	0	0	0	0	0	37
Tamshiyacu	14	71	2	1	0	8	3	0	1	0
La Unión	79	12	7	1	0	1	0	0	0	0
Nueva Tarapacá	28	12	5	11	13	2	27	0	0	1
Santa Ana	39	41	0	11	0	0	8	0	0	2
Señor de los Milagros	61	28	11	0	0	0	0	0	0	0
Tarapoto	57	3	17	4	0	3	1	4	0	11
Libertad	62	16	0	15	0	0	0	0	0	6
Shiriara	72	2	8	5	3	0	0	3	0	8
Mishana	24	4	24	12	15	0	3	3	0	15
Yarina	70	1	6	9	1	4	1	9	0	0
Brillo Nuevo	15	2	1	57	7	18	0	0	0	1

* See Table 3 for use categories.

marketed, together with many other fruit and fibre products. The species mentioned are only those that are most commonly sold. Despite the restriction of this list to those products that most often appear in the markets, Table 3 indicates that a large spectrum of forest and fallow species are traded in the markets of the Iquitos area, including many of the species found by the project in the fallow fields at Brillo Nuevo.

In Table 4, the total average income of the households interviewed in each village is divided into the percentages derived from the marketing of products in each of the categories described in Table 3. (A total for an inclusive 'forest and fallow products' category can be found by adding together all categories except 1 and 10).

That considerable variation in how residents of various villages obtain their monetary income exists can be seen in Table 4. Some communities, such as San Antonio and Aucayo, situated close to Iquitos and having access to seasonally flooded lands for intensive annual crop cultivation, get most of their income from the intensive cultivation of agricultural crops as well as from the marketing of fresh fish in Iquitos. The Bora of Brillo Nuevo, on the other hand, largely sell easily transported and non-perishable items such as handicrafts. Other villages tend to exhibit a more balanced distribution of income sources.

Table 4 shows that apart from a few villages, the forests and fallow fields of the Iquitos area supply rural households with a significant amount of income. Some villages, particularly Tamshiyacu, bear special mention. The great part of the income earned by the residents of this community derives from the selling of fruits, with umarí (*Poraqueiba sericea*), the most important product harvested. The production of this fruit takes place within an agroforestry system of cultivation. The relative ease with which the residents of Tamshiyacu can bring their produce to market is no doubt a determining factor in the pattern of marketing developed in this village. However, the development of better transport, new markets, and/or processing facilities in other areas would certainly allow for the greater commercialization of fallow fruits such as umarí in more distant settlements such as Brillo Nuevo. The marketing of fruits produced in swidden fallow not only accounts for a very high proportion of the income earned by Tamshiyaquenos, but it also provides them with a relatively high annual income for the region, an average of about $1200 per household, while the Bora of Brillo Nuevo earn about $500.

It should also be mentioned that apart from variation between villages, there are also considerable differences among households in any particular community. The sources of variation within villages are in part the same as those mentioned above as accounting for differences between communities. Differential access to resources such as prime rice cultivation land is one important factor. Others include the demographic composition of the household. Many products are heavy to carry and are frequently located far from the house. Therefore households with enough able-bodied members, particularly young men, tend to engage in more forest fruit collection than do those with different age-sex structures. Households with unmarried women often market more handicrafts such as chambira fibre bags and hammocks. Differences in ethnic affiliation also may account for some

Table 5. Variability in source of income among five households in Nueva Tarapaca.

	Percentage of income derived from marketing of products						
Category	**HH1**	**HH2**	**HH3**	**HH4**	**HH5**	**Range**	**Average**
1. Intensive crops	41	38	4	36	23	. 4-41	28
2. Fruit trees	0	0	0	40	19	0-40	12
3. Forest fruits	0	22	1	0	0	0-22	5
4. Handicrafts	0	40	14	3	0	0-40	11
5. Roofing/wall	0	0	0	22	44	0-44	13
6. Animal products	0	0	12	0	0	0-12	2
7. Charcoal	55	0	69	0	13	0-69	27
8. Firewood	0	0	0	0	0	0	0
9. Medicinals	0	0	0	0	0	0	0
10. Fish	4	0	0	0	0	0-4	1

marketing differences. Members of tribal groups, for instance, often sell traditional manufactures using forest plant and animal materials. Some, although by no means all, non-indigenous residents of the area consider the production of handicrafts a tribal occupation and thus demeaning or unsuitable for non-tribal people. Other differences in production and marketing strategies can be attributed to varying preferences, skills, and needs. Table 5 provides an illustration of the variability found among households in the percentage of income they derive from the marketing of various categories of products. This table examines the situation in the village of Nueva Tarapaca, situated along the Río Tamshiyacu. It is evident that average figures give a very generalized picture of an extremely complex pattern.

The ranges of variation found among households in other villages, including Brillo Nuevo, are as wide or even wider. Thus while many villages are classified locally as centres of specialization in the production of particular products, in reality there is no unvarying pattern of economic behaviour, including marketing, among the residents of any community.

The great complexity of marketing in the Iquitos region reflects not only the considerable variation among villages and individual households outlined above, but also the continually changing nature of production and trade. Changes in marketing patterns can be seen as occurring both seasonally and over the longer term.

Seasonality in production and marketing stems from a number of factors. Fruiting seasons are obviously an important determinant. Many of the forest and fallow species important to the Bora and other Amazonian residents fruit twice annually. Whether and when these products are marketed, however, depends not only on production seasons but also on varying river levels. Villages such as Brillo Nuevo which are located on smaller streams are relatively isolated from the market at times when water levels are too low to allow for the passage of heavily-laden boats. Larger trading boats often cannot navigate these streams for several months of the year, making the buying and selling of trade items difficult. When water levels are low, many resources such as logs for marketable firewood cannot be extracted at all. Changing water levels also determine when villagers will engage in occupation other than forest and fallow product collecting and sale. Cultivation of seasonally inundated areas, playas and barreales, must obviously follow river levels. And fishing is far more profitable when river water is low. When people are busy with other occupations, trade in forest and fallow products is often neglected. Other factors influencing seasonal patterns include special market periods. For instance, during the week preceding Easter, palm hearts are a favoured food; many villagers collect and market *Euterpe* palm hearts in quantity only during that one week of the year.

Other than seasonal variations, longer-term changes affect marketing behaviour. Prices of many products both for internal use and for export change frequently due to many factors. Collecting and marketing of various items becomes accordingly more or less profitable and frequent. The history of forest product exploitation, noted above, is one of great variation in market prices and consequently production and trade in the Iquitos region.

The exploitation and marketing of some forest products is regulated or controlled by government agencies. For instance, trade in animals and animal products, especially skins and live primates and birds, an important occupation for many Amazonian residents in the past, is now restricted by the Peruvian government. Although the commercial sale of many animal products continues in a more or less clandestine fashion, it has declined greatly as a source of regular income.

Longer term variation in marketing patterns can also be attributed to changes in resource availability. Many forest products have been and are exploited at rates and in ways that do not allow for adequate regeneration and sustained use. Thus many resources are becoming more scarce and therefore more difficult to collect, consequently trade has declined.

Finally, it should be noted that changes in the transportation and market facilities greatly contribute to the variation in trade. In remote areas, collectors and producers are dependent on travelling traders to sell their goods. Such traders vary their trips according to their own needs and schedules, often leaving certain areas without any reliable means of marketing their products. Enhancement of transport or creation of scattered regional markets would greatly stabilize the marketing situation in the area.

Trade patterns

The trade patterns of marketing of forest and fallow products in the Iquitos area are highly varied and complex. Arrangements may be simple, such as a producer or extractor selling his or her own household products in the same village or a regional market; or they may be extremely complex, such as the extraction of forest products by an upriver settler on contract to a local buyer who in turn is under contract to a regional subcontractor who delivers the goods to a major contractor in Iquitos who then sells to a wholesaler for export. The simplest transactions are perhaps the most frequent in far upriver areas. A socioeconomic study conducted on the Amazon and Napo rivers found that 60 per cent of Napo producers interviewed sold most of their produce in their home villages (IPA, 1974, II: 122). Villagers along the Amazon who generally have easier access to larger markets tended to sell in Iquitos or other regional centres: Tamshiyacu; Indiana; Pebas; San Pablo; Caballococha; Leticia or Benjamin Constant. In these transactions some middleman is usually involved.

Much of the produce that arrives in the market in Iquitos is brought in by a producer or member of his or her household by river, either in a privately owned boat (if the distance is small) or more frequently, by collectivo or 'river bus'. The expenses involved in transporting goods to market can be a determining factors in what is marketed and in what quantities. When products are brought in by collectivo, the seller must pay both his or her round-trip as well as cargo charges for the produce for sale. Charges are usually figured on the basis of cost per large gunny sack (used for a large variety of goods), or in the case of some fruits, cost per raceme. Goods are generally not weighed, although in a few cases distinctions are made between a sack of heavy goods and lighter produce such as charcoal.

From some areas, such as most villages along the Río Nanay, marketers usually carry their goods by boat to a point (Puerto Almendras or Santa Clara) where they and their goods transfer to trucks or buses for the rest of the trip to Iquitos. The need to pay two fares generally makes transport quite expensive; cargo charges on such trips tend to be especially high.

Table 2 gives an indication of the importance of transport costs to village producers and collectors. The percentage of the average sale price of ten sacks of fruit such as aguaje (*Mauritia flexuosa*) that a resident of a number of villages along the Amazon and Nanay would have to pay to transport himself and his goods to the Iquitos market is computed. The transport of lower priced but bulky items such as charcoal is often even less profitable. Transporting ten sacks of charcoal from Tamshiyacu to Iquitos would consume 20 per cent of the expected return on sale, while from Tarapoto on the Nanay River a prohibitive 83 per cent of the market price would be expended for transport costs. As might be expected, the residents of Tarapoto never bring their charcoal to market; they only sell the product when the rare travelling trader purchases it at the village itself.

The costs of transportation from Brillo Nuevo to Iquitos are extremely high. A round-trip fare for one person (without cargo) in August 1983, cost nearly $12. Since the price of a sack of aguaje in the Iquitos market averages less than a third of a person's fare, marketing fruits in Iquitos by Brillo Nuevo producers is generally not feasible. What fruits are marketed are usually sold in the very limited market at Pebas or to travelling traders. Occasionally the headman of the community or the missionary resident in Brillo Nuevo will take large boatloads of their own and their neighbours' produce directly to the Iquitos market for sale, avoiding the high cost of travel by public transportation.

Goods brought into Iquitos are usually sold to a wholesaler who in turn sells them to a retailer with a stall in the market. Most of the producers interviewed complained bitterly of what they considered the unfairly low prices paid them by the wholesalers who usually intercept collectivos and smaller boats bearing produce before they arrive in the market itself. Villagers termed the buyers 'pirañas' or 'lagartos' lying in wait to take advantage of arriving producers. Although they are not literally forced to sell their goods to wholesalers, few villagers, little skilled in marketing produce in a large and busy marketplace like Iquitos, ever successfully retail their own produce.

Producers who arrive in Iquitos by truck or bus, mostly from villages along the Nanay River, largely avoid the wholesalers who operate in the port area and tend to market most of their own produce directly to the consumers along the streets on the edges of the busy Iquitos market.

Where distances from areas of production to markets are very great, public transportation facilities lacking, the market specialized, or necessary credit unavailable, the arrangements for selling forest and fallow products become far more complex. Between producer and consumer there often enters a large number of middlemen.

In the Amazonian minor forest products trade, middlemen include large urban wholesalers (mayoristas), who buy goods in large volume and turn over capital which may equal $10,000. Mayoristas often possess their own large boats and storage facilities. These major wholesalers probably number less than ten in Iquitos and engage in trade of a large variety of products as well as other commercial enterprises. Mayoristas often employ corredores of travelling agents who buy goods at the place of production or extraction. The smaller wholesalers (rematistas) operating in the principal ports of the city, as well as on boats that ply the Amazon and major tributaries, number in the hundreds. Most of them deal almost exclusively in agricultural products, but many also buy and sell minor forest products when the opportunity presents itself. These traders vary enormously in the volume of trade they handle and in the value of their operations. Some rematistas also act at times as vendedores or retailers of the products in the market, although many only sell the products to the consumer.

The marketing process often begins in the hamlets and villages where producers and collectors reside. The first purchaser of minor forest products is frequently a comprador or buyer, often a small shop owner who resides in a town or village along the river and purchases goods for subsequent transport to the market in Iquitos. Also involved in the marketing network are transportistas, owners of boats that carry passengers and cargo. Boat owners frequently purchase goods for resale in Iquitos. Some may act as negociantes who buy products not for direct payment in cash but as exchange goods with the producers or extractors of minor forest products. Some negociantes do not own boats but travel in boats belonging to others and make their sales and purchases when the boats stop at riverine villages. Among wholesalers one can also count regatónes or river traders, who carry on their commercial activities in areas such as Brillo Nuevo, that are far removed from market centres. These traders carry a store of daily necessities and other goods aboard their boats. Although not nearly as numerous as in the past, some regatónes still operate out of Iquitos making trips which normally last 15 days to a month, during which time they contact many producers and collectors along the upper tributaries of the Amazon. Regatónes usually pay their suppliers in merchandise in exchange for the promise of future production; at times they also advance cash to their contacts.

In remote areas the regatón often acts as a contractor (habilitador) or subcontractor (subhabilitador), although those two functions are also performed by other types of middlemen. Contractors generally advance cash to subcontractors, compradores, group of producers, or individual producers in exchange for exclusive rights to extracted products or agricultural harvests. Many of these functions were, until the 1950s, performed by patrones, owners of tracts of land containing valuable forest products and virtual owners of populations of collectors of these products. In remote villages shop owners and others still often act as patrones of villages, although in a much reduced and changed fashion. While the worst abuses associated with the patrón system are probably a thing of the past, perpetual indebtedness of rural folks is still not uncommon. The regatón and other intermediaries buy minor forest products cheap and sell manufactures and other goods dear to their upriver clients. The extractor generally gets little for the valuable products which he delivers. A government publication estimated that in 1969 extractors as a group received less than 25 per cent of the value of the extracted product, although those extractors represented 85 per cent of the work force involved in the entire process (ORDEORIENTE, 1971: 149). The same report estimated that the share of the profit from an extracted product that an individual extractor received was only 1.6 per cent of the share going to the habilitador who was involved, 3.2 per cent of the share taken by the subhabilitador, and 13 per cent of the share received by the local comprador or patrón.

Having briefly outlined the roles played by the several categories of middlemen or intermediaries, it is evident that the potential combinations involved in a commercial forest products transaction in the Iquitos area are many and the possible complexity of commercial networks great. Much of the difficulty of assuring consumers a reliable supply of forest and fallow products, of promoting more conservative extraction methods and insuring long-term availability of resources, and of redistributing the benefits and risks of the trade more equitably, so that rural dwellers might gain a reasonable return, can be traced back to the extended and complex marketing arrangements. Much has been said in favour of reforming or simplifying the system by eliminating middlemen. Even a cursory examination of the present situation suggests that no such easy solutions are readily available.

Markets for forest and fallow products

The principal regional trade centre of the area

under study is Iquitos. Apart from many retail stores and stalls located throughout the city, Iquitos contains several market locations: Belén, Modelo (Camal), Central, Norteñita, Trujillo, Bellavista, and a few smaller, less established markets. The principal market, Belén is by far the most important in both wholesale and retail trade. At the port of the Belén market, near the confluence of the Itaya and Amazon Rivers - an area known locally as Venezia - wholesalers and retailers intercept incoming goods. Among the significant forest and fallow products brought into the market are fruits, including various palm fruits, palm heart, medicinal plants, small manufactures, charcoal, and handicraft items such as hammocks, baskets, and brooms. The trade in some goods, especially fruits, varies considerably with the seasons (Novoa Miranda, 1970).

While daily, semi-weekly, and weekly markets are also held in a few other towns of the region, Iquitos dominates the larger scale trade. Only near the eastern end of the study area are goods in any quantity shipped elsewhere for sale, usually to the Colombian port of Leticia or to Benjamin Constant in Brazil.

Apart from sale at the market to a wholesaler or retailer who will then sell the product directly to a consumer, there are several processing industries that buy forest and fallow products for elaboration of consumer products. Ice-cream and chupete (popsicle) makers buy large quantities of aguaje (*Mauritia flexuosa*) for processing, and juguerías (juice bars) and restaurants purchase a variety of fruits including camucamu (*Myrciaria dubia*), cocona (*Solanum sessiliflorum*), and araza (*Eugenia stipitata*) for the manufacture of drinks. Other forest products consumed by restaurants are palm heart and some game, notably peccary (*Tayassu* sp.) and tortoise (*Testudo* sp.).

The several restaurants in Iquitos that specialize in the preparation of barbecued chicken consume great quantities of charcoal, while 90 to 95 per cent of the 30 or so bakeries in the city use large amounts of firewood to heat their ovens. Another significant consumer of firewood is the brick making industry. Both bakeries and brick makers generally receive regular deliveries of the fuel. Middlemen process and haul the wood from the village of Santa Clara on the Nanay River, a central distribution point for firewood for the entire urban area of Iquitos.

Two processing industries in Iquitos also provide a market for forest and fallow products. The Astoria Company, a United States-owned enterprise, operated in Iquitos for over 50 years and exported many products including timber, barbasco (*Lonchocarpus* sp.), ojé (*Ficus insipida*), and curare (*Chondrodendron* sp.) to North American markets. Since 1972 the company has been Peruvian-owned, and its scale of operations has declined notably. The Peruvian owners have diversified into production of some non-forest products but also continue to export small quantities of the company's traditional goods such as barbasco and ojé. Most of the barbasco exported by Astoria Peruana is now grown outside the Iquitos region, but the ojé is harvested in the area, mainly in remote spots such as the Upper Napo. Astoria Peruana contracts with collectors to tap trees bearing the natural antihelminthic and provides them with necessary tools and supplies.

The present directors of Astoria Peruana hope that

the growing opposition among Europeans and North Americans to synthetic poisons will soon boost the currently depressed market for their products. They also wish to expand their operations to include other products such as the medicinal sangre de grado (*Croton* sp.), and the processing of papain. However, the testing facilities and scientific expertise formerly found at the Astoria Company left with its North American owners, and the present management has little knowledge of new market possibilities or the optimum ways of exploiting them.

The only other large processor of forest products in Iquitos is a palm heart canning operation, Conserveras Amazonicas, SA (CAMSA). The plant processes and cans the heart of the naturally-occurring husasaí palm (*Euterpe precatoria*) for export to Canada, Argentina, Venezuela, and Colombia. The palm hearts are brought occasionally to the factory by individual collectors, but more frequently by contractors who travel the Napo, Ampiyacu, Apayacu, and Amazon Rivers buying the product from villagers. The factory is now operating well below its capacity, and the managers complain of considerable variation in the availability of their raw material. Plans are now being made to solve some of those problems by attempting to plant the palm in plantations.

There is some furniture manufacture in Iquitos, although at present it is conducted on a small scale with little, if any, production for export. Forest products in the form of special woods as well as fibres used for caning and tying are purchased by manufacturers from collectors. Fibres used include: tamshi (*Heteropsis jenmanii, Carludovica divergens*), bombonaje (*Carludovica palmata*), and; baras-casha or cashabara (*Desmoncus prunifer*). A small manufacturer and former exporter of furniture in Iquitos placed the blame for the relative underdevelopment of the industry on the lack of skilled and diligent manpower and on the difficulty of reducing the moisture content of woods to acceptable North American standards.

The tourist industry in Iquitos provides some outlet for handicraft items made in the area. Largely, though not exclusively, dealing with native-made crafts are several shops in Iquitos, including one operated by a government agency. Some export of items directly to importers of handicrafts in the United States and western Europe also figures in the forest products trade. Baskets made of various forest fibres, hammocks and bags of chambira palm fibre, wooden carvings, carved and feather-adorned bows, spears, and arrows are among the many forest-derived products. Animal products such as skulls, bones, teeth, claws, and plumes are also important craft items offered for sale. A few specialists in taxidermy and the preparation of other animal and plant handicraft reside in Iquitos, but much of the material sold is produced by village farmers who supplement their incomes with craft making.

Also of some importance is the trade in medicinal plants. We have already mentioned substances such as ojé and curare that at various times enjoyed a major export market. There is, as well, a significant local and national trade in medicinal products, which are sold in the markets and in specialized shops. Many of the medicinals are sold in somewhat processed form, such as infusions in alcohol, which are bottled and then are sold in various retail stores throughout the city of Iquitos.

Many economic botanists and other researchers have stressed that the potential for export of medicinals from Amazonia is much greater than is now realized.

It should also be noted that trade in coca leaves, cocaine base (pasta basica), and cocaine is of considerable importance in the Iquitos area. Other than noting its significance, we have not examined this trade.

Conclusions

The sub-project on the economic importance and marketing of forest and fallow products had as its goal the addition of an economic component to the essentially ethnographic and ecological studies carried out by the other sub-projects. As the ultimate purpose of the entire project was to make environmentally, socially, and economically sound recommendations for the development of agroforestry systems in the Peruvian Amazon, the collection of data on the present and potential economic role of forest and fallow products was essential. Although scheduling problems prevented data collection over a year-long period and in a large number of locations, as had been originally planned, a substantial amount of valuable information was collected in the course of two research periods. These data, presented briefly above, point to the following general conclusions:

1. Historically the extraction and export of minor forest products, as well as products grown in some swidden fallows, have been important in the Peruvian Amazon. While a number of extractive activities produced economic booms in the region, these tended to be short-lived. Much of this activity in the past was characterized by destructive harvesting practices, exploitation of local collectors, export of materials in raw form, and little local permanent development.

2. The forest and fallow products that were and still are extracted or produced in the Iquitos region are varied and often occur in substantial quantity. Many of the fruits, fibres, and other products found in Bora and other swidden fallows have a potential for greater market development.

3. Although agriculture, largely of annual crops, has replaced forest extraction as the most important economic activity in the region, the contribution of plant and animal products from the forest and fallow fields of the area continues to add significantly to the regional economy. The precise value of forest extraction was impossible to measure as data of a regional nature are collected in an incomplete and inconsistent fashion.

4. Many of the rural households of the region depend on the produce of the forests and their agroforestry plots for 50 per cent or more of their annual monetary income. Virtually all village residents depend at least seasonally for part of their household budget on these products. As illustrated in examples such as Tamshiyacu, more intensive cultivation of agroforestry plots can yield incomes surpassing those gained by annual crop cultivation, with minimal need for outside material inputs and with low labour requirements.

5. In the region, both communities and individual households within such communities vary greatly in their dependence on forest and fallow products for income and on the types of products they market.

There is no 'typical' village, household, or marketing pattern. Some generalizations can be made concerning a positive correlation between the importance of marketing of forest and fallow products and proximity to Iquitos. However, the factors that account for the observed variation in economic patterns are many and complex.

6. The cost and seasonal transportation problems of bringing produce to the market in Iquitos is a major constraint on marketing activities for all but residents of the nearest villages. Outlying villages such as Brillo Nuevo have very poor and seasonally highly unreliable transportation facilities. These constitute important constraints on the types and quantities of products that can be marketed.

7. Markets and other commercial activities of the region are almost totally centralized in Iquitos. Other regional markets are poorly developed and provide little outlet for forest and fallow products. Travelling traders or regatones often provide the only market links for residents of remote villages.

8. Most commercial transactions involve one or more intermediaries. The economic dealings of these middlemen both in and outside the markets of Iquitos are strongly criticized by producers, virtually all of whom feel exploited by traders. While it is certain that some intermediaries make exorbitant profits in their transaction at the expense of underpaid producers, the elimination of middlemen as a group is neither possible nor advisable. Long distance traders do provide an essential service in remote areas, and the majority of rematistas who operate in the ports and markets of Iquitos hardly make an adequate living. The present economic crisis in Peru, which has resulted in increased unemployment and loss of buying power, has literally forced many town dwellers to engage in at least part-time trading. While some control and change of the marketing situation is desired by many, viable alternatives for isolated communities and for those now engaged in market trade are still lacking.

9. Marketing of many forest and fallow products, especially fruits, is highly seasonal and prices received for these products vary greatly throughout the year. Many producers are at a disadvantage in dealing with merchants since they often do not have access to accurate market information.

10. The processing and export of forest and fallow products out of the area is now done on a very limited scale. Only two companies are involved in the export of any significant quantities of local products. Both of these companies are operating below their capacity and express interest in expanding and diversifying their operations. No processing of important fallow products such as fruits is now being done on a commercial scale.

Acknowledgments

During the first period of field research in June 1982, data were gathered by Christine Padoch and agronomist Douglas Pool (consultant from Puerto Rico), with aid from Alberto Bashanashi (UNAP) and Augusto Vargas (UNAP). The second period of field research, in July and August 1983, was carried out by Christine Padoch with the assistance of ecologist Jon Unruh (University of Wisconsin) and forester Jomber Chota Inuma (UNAP). Throughout both periods we received valuable help and advice from Salvador Flores Paitán, as well as from other staff members of UNAP. We also wish to acknowledge the assistance of the staff at the Iquitos offices of the Ministerio de Agricultura, the Corporación de Desarrollo de Loreto (CORDELOR), Astoria Peruana SA, and Conserveras Amazonicas SA; several scientists at the Universidad Nacional Agraria at La Molina in Lima; and numerous residents of Iquitos and the various villages where we conducted our research.

References

CORDELOR (1985). *Estadisticas Para Planification en el Departmento de Loreto, 1980-84.* Corporación de Desarrollo de Loreto (CORDELOR), Iquitos

IPA (1974). *Estudios Socio-económicos de los Rios Amazonas y Napo.* Two volumes, Investigación y Promoción de la Amazonia (IPA), Iquitos

Ministerio de Agricultura (1980). *Anuario de Estadista Forestal y de Fauna Silvestre.* Lima, Peru

Novoa Miranda, W A (1970). *Estudios de Flujo de Productos Agricolas Llegados por via Fluvial al Mercado de Iquitos.* Thesis, Universidad Nacional de la Amazonia Peruana, Iquitos

ORDELORETO (1980). *Ordeloreto: Memoria del Desarrollo.* Organismo Regional de Desarrollo de Loreto (ORDELORETO), Proceso, Lima

ORDELORETO (1981). *Información sobre Indicatores de Población de Loreto, 1981 (e) Indice de Precios de la Ciudad de Iquitos.* Oficina Regional de Planificación, Oficina de Estadistica, Iquitos

ORDEORIENTE (1971). *Política de Desarrollo de la Región Oriente.* Organismo Regional de Desarrollo del Oriente (ORDEORIENTE), Instituto Regional de Planificación, Iquitos

Schery R W (1949). Problems associated with the procurement of plant products from the American tropics. *Economic Botany* 3: 413-427

Villarejo, A (1979). *Así es la Selva.* CETA, Iquitos

Watson Cisneros E (1964). *Comercio y Tendencias del Mercado en los Productos de la Región de la Selva Peruana.* Universidad Agraria, Lima

Wille, J E, J Alcides Ocampo, A Weberbauer and D Schofield (1939). *El Cube (Lonchocarpus utilis) y Otros Barbascos en el Peru.* Ministerio de Fomento, Dirección de Agricultura y Ganadería, Boletín No 16, Lima

Williams, L (1962a). Laticiferous plants of economic importance, I: Sources of balata, chicle guttapercha and allied guttas. Economic *Botany* 16:17-24

Williams, L (1962b). Laticiferous plants of economic importance, III: *Couma* species. *Economic Botany* 16 251-263

Discussion

Panel
Dr Brian Boom, Dr Kent Redford, Yance de Fretes, Xie Jiwu, Julia Falconer

Oliver Tickell, Tambopata Reserve Society/ Oxford Friends of the Earth. I would like to thank Dr Kent Redford for his excellent presentation. I suggest that there is an alternative - the specific farming or ranching of wild animals in the rainforest. I know this has been tried with iguanas with great success and I believe also with armadillos and peccaries in certain parts of the world.

Dr Kent Redford. I do not think these ideas have a place in the overall scenario and I adopt what has been an unpopular point of view on this issue. The jury is still out on all of the projects you mentioned. The last peccary domestication project was tried with the Lacandon Indians in southern Mexico. They were doing reasonably well with reproduction, though sales were limited, until the time came for a traditional Lacandon fiesta, when, requiring a lot of meat, every animal was slaughtered and eaten. Calculations have been done on the domestication of paca on Barro Colorado Island which suggested that it would cost approximately $6 to $7 a kilo to produce these animals.

The iguana project is perhaps the best option, although interestingly iguanas are not a favourite game, nor a favourite meat in the areas I am familiar with outside of Central America. There has been an enormous amount of time and effort put into the green iguana project and perhaps it might work.

My own feeling is that farming of wild animals has no place in the future, but the ranching of game animals has. I distinguish between farming and ranching in the sense that farming involves control of reproduction and extensive involvement and manipulation of ecosystems to produce the organism you wish. Ranching means limited involvement and no control over reproduction. I do not think this is possible in the rainforest, but would be in much simpler ecosystems such as the Llanos grasslands and the Pantanal.

Dr Jonathan Okafor, Formerly of the Forestry Research Institute, Nigeria. My comment is on the paper by Brian Boom. I have two questions, one dealing with methodologies, the other on conservation implications. When you accounted for the trees that have been harvested in Bolivia and you showed the packs being used to identify the trees, I wondered whether, as part of the information gathering, you included shrubs and herbs. Secondly, I wondered how you ensured that the interviews you had with the local people gave you useful and relevant information, because obviously it would vary according to the age and experience of the interviewees.

Regarding the implications for conservation, in Nigeria we found that the collection of bush mango by local people can be considered to pose a considerable threat to the survival of certain trees because the people, camping in the bush, collect the fruit as they fall, and cut them open which reduces natural regeneration. I was wondering whether for Bolivia Dr Boom could give us some examples of similar kinds of harvesting which poses a threat to the conservation or natural survival of certain plants. One must also remember that the use of some plants for medicinal purposes usually involves debarking or the breaking of the plant to get to the roots.

Dr Brian Boom. First of all, the data I presented were just on trees. However I collected everything, lianes, shrubs, herbs, epiphytes and parasites though these were not so easily tabulated. In fact, the majority of the medicinals were not trees, they were in fact herbs or lianes. If we include all these, the percentage of things used was much higher than I presented. I do not have data per unit area.

To answer your question on interviewing, it is very important how the interview is conducted. The principle guiding factor I used was not to ask leading questions. Any tree might be said to be used as fuelwood if really pressed on the matter and obviously they all burn to a greater or lesser extent. So when recording fuelwood, I only did so when the subject suggested and said, for example, "yes, this burns with a dense, acrid smoke which we use in smoking rubber".

Obviously the interviewing process will vary according to the level of knowledge of the informant, his or her interest in talking to me and my interpretation of what he or she says. It is fraught with problems, but overall, and over time, once you establish a rapport with the people you are working with, then the more reliable kinds of results come in; and obviously the goal is to get as reliable information as possible.

On the conservation aspect, my limited experience in Bolivia was with two kinds of harvested product - nuts and rubber - and in both instances, the Chácobo Indians had minimal access to the market and consequently there was no problem of over-exploitation. However, the people did complain about the lack of suitable rubber trees to tap in their area. In the early 1960s, the Summer Institute of Linguistics arranged for the declaration of 43,000 hectares of land for the Chácobo Indians, and the Bolivian government set aside this area for the Chácobo. However, by delimiting this area they started to run out of resources; they have now over-fished and over-hunted the area and cannot find enough rubber trees to tap. Now, they are over-exploiting resources because their natural range had been restricted when previously they were used to being semi-nomadic and moving around to find game and rubber trees. Brazil nuts are not over-exploited because they are sparsely distributed and they do not find that many.

George Monbiot, Journalist. I am writing a book on certain developments in the Amazon basin. Dr Redford, you have revealed to us that game commercialization is not sustainable, and we already know that cattle ranching in the Amazon certainly is not. But as you know there is a very large urban population in the Amazon which is growing very rapidly. Could you suggest a useful sustainable protein source from which this population could survive?

Perhaps I can give you an opinion, although it is not one I necessarily agree with. Fish have been exhausted in many areas of the Amazon through ruthless over-exploitation, where the people say that for every boat load of fish that comes into the major markets, two boat loads are dumped overboard. If they find a more valuable commercial fish they simply throw out what they have already caught. So, combined with mercury contamination, siltation from cattle ranching and deforestation, the fish fauna have been severely disrupted. There is an adequate array of domestic animals and if I were in the business, I would intensify the production of domestic meat. There are people who want to domesticate iguanas and currasows, for example. In an recent article written by Louise Emmons, she calculates that a pair of currasows would produce two to three eggs a year and a chicken will produce 250. Now I ask you, what kind of sense does it make to devote your time to domesticating currasows in a circumstance like that?

Chair: Dr John Hemming. Perhaps I can come in here. If you read Orellana's descent of the Amazon in 1542, you find that turtles were farmed on an enormous scale. The Spanish conquistadors plundered vast numbers of turtles outside every Indian village. At breeding times the Indians simply let the turtles go out, lay their eggs and then as the young turtles hatched they drilled a little hole in the shell and towed them all back to the pens outside the village. It should not be beyond the intelligence of modern man to revive turtle-farming. In the eighteenth century the Jesuits would only allow half of each sandbank of the turtle laying sands to be exploited; the other half being left for reproduction. But as we have heard in one of the papers, literally millions of turtle eggs were destroyed, mostly to light the lamps of Manaus in the nineteenth century. However, I do think this provides a possible potential resource.

Don Dennis, Green Woodturners' Group and Milland Fine Timber, agents for the Ecological Trading Company. My question is for Dr Redford. I much appreciated your comments on bushmeat which, personally, gave me some comfort in the overall picture. I was rather horrified at the notion of commercial exploitation of rainforest animals. On the other hand, I am concerned with what you said about the impact of Brazil nut harvesting and other items of extraction which reveals a rather bleak prospect for any positive, protective, and sustainable operations in the rainforest. If that is your view, then do we just sit back and let destructive, commercial forces - that are already in operation - continue or do we hope that governments create national parks? Do you see any prospects for truly positive, sustainable commercial projects that can give value to the rainforest and to rainforest harvests which is what this Conference is concerned with?

Dr Kent Redford. Yes I do. I think you need to disassociate the presumption that biodiversity conservation can go hand in hand with extractive reserves and instead remarry extractive reserves with ecosystem services. This is a concept that the World Bank is so fond of and, which means amongst other things, one tree does much the same thing as another tree in terms of fixing carbon, decreasing siltation, erosion and so on. I think that when you have humans operating in an area, certain plant and animal species will not survive.

Now I think the forest will survive but biodiversity, by

definition, will not because people living in extractive reserves kill animals in order to eat. But I do not think we are in a position to tell them that they cannot do this. Instead, I believe you should set aside separate areas of land specifically for those animal and plant species which will not survive in extractive reserves; and the reserves themselves will perform an enormously important service for the 99 per cent of the fauna that is probably not severely effected by extractive activities.

Julia Aglionby, Oxford student. I would like to ask Yance de Fretes if he sees the Indonesian government changing their attitude towards community plantations and moving away from using forestry and non-wood products as cash crops. Furthermore, do you think that the consumers of cash crops, such as in Japan and Europe, can do anything to encourage a change in the Government's attitude?

Yance de Fretes. Right now one of the aims of the Forestry Department is to try and get the people involved in forest management - in other words, trying to implement a social forestry programme. It is an encouraging sign although it is still in its conception stage and not yet operational in the field.

In some plantations in Java, for example, they allow the farmers to plant crops on state land which they then harvest for themselves. At the same time they also have to plant teak for the company. This does have its problems, however. The farmers are under contract for two years and the crops bear fruit only every seven years. Contract renewal is not guaranteed and the farmers may well lose their harvest, so, work still needs to be done on this. I think the biggest problem is that forestry instructors and the programmes they are working with lack concern for the people working on the land.

Indian Reserves: A Feasible Alternative for the Conservation and Proper Use of the Colombian Amazon Forest

Thomas Walschburger, Patricio von Hildebrand,
Fundacion Puerto Rastrojo, AA 241438 Bogotá, Colombia

Summary

Nearly 50 per cent of Colombia's Amazon forests have been designated as 'Indian resguardos'. The plan to hand over vast areas of the forest is relatively new and long-term success depends on the implementation of certain strategies. However, the Indians' uses of the forests represent various restrictions when faced with the dynamics and philosophies of a capitalist market economy which would stand at odds with the cultural structure of many Amazonian tribes. When handing over the responsibility of maintaining and keeping their ancestral territories to the Indian communities, Western civilization must also assume a responsibility for making this alternative feasible and successful.

The Colombian Amazon forests cover around 38 million hectares, of which 18 million are under the 'Indian resguardos' category and 5.7 million are national parks and natural reserves. The remainder of this jungle area is legally considered 'forest reservation', but areas of this territory can be subtracted for colonization purposes. This means that for 50 per cent of the Amazon region, there exists a shared responsibility between the Colombian State and the Indian communities in order to ensure its proper and adequate use.

The present Government has expressed, on one hand, a clear conservationist policy, especially on the eastern part of the Colombian Amazon area (Colombia, Government of, 1990), but, on the other hand, in the colonization fronts along the foothills of the eastern cordillera of the Andes and the Guaviare River (high biodiversity areas) there are contradictory policies. However, we can now observe a transition within different governmental institutions regarding the forests and their potential use which are now trying to improve levels of co-ordination among them. The inadequate agricultural techniques that have been promoted in the area have not been able to stabilize the colonization fronts, generating a continuous migration of colonizers from the recently degraded areas to new forest frontiers. This model of unstable occupation of jungle lands has produced a generalized social and economic disorder in which coca fields, guerrilla movements and 'narcotrafficers' prosper.

Once used and degraded, these frontier areas do not have, at present, the potential for quick socioeconomic and environmental stabilization because of a lack of proper technologies and the lack of a determined, clear government decision to discontinue the advance of colonization, and subject the areas to firm governmental action. The national parks and natural reserves have been legally declared but no resources are available to transform them into truely protected areas, within a wide territorial ordination plan and a sustainable management policy for their proper use and protection. The majority of these parks have the advantage of not being directly threatened by colonization and can remain temporarily unprotected. However, parks such as the Marcarena, Tinigua, Picachos and la Paya (totalling around 1 million hectares) are seriously threatened.

Finally, the relatively new plan to hand over the responsibility for the conservation of vast areas of Amazon forest to the native Indians is, at first glance, encouraging (see paper by Martin von Hildebrand, this volume), but the long-term possibility of success depends on the implementation of certain strategies.

Various premises, which seem valid *a priori*, support this strategy to save the forests:

- the Indian communities have managed and used the jungle properly over several millennia;

- the Indian communities have the knowledge of the biotic elements that form the ecosystems, and know the dynamics and regenerative processes therein (Fundacion Puerto Rastrojo, 1987);

- within their cosmological and cultural conception they have assimilated their knowledge of the natural environment which is expressed in different myths, rituals, shamanist management and oral tradition (von Hildebrand, 1987);

- the shaman acts as a regulator of energy withdrawn from the natural environment by Indian communities so that the ecosystems are able to regenerate themselves (von Hildebrand, 1983);

- the use of resources is based on the ecological diversity of ecosystems, which means that the subsistence activities are equally diverse in time and space. This strategy allows biological processes to be maintained in the long-term (Walschburger and von Hildebrand, 1988);

- subsistence is obtained by means of intensive use of culturally transformed spaces, such as the home-gardens and cultivation areas which, when they become weak, are abandoned to regeneration. On the other hand there is an extensive use of wild spaces for collecting resources, such as animals, fish and different forest products (Walschburger and von Hildebrand, 1988).

However, the Indian models of the use for the forests represent various restrictions when faced by a capitalist market economy:

- they function best at low human densities;

- there is no possibility of maximization, nor massive marketing of resources, in order to participate with an advantage in the market economy;

- the areas in question have very few infrastructural services, which makes the access to markets difficult;

- several forest products are seasonal, which does not allow sustained production throughout the year.

A diversified use of resources may be elaborated, which would call for permanent variations in the commercialization mechanisms over time;

■ the Indian culture regulates the intensity of the use of forest products. The commercialization of surplus products brings a contradiction with the traditional use of the environment. The dynamics and philosophy of the market economy would stand at conflict with the cultural structure of the majority of the Amazonian tribes and would necessarily generate an irreversible cultural transformation. The Amazonian cultures are highly dynamic, with a strong capacity for assimilation and acquisition of new values, but the forces of a market economy bring along their own dynamics which deny and subdue all independent or autonomous cultural expression. An Indian shaman cannot simply define new negotiation terms with the 'owners of the animals and plants', who are the natural distributors of 'crop quotas' for the Indian communities. If these quotas are not adhered to, the Cosmos will begin to show disorders, and illness and death will creep into the communities. These are the mechanisms which the owners of the natural wild energy employ to recover the excess energy accumulated in the human communities.

When handing over the responsibility of maintaining and keeping their ancestral territories to the Indian communities, the Western civilization must also assume a responsibility for making this alternative feasible and successful.

We all know that the Indian can become the worst predator of natural resources if he loses the constraints of his traditional culture. At this moment, most of the Indian cultures find themselves faced with the dilemma of how to deal with the Western culture. Contact with this culture has mostly been chaotic and deadly. During the past, they have been enslaved and indebted for the exploitation of rubber, furs and gold. They have been denied the value of their own cultures; this denial is still reflected, for example, in the fact that education and health, which is brought to them, correspond to a Western logic. And even though the Colombian government has established laws that allow the Indians to participate in the definition of their own education and health programmes, the mechanisms to reach them have yet to be found. The same government officers find themselves often unable, or simply too arrogant, to enter into open dialogue with the communities.

The list of created material 'necessities' has grown continuously during the present century in the Indian communities. The answer, in order to obtain the necessities, has been the establishment of a relationship of dependence with merchants who buy the Indian products at ridiculously low prices and sell commodities at high prices so as to maintain permanent debts and access to products. The Indians have to agree since no other alternatives exist.

This somewhat sombre view does not imply that it is already too late for us to act. Numerous Indian groups are making great efforts to break up this situation. They are aware that solutions do not appear by themselves, nor by waiting passively for the Government to act, but that solutions lie in their own traditional cultural background.

For example, in the lower Caqueta River in the Colombian Amazon region an intense phenomenon of cultural recuperation is taking place. They are conscious that they cannot totally isolate themselves from all Western pressures, but if they can understand how the Western world functions, they can fight to enforce the legal space granted to them by the State. And at the same time, they are finding ways to harmonize Western education and health programmes with their traditions (FBPR, 1989).

Work is being done in order to find new economic alternatives that highlight the biological diversity of the jungle as well as domesticated varieties, in a strategy that diversifies the use, in both time and space. The intensity of use should not become contradictory with traditional culture and must lend itself to the natural processes of regeneration of ecosystems (FBPR, 1990).

The responsibility and commitment that we must accept is to recognize and give support to these efforts.

We should assume the following actions and/or responsibilities:

■ the ability of the Indian communities to face their own destiny and to manage the Amazon jungle properly should be accepted;

■ internal processes should not be imposed, nor 'solutions', handed over, to avoid proselytizing to religious or ideological beliefs that are different from the Indians' own traditions. Relationships have to be established, on an equal basis of exchange, that reinforce traditional forms of organization and do not promote alien decision-making instances within communities;

■ political fora must be opened up to allow the Indian communities to participate in and contribute to the decision-making processes that directly affect them;

■ it should be recognized that these communities are lending a service to all mankind by the conservation of large areas of Amazonian jungle. This service should be paid, for example, with a compensation (subsidies) for the products that would be extracted from the forests. Why push them into a market economy?

■ if the West utilizes biological resources, either domesticated or wild, it should acknowledge the Indian communities' intellectual rights over technologies and use of resources, and give them compensatory services;

■ recognition should be given to the Indian communities for the ecological debt that we have acquired with them as a result of their proper up-keep of the Amazon jungles over the last millennia;

■ we should accept that the rationale of capitalism stands in clear contradiction with Indian traditional forms of forest use. There is still no way to harmonize these two interpretations of how the world works. Both cultures have to make strong efforts to succeed in the intention to save Amazon forests and to respect each other.

Ecosystems and cultural systems

Finally, it is important not to forget that we are dealing with ecosystems and cultural systems. Every component is essential to the dynamics of the system. There is a great danger from extraction of products from the forest if we are not aware of the impact we are causing on the equilibrium of ecosystems.

Amazon ecosystems are poor in nutrients. If we extract tonnes of biomass, for example fruits, the system loses nutrients which are very difficult to regain.

The fruits or other products to be harvested are, to be sure, also a food supply for many animal populations of the forest. For example, different fish feed on fruits during several periods of the year. If fruit supply is lowered the fish populations will also decrease. With high levels of extraction we disturb the whole nutrient balance of forests.

Amazon Indian cultures strongly regulate the energy withdrawn from the ecosystems. The harvest of products can be managed if it occurs at low levels. Most Indian cultures have been exposed to occidental culture and the needs for different material goods are growing continuously. They are pushed towards the created need of rapidly increasing their income capacity through new commercial products from the forest, traditional leaders and shamans will not be able to hamper an increasing consumerist process and the whole organization of the community will be endangered. So, both ecosystems and cultural systems, which once co-existed in harmonic articulation, will lose their internal regulation capacity and the future task of conservation of the Amazon's forests will be immense.

References

Government of Colombia (1990). *Policy of the National Government in Defense of Indigenous Rights and in the Ecological Conservation of the Amazon.* Republic of Colombia

Fundación Puerto Rastrojo (1987). *Participación Indígena en el Desarrollo del Amazonas. Elementos Para Definir un Modelo Económico Local.* Fundacion Puerto Rastrojo, Bogotá

von Hildebrand, M (1987). An Amazonian tribe's view of cosmology. In P Bunyard and E Goldsmith (eds), *Gaia, The Mechanisms and the Implications.* Quintrell and Company Limited, Cornwall

von Hildebrand, M (1983). Cosmovisión y el concepto de enfermedad entre los Ufaina. En, *Medicina, Shamanismo y Botanica.* Funcol, Editorial Presencia, Bogotá

Walschburger, T and P von Hildebrand (1988). Observaciónes sobre la utilización estacional del bosque húmedo tropical por los indígenas del río Miriti. *Colombia Amazónica.* Volume 3, No 1, Bogotá

FBPR (1989). *Memorias de la Primera Reunión de Capitanes y Líderes Indígenas de los Resguardos de Miriti, Yaigoje, Puerto Cordoba y Comeyafú.* FBPR, Bogotá

FBPR (1990). *Sustainable Use and Cultural Flourishing in the Lower Caqueta River Region, Amazonas, Colombia.* (In preperation), FBPR, Bogotá

Social Movements and Natural Resource Conservation in the Brazilian Amazon

Dr Stephen Schwartzman
Environmental Defense Fund, Washington DC, USA

Summary

This paper is about the creation of extractive reserves and the legal mechanisms devised by the National Rubber Tappers' Council (CNS), the Institute for Amazon Studies (IEA) and their supporters within government agencies, and the implications of these mechanisms. Also, it discusses the similarities and overlap of the groups involved in this initiative with other organizations in Brazil that are concerned with the course of development. Finally, some concluding comments are made on the importance of the social basis of extractive reserves for investment and marketing strategies as a means of protecting tropical forests.

Introduction

The recent discussions concerning the economic potential of extractive economies are important, but not because they are more profitable than cattle ranches or colonization projects (although they are in many instances, as much recent research has shown). The reason that 7.5 million acres of extractive reserves exist in Brazilian Amazonia today is due to an organized social movement in the Amazon that invented them as a strategy to deal with immediate, pressing social problems (deforestation, expulsion of local communities, assassinations, working conditions similar to slave labour). This was followed up with the creation of these reserves through the formation of alliances with various groups in Brazil, and internationally. An apparently archaic form of land occupation, the rubber estate or *seringal* was developed by the National Rubber Tappers' Council (CNS) and the Institute for Amazon Studies (IEA) into a new way of legally occupying land in the Amazon - the extractive reserve.

The evolution of extractive reserves in the Brazilian Amazon

The opening of the Amazonian frontier has played an important part in Brazil's immense economic growth over the last thirty years. The Amazon has figured as a safety valve for the poor and landless that have been displaced from other parts of country, but government policy has also ensured investments of billions of dollars in subsidies to large landholders. Landholding relations have been totally transformed; areas of largely public land, or those held under traditional peasant or Indian systems of land tenure, have become private and a huge land boom has taken place. This has resulted in deforestation of around 12 per cent since 1970, and also a concentration of landholdings in fewer and fewer hands. 15 of the largest 18 landholdings in Brazil are in the Amazon and total an area equal to Austria. Increasingly, land cleared by colonists is subsumed into large cattle ranches as smallholders fail and sell out, or are forced off. Concentration of landholdings has engendered intense rural violence; since 1980 there have been 1000 assassinations during rural violence in Brazil, of which almost one half occurred in Amazonia, an area with only 10 per cent of the country's population.

The rubber tappers' movement began in Acre in the mid 1970s as a spontaneous resistance to this process. This was channelled into the Sindicato dos Trabalhadores Rurais (STR - Rural Workers' Union) which, from the outset, included colonists as well as rubber tappers. The colonist farmers' major concern was pressuring state agencies to deliver services promised, namely; credit, local transportation and infrastructure, health and education.

By 1985, unions in Acre had made substantive advances. They had forced expropriations of some areas by the Land Agency (the National Institute for Colonization and Agrarian Reform, INCRA). They stopped deforestation in many instances, but they recognized that many of the processes that they were confronting were not caused at the local level. Federal government policy was important, and also new actors were appearing - the World Bank and Inter-American Development Bank (IDB) - whose large-scale infrastructural projects were speeding migration and exacerbating land concentration and conflicts.

In 1985, the STR, from Acre, took the step of organizing a national conference of rubber tappers, out of which came the CNS and the proposal for creation of extractive reserves. The CNS established two kinds of alliance to move this proposal forward: with national Brazilian groups, for the technical assistance and support required to find means to create reserves, and with international groups to pressure the multilateral development banks into halting destructive development programmes and opening the decision making process to the concerns of the people affected by their projects.

By 1987, the CNS and IEA had designed, with a working group from INCRA, the first legal form for creating extractive reserves; the Projeto de Assentamento Estrativista - Extractive Settlement Project (PAE), and both the IDB and the World Bank had endorsed the concept.

The PAE was an important innovation in land law. It was the first time that the Land Agency recognized not only socioeconomic but also environmental criteria as grounds for action. In PAEs, the Government is the owner of the land, but a local community, association or co-operative contracts to hold long-term rights of use. Deforestation is prohibited, except as required for subsistence agriculture, and so is the sale or transfer of use rights. When PAEs are created, INCRA delimits a single continuous area rather than dividing up the land into individual lots. The rubber tappers already had some experience of division into individual lots after INCRA had carried out its mandate and expropriated areas in conflict. Such division was not viable; the seringal or rubber estate is a social and economic unit where both individual family and collective rights and obligations play a part in resource management. The great advance of the PAE, however, was to allow the Land Agency to take the land out of the speculative land market and turn it over to local groups to manage collectively.

This model was based on the experience of autonomous rubber tappers. Those that had already escaped the debt peonage in which many if not most extractive communities live in the Amazon (where all commerce is controlled by a patron or middleman, and rubber tappers go further into debt the harder they work). The autonomous rubber tappers, like Chico Mendes and the unionized rubber tappers of the Acre River valley, had been the impetus behind creating the CNS. The premise supported by rubber tappers from other areas, where debt peonage still reigns, however, is that debt peonage, being a social relationship, can be changed by social action.

The situation in the Upper Juruá extractive reserve is a good example. Until about 3 years ago, rubber tappers in this area were completely subject to brutal exploitation by rubber baron patrons. They claimed ownership of the land and exacted rent payments from the tappers on the trails of rubber trees as well as maintaining a system of labour relations characterized recently by the Federal Prosecutor's Office as 'analagous to slavery'. The CNS sent one organizer, Antonio Macedo, and an advisor, Mauro Almeida, to work in the area. They discovered local leaders who had worked in isolation for years and established contact and a CNS presence among them. The result was that, in 1988, the CNS established a co-operative that broke the patrons' stranglehold on the trade, the rubber tappers stopped paying rent, and the population mobilized behind the proposal of creating an extractive reserve. In January 1989, an extractive reserve was created covering 500,000 hectares, and protecting key upper watersheds of the Juruá River, a major affluent of the Amazon.

This suggests that with minimal support, extractive reserves can work in areas of so-called traditional extractive production, and as an organizing strategy can work to transform anachronistic, semi-slave working conditions. Of the 25 local commissions of the CNS, at least 14 represent areas of traditional extraction, areas that have more in common with the Upper Juruá than the Acre River valley.

Also, in January 1990, a new mechanism for establishing reserves was created. A decree, drafted by a working group in IBAMA - the Instituto Brasileiro de Meio Ambiente (Brazilian Environmental Institute), including the CNS and IEA - was signed by the then President Sarney creating the figure of the extractive reserve. The new figure maintains the basic character of the PAE, but is stronger and its first application in the Upper Juruá contained an historic innovation. Once the extractive reserve was declared, those claiming property rights within it were obliged to present legal documentation of valid land title to the Federal Prosecutor's Office, which determined the legitimate claims in the region. This reversed the burden of proof of legal occupation of land that has prevailed in the Amazon for the last 25 years, where the presumption has always been on the side of the title holders, no matter how dubious their claims. It also removed the decision on this issue from local offices of INCRA - notoriously subject to pressure and manipulation by local elites - and placed it with an extremely capable and professional federal agency.

Patrons in the Upper Juruá presented dozens of claims to almost the entire 500,000 hectares of the reserve. Four titles, covering a small portion of the reserve, were judged valid. Three other extractive reserves were created under the new law in March. The four new reserves total over 2 million hectares, including some of the most biologically diverse areas of the Brazilian Amazon as well as areas that have been in conflict for the last 15 years, notably the Chico Mendes extractive reserve in the Acre River valley.

Extractive reserves in a wider social context

Extractive reserves are not a panacea for environmental and social problems in the Amazon. They do, as an organizing strategy, have a great deal in common with the concerns of other constituencies in the Amazon and in Brazil - colonists, landless peasants, Indians, riverine communities and populations displaced by dams (Almeida, 1989). Some researchers have suggested that extractive reserves may be socially inequitable in that they typically allocate more land per family than do colonization projects. This overlooks the fact that the consolidation of large landholdings, particularly for cattle ranching, has not only displaced rubber tappers, but relied on the failure of agricultural colonization for the labour force to open and expand pasture lands (Partridge, 1989). The creation of extractive reserves does not imply 'extractive fortresses' and the need to send colonists back on the next bus, nor could it.

First of all, many of the members of the unions out of which grew the CNS (and with which their membership is still largely coterminous) are small farmers and colonists. This is so in the reserves in the Acre River valley, and especially in Amapá, where many of the communities are small farmers who are interested in re-introducing the extraction of Brazil nuts and other products as a means of increasing very low incomes.

Affiliates of the CNS in Pará include members of rural workers' unions of small farmers, some of whom are also Brazil nut gatherers. Unions and union-based organizations in the south of Pará have founded agricultural co-operatives as well as sustainable agriculture research projects for smallholder colonists seeking to improve incomes through a mix of annual crops, perennials, and Brazil nut extraction. These include the Agriculture Centre of the Tocantins, and the Centre for Research and Union and Popular Support (CEPASP).

There is also some evidence that government land titling programmes for colonists in some parts of the Amazon have speeded migration and land concentration through disruption of peasant common property resource management practices (common forest reserves, water sources and fallow systems). In particular, this is shown by Alfredo Wagner de Almeida's work on colonist communities in Pará (Almeida, 1989). For such groups, forms of landholding that allow for common property resource management may be an important part of a sustainable solution.

Rural workers' unions, made up largely of small farmers, the landless and colonists, share fundamental concerns with the CNS. Various researchers have noted that any long-term answer to deforestation requires more research and extension work, seeking viable smallholder farming systems for at least the colonists already in the Amazon. This, however, will not happen in a social and political vacuum. The literature amply recognizes the inefficiency, inaccessibility and outright corruption of the government agencies charged with providing services to smallholders on the frontier. If small farmers are to get the credit, local infrastructure, research and extension work that they need from the patronage-ridden state agencies they depend on, public pressure from vocal and organized local constituencies will be of considerable importance.

A good example is shown by the consequences of pressure that the CNS has brought to bear on state and federal agencies to open their decision-making process, and act to fulfil their legal mandates. Acre now has a state environmental institute, which has a licensing procedure for deforestation, requiring environmental impact statements, and which fines illegal deforestation. This month, for the first time anywhere in the Amazon, there was a public hearing on an environmental impact statement filed by a cattle ranch. This is a credit to the capable public servants who have pushed these innovations in state agencies; but they would not have had the opportunity to do this without the public demand created by the CNS.

Producers' associations, agricultural co-operatives and rural workers' unions all have a common interest with the CNS in the accountability of public agencies. This is clear in recent communications from local colonist groups in Rondônia, as well as rubber tappers, to the World Bank. All these constituencies have expressed the same concern that a new project, under consideration by the World Bank, to support environmental and agricultural zoning in the State will not work unless the project includes greater participation of, and consultation with, local people. Without greater public accountability of the state agencies, money may never get to where it is supposed to.

Conclusion

In conclusion, I want to make two points. First, in seeking to expand the extractive reserve concept outside the Brazilian Amazon, equally important to finding products that are, or can be, sustainably produced is identifying local social movements or organized constituencies with an interest in sustainable management of tropical forest. Second, for private sector marketing strategies, which I think are exceptionally important, there are few, if any, products that are naturally and inevitably sustainably produced. Dealing with organized local groups that are seeking to maintain and modernize sustainable uses of tropical forest is the best means to ensure that the product in question is really green. Beyond this, halting the concentration of landholdings into fewer and fewer hands, and making forest communities and smallholders economically viable in the long run is essential to a long-term solution for the Amazon. This is what extractive reserves propose, and it is important that marketing initiatives support this approach.

It is not remarkable that extractive reserves have not attained these goals. Billions of dollars have been invested in cattle and colonization projects in the Amazon. In comparison, the resources invested in research on alternatives - identifying new products, sustainable smallholder agroforestry systems as well as the implementation of extractive reserves, have been infinitesimal. New marketing strategies that involve and benefit the direct producers and their organizations can help immensely to redress this situation.

References and further reading

Allegretti, M H (1990). Extractive reserves: an alternative for reconciling development and environmental conservation in Amazonia. In A Anderson (ed), *Alternatives to Deforestation: Steps Toward Sustainable Use of the Amazon Rainforest.* New York, Columbia University Press

de Almeida, A W B (1986). Estrutura fundiara e expansao camponesa. In J M G de Almeida Jr (ed), *Carajas: Desafio Politico, Ecologica e Desenvolvimento.* Sao Paulo, Editora Brasiliense

de Almeida, A W B (1989). Os tempos dos primeiros encontros. *Tempo e Presenca.* Numbers 244 and 245, Agosto/Setembro 1989. Publication of CEDI (Ecumencial Center for Documentation and Information), Sao Paulo

Partridge, W L (1989). The human ecology of tropical land settlement in Latin America: overview. In D A Schumann and W L Partridge (eds), *The Human Ecology of Tropical Land Settlement in Latin America.* Boulder CO, Westview Press

Schwartzman, S (1989). Extractive reserves: the rubber tappers' strategy for sustainable use of Amazon rainforest. In J O Browder (ed), *Fragile Lands of Latin America: Strategies for Sustainable Development.* Boulder CO, Westview Press

Land-use Strategies for Successful Extractive Economies

Dr Anthony Anderson
Programme Officer, The Ford Foundation, Praia do Flamengo, 100
22.210, Rio de Janeiro R J, Brazil

Summary

Extraction of tropical forest products has taken on new appeal in recent years as a potentially sustainable alternative to deforestation. Yet the economic viability of extraction is highly questionable. Following a critical analysis of extraction as it has been practised historically, this paper examines alternative land management strategies that could enhance economic viability without sacrificing ecological sustainability.

Introduction

Extractive reserves have emerged as one of the most promising development strategies for Amazonia. Supported by a grassroots movement involving thousands of rubber tappers, these entities are defined as discrete areas where populations can continue to subsist through extraction of forest products such as rubber and fruits. The concept has gained legal recognition in Brazil and, to date, 16 extractive reserves have been established in the Brazilian Amazon, encompassing a total area of over four million hectares.

Extractive reserves have attracted attention because they appear to represent a socially just form of land-use that can reconcile economic development and environmental conservation. Yet, the enthusiasm with which extractive reserves have been greeted by researchers and policy makers is at the very least curious, especially if one takes a critical look at forest extraction in Amazonia. Until recently, extraction has been the basis for virtually all major economic activities in the region, and is historically associated with resource depletion, environmental degradation, socioeconomic disruption, and cultural decimation. In terms of economic viability, environmental conservation, and social equity, the prospects for extractive economies are far from promising. Let's examine each of these components - economic viability, environmental conservation, and social equity - more carefully.

Economic viability

Extractive economies are notoriously unstable and subject to disruption, due to competitive displacement of the production system - as occurred in the case of rubber (Weinstein, 1983) - or degradation of the resource base - as is currently taking place in natural stands of Brazil nut (Kitamura and Muller, 1984). Of 15 major extractive products for which data are available between 1974 and 1986 in the Brazilian Amazon, only four showed an increase in production, and a mere two in unit value (Table 1). Rubber production in

Table 1. Production of selected extractive products derived from native plant species in the Brazilian Amazon region during 1974 - 1986. The Brazilian Amazon region defined as including the states of Amazonas, Pará, Rondônia, Acre and Amapá (Values expressed in $1000).

Product/Scientific Name	Vernacular Name	1974		1978		1982		1986	
		Tons	Value	Tons	Value	Tons	Value	Tons	Value
Natural Rubbers									
Hevea brasiliensis (Willd ex A Juss) M Arg	borracha								
- coagulated latex		18001	17703	20795	23585	25813	51609	26880	27485
- liquid latex		896	377	1062	708	1005	1008	1520	954
Castilla ulie Warb	caucho	154	133	1074	837	914	1313	200	136
Non-elastic Gums									
Manilkara bidentada (DC) Chev	balata	279	152	407	426	216	249	22	12
Manilkara elata (Fr All) Monac	maçaranduba	526	227	451	271	426	292	376	167
Couma utilis M Arg	sorva	3787	133	5555	2373	5461	3202	3002	1160
Fibres									
Mauritia flexuosa Lf (Plate 5)	buriti	-	-	-	-	862	115	893	83
Leopoldinia piassaba Wall	piaçava	2360	732	2321	779	38	15	303	127
Oils									
Orbiqnya phalerata Mart	babaçu	1354	186	254	57	48	16	43	7
Copaifera lanqadorffii Desf	copaiba	160	341	120	180	68	124	43	37
Dipteryx odorata (Aubl) Willd	cumaru	24	19	37	68	48	92	457	754
Scheela huebneri Burret	urucuri	-	-	719	8	4179	23	4642	27
Foods									
Euterpe oleracea (Mart)	açaí								
- fruits		134	10	46092	6483	80871	16436	133847	41600
- palm hearts		21246	524	20573	1871	95084	6991	124315	6423
Bertholletia excelsa HB	castanha-do-Pará (Brazil nut)	35276	7791	40244	15596	36419	14595	35563	6990
TOTAL			29513		53242		96080		85962

Sources: IBGE; 1976, 1981, 1984, 1988.

Amazonia is currently sustained by price subsidies.

This is a most precarious base for a major development strategy and it is reflected in the economic welfare of extractive populations in Amazonia. In the popular imagination, rubber tappers subsist in idyllic bliss on the natural bounty of the rainforest. In reality, however, extractive resources such as rubber and Brazil nut are sparsely distributed, access to markets is poor, and social services such as education and health care are minimal. As a result, the welfare of most extractive populations in Amazonia - whether in terms of income, health, or education - is marginal at best.

Environmental conservation

Much of the current charm of rubber tappers, Brazil nut harvesters, and other extractive populations lies in their potential to reconcile economic livelihood and environmental conservation. Yet the economic fragility of extraction can act to undermine such reconciliation. This is apparent in one of the Amazon's first extractive reserves - São Luís de Remanso, approximately 50 kilometres south-east of Rio Branco, capital of the western Amazon state of Acre - where over 15 per cent of the reserve has been degraded by the resident population for shifting cultivation and pasture conversion (FUNTAC, unpublished field data). Land-use pressures are increasing in this reserve due to expulsion of rubber tappers from surrounding areas, combined with a growing desire for economic improvement among the resident population. Despite their reputed environmental consciousness, when short-term needs can only be met by destroying the forest, rubber tappers act no differently than peasant farmers or ranchers.

Social equity

Finally, the economic and ecological sustainability of most extractive populations in Amazonia depends on access to extraordinarily large land areas. Among rubber tappers in Acre, for example, the average size of each family production unit (*colocação*) is 300-500 hectares (Allegretti, 1990). This area is far greater than the size of family lots generally utilized in regional colonization projects (25-100 hectares). If land were distributed throughout the Brazilian Amazon according to the rubber tappers' standard, the current population of the region would have to be reduced. Obviously, this discrepancy raises serious questions about social equity. Are extractive reserves only to include populations that carry out potentially sustainable forms of extraction? What about colonists from other locations? Do extractive reserves represent a viable model for development, or merely a means of preserving a favoured group's way of life?

Land-use strategies

Many of the problems inherent in extractive systems can be resolved once we stop viewing them as panaceas. The truth is that the economic viability of these systems is marginal and, as a development model, their social inequity is unjustifiable. Furthermore, without a strong economic and social foundation, the long-term ecological sustainability of extractive reserves is likely to be undermined.

To function, then, extractive reserves must evolve. Extraction can be defined as the removal of natural resources with no provision for their replacement. I would argue that, to be successful, extractive reserves will have to move beyond extraction and incorporate alternative forms of land-use. Ideally, these alternatives will intensify production per unit area without sacrificing the resource base. In this way, economic viability and social equity can be enhanced and natural resources maintained.

What are the options for intensifying land-uses in extractive reserves? To answer this question, let us examine forest extraction among a population of rubber tappers, and then compare this land-use with agroforestry systems practised by two other social groups in Amazonia.

Forest extraction

My analysis of forest extraction is based on a case study of the Cachoeira extractive reserve, located in the municipality of Xapuri in the state of Acre (Schwartzman, 1989). This reserve covers 24,898 hectares and contains 67 rubber tapper families; the average size of each land holding or *colocação* is 372 hectares. In a typical *colocação* the principal form of land-use is extraction of rubber (*Hevea brasiliensis* [Willd ex A Juss] M Arg, Plates 24, 25 and 26) and Brazil nut (*Bertholletia excelsa* H B, Plates 27 and 28) from extensive tracts of unmanaged forest, which cover about 98 per cent of the land area. In addition, small areas are cleared for pasture and swidden plots (Figure 1). Trails are cut in areas designated for extraction but there is no evidence of manipulation of the forest structure in any way resembling management.

An analys is of inputs and returns illustrates the non-intensive nature of forest extraction (Table 2). In the Cachoeira reserve, an average of 0.53 person-days of labour and $0.24 in materials are allocated per hectare each year. Gross annual return per hectare in the form of rubber and Brazil nuts is also small ($2.58). Subtracting inputs from outputs, the average net annual return is $872.35 per holding and $2.35 per hectare. The return per day of family labour ($4.38) is greater than the prevailing daily wage ($2.60).

The principal advantage of this land-use lies in its extremely low level of capitalization; a family practising forest extraction requires an annual outlay of only $87.65. This factor is crucial for producers living in extremely remote areas, which is the case for most extractive populations in Amazonia. On the other hand, the low labour and material inputs characteristic of forest extraction result in extremely low returns, both on a per-holding and a per-hectare basis. Regardless of regional development policies, the diffuse nature and low economic returns of forest extraction make it highly susceptible to disruption by more intensive land-uses.

Extensive agroforestry

This example is based on a case study of a population of river dwellers or *ribeirinhos* on Combu island, 2.5 kilometres south of the port city of Belém in the Amazon estuary (Anderson and Ioris, 1989). Combu has a total resident population of approximately 600 people dispersed over an area of 15 square kilometres. In contrast to the Cachoeira reserve, land holdings on Combu are relatively small. In a sample of five households in which economic production was studied, the mean holding contained 36 hectares. 95 per cent of Combu is covered by managed or unmanaged

Table 2. Comparison of three land-use strategies in Amazonia

	Forest Extraction[1]	Extensive Agroforestry[2]	Intensive Agroforestry[3]
Area utilized per household (ha)	372	36	28
Annual labour requirements			
Persons-days per holding	199	661	2477
(% family labour)	(100%)	(92.2%)	(23.3%)
Person-days per hectare	0.53	18.36	88.46
Hired labour costs[4] per holding	0	$134.05	$4939.63
Hired labour costs per hectare	0	$3.72	$176.42
Material costs[5]			
Fertilizer/pesticides	0	0	$13490.02
Utensils/machinery[6]	$87.65	$51.77	$1738.24
Material costs per holding	$87.65	$51.77	$15228.26
Material costs per hectare	$0.24	$1.44	$543.87
Gross return			
per holding	$960.00	$2733.45	$29667.39
per hectare	$2.58	$75.93	$1059.55
Net return			
per holding	$872.35	$2547.63	$9499.50
per hectare	$2.35	$70.77	$339.27
per person-day family labour	$4.38	$4.18	$16.46

Notes for Table 2:

1. Data base: sixty-seven producers in Seringal Cachoeira, municipality of Xapuri, State of Acre, Brazil. Source: Schwartzman (1989).

2. Data base: five producers on Combu island, municipality of Acara, State of Pará, Brazil. Source: Anderson and loris (1989); annual labour requirements and material costs estimated by Anderson (unpublished data).

3. Data base: six producers in the municipality of Tomé-Açu, State of Pará, Brazil. Source: Florhschutz (1983).

4. Hired labour costs calculated at US$2.60 per day, following Schwartzman (1989). Similar values were used by Florhschutz (1983) for contracted labour in Tomé-Açu, and by Anderson and Jardim (1989) for the daily wage rate in the Amazon estuary.

5. In all cases transport expenses were not included.

6. For the Cachoeira case study, it was assumed that each household would require 500 cups for collecting rubber, two knives for cutting rubber trees, four machetes, and one axe. For the Combu case study, each household was assumed to require 15 baskets fo collecting açaí fruits and cacao, 100 cups for collecting rubber, one knife for cutting rubber trees, and one machete. All values were converted from Brazilian currency using the official exchange rate.

tracts of floodplain forest in various stages of succession. Shifting cultivation is not currently practised on the island and forest clearing is only carried out for establishment of house gardens. A typical holding is surrounded by a house garden, a zone of managed forest, and a zone of unmanaged forest (Figure 2).

I refer to this combination of land-use zones as 'extensive' agroforestry, in which the native forest cover is an integral component. One of the most distinctive features of this system is the zone of managed forest, which is described elsewhere in detail (Anderson *et al.,* 1985; Anderson, 1990). Management of this zone consists of manipulating the existing forest (primarily through selective thinning) to promote regeneration and growth of selected species; conventional plantations are rarely established and then only in the forest understorey. By maintaining the native forest, labour requirements are minimized but by manipulating its structure and composition, yields of economic species are substantially increased (Anderson and Jardim, 1989). On Combu, the principal market products obtained from managed forests include fruits from native açaí palms (*Euterpe oleracea* Mart, Plate 1) and understorey plantations of cacao (*Theobroma cacao* L), as well as latex from wild rubber trees (*Hevea brasiliensis*).

An economic analysis shows that the inputs as well as the outputs of this extensive agroforestry system are greater than those associated with forest extraction (Table 2). In the sampled households on Combu, an average of 18.36 person-days and $51.77 in material costs are allocated per hectare each year. Gross annual return per hectare from sale of forest products is a moderate $75.93.

Figure 1. Schematic representation of a forest extraction system.

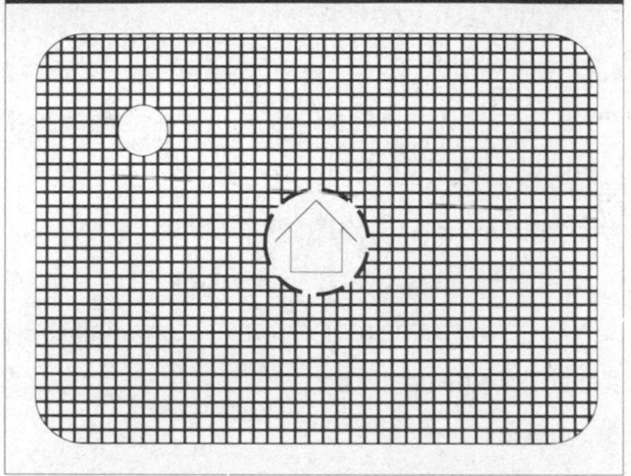

Figure 2. Schematic representation of an extensive agroforestry system.

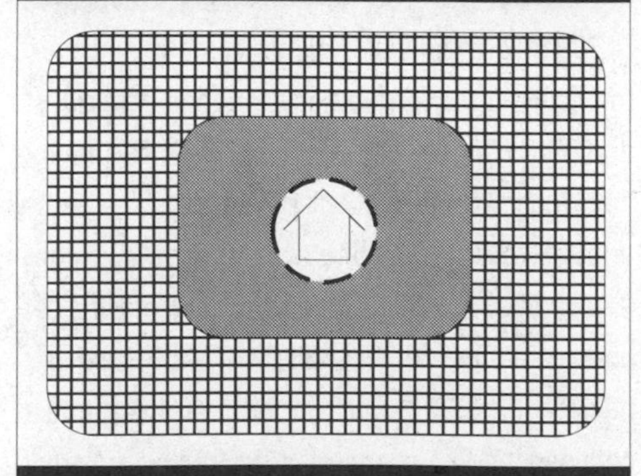

Key to Figures 1-4

Intensive Agroforestry

Subtracting inputs from outputs, the average net annual return is $2,547.63 per holding and $70.77 per hectare.

For a family practising this extensive agroforestry system, the annual cash input ($185.82) is approximately twice that of a family engaged in forest extraction. Yet, net return per holding ($2,547.63) is nearly three times that of the forest extraction case, and net return per hectare ($70.77) is thirty times as great. The net return per person-day of family labour ($4.18) is practically equivalent to that obtained under forest extraction.

These data suggest that extensive agroforestry could be a promising land-use alternative for extractive reserves. Although higher than in forest extraction, cash input remains modest and is probably within reach of most extractivists in Amazonia. Material inputs are minimal and can be readily obtained even in isolated areas. Land-use intensity - as measured in labour requirements and cash return per hectare - is far greater in extensive agroforestry, thus potentially resolving one of the critical limitations of forest extraction systems.

Yet, extensive agroforestry has its limitations, as well. The system described on Combu island is situated in one of the highly specific 'oligarchic' forest types described by Peters *et al.* (1989), which, in this case, is dominated by the economically important açaí palm. Because this forest contains a high density of economic species, modest inputs in the form of management can produce rapid and substantial returns. This is not the case for most forest types in Amazonia, which are characterized by high biotic diversity and low densities of economic species. In these forests, management could increase densities of economic species through thinning of undesirable competitors and enrichment via seeding or underplanting. Such practices, however, are likely to take many years or even decades to produce economic results.

In summary, extensive agroforestry represents one alternative for increasing land-use intensity in extractive reserves. The low cost of this system places it within the economic reach of most small-

Figure 3. Schematic representation of an intensive agroforestry system.

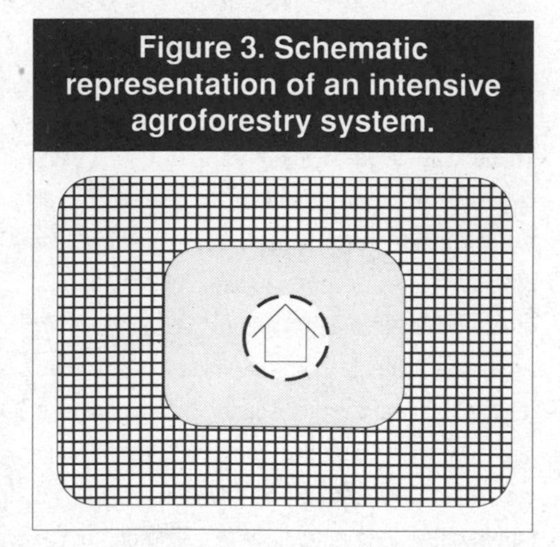

scale producers in Amazonia. But the slow returns that probably characterize this system in most areas diminish its potential for meeting the short-term needs of extractive populations. Only a more intensive form of land-use can meet these needs.

Intensive agroforestry

The third system that I shall describe was developed by Japanese immigrants and their descendents near the town of Tomé-Açu in the State of Pará (Florschutz, 1983; Subler and Uhl, 1990). This system probably represents the most intensive form of land-use currently practised in Amazonia. It is characterized by extraordinarily high inputs of labour and materials on small areas of land, which average 28 hectares in the sample of six farms analyzed by Florschutz (1983). In intensive agroforestry systems, the native forest cover is largely replaced by intensively managed crop plantations (Figure 3), occasionally represented by monocultures but more frequently by complex polycultures. Plantations range from annual food crops to a wide variety of perennial fruit and timber species.

In economic terms, both the inputs and outputs of this intensive agroforestry system are extraordinarily high (Table 2). The annual labour requirement is 88.46 person-days per hectare, and the per-hectare cost of hired labour averages $176.42. The annual material costs per hectare (primarily in the form of fertilizers and pesticides) are $543.87 - literally hundreds of times greater than those in the preceding systems. The gross annual return per hectare is likewise high: $1,059.55. Subtracting inputs from outputs, the net annual returns per holding ($9,499.50) and per hectare ($339.27) are far greater than those obtained under extensive agroforestry or forest extraction. And, most significantly, the net return per day of family labour ($16.46) is nearly four times that of the other two systems.

In short, the intensive agroforestry exemplified by the Japanese immigrants and their descendents in Tomé-Açu provides extremely high returns. Furthermore, the removal of the native forest cover in intensive agroforestry reduces establishment time and makes this system far more productive on a per-area basis. Managing this intensive land-use system, however, requires extremely high material, labour, and capital inputs, which are generally beyond the reach of small-scale producers in Amazonia. One of the key elements in the success of this system at Tomé-Açu is the farmers' co-operative, which provides financing, extension, and marketing of produce.

Establishment of such a vertically integrated, highly capitalized system in areas of Amazonia currently inhabited by extractive populations seems most unlikely at this time. In a less capitalized form and on a smaller scale, however, intensive agroforestry could represent an attractive land-use alternative for these populations. If current efforts by the rubber tappers and their allies succeed in strengthening community organization in extractive reserves, the chances of establishing intensive forms of agroforestry could improve.

Figure 4. Schematic representation of an alternative land management scheme for extractive reserves

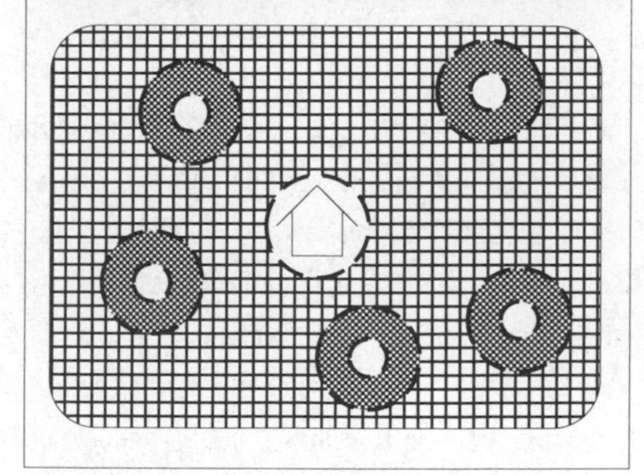

Land-use alternatives for extractive reserves

Each of the land-use systems described above has its strengths and weaknesses. Forest extraction requires minimal inputs but also produces minimal outputs. On the other hand, intensive agroforestry provides high outputs, but at a seemingly prohibitive cost in terms of labour, materials, and capital. And, finally, although extensive agroforestry appears to combine the best of the other two systems, it is most successful under highly specific ecological conditions. Elsewhere, it may require inordinately long periods to become established.

In view of the limitations inherent in each land-use system, the best strategy for extractive reserves may be to combine all three. One scheme for accomplishing this could involve utilizing swidden plots as sites for agroforestry systems (Figure 4). In most extractive areas today, such plots are abandoned after a short period of cultivation. Instead of being abandoned, these plots could be used to establish plantations of perennial tree crops. As in other systems of swidden-fallow agroforestry (*eg* Denevan and Padoch, 1987; Posey, 1983) in Amazonia, the degree of intervention could decrease as one proceeds from the centre of the plot, with intensively maintained plantations giving way to manipulated forest fallow. A wide range of plant and game resources could be exploited along this management gradient, thus diversifying the range of economic goods produced in extractive reserves. Moreover, such systems are frequently practised by groups that have little or no access to biocides or other energetically expensive inputs. And these systems can be linked to local markets, thus providing substantial monetary returns (Padoch *et al.,* 1985).

Other land-use models can and should be proposed for extractive reserves. Before we can work to improve extractive reserves, however, we need a critical vision of their limitations. While it is necessary to clear the air of some of the romantic myths associated with extraction, I would disagree with the contention that extractivists are marginal elements in the process of frontier expansion in Amazonia and that we should, therefore, concentrate our efforts in improving land-uses among the numerous colonists (Browder, this volume). In a practical sense, the forces struggling against deforestation in Amazonia are vanishingly small, and it is imperative that allies and battlegrounds be chosen carefully.

I would argue that we should develop a research and policy agenda aimed at transforming extractive reserves into viable enterprises. This agenda should include further studies on the potential valuation of a wide range of forest types in Amazonia, as well as on the costs and benefits of subjecting these forests to management. Extractive populations are hungry for knowledge of alternative land-use techniques that can increase their returns without undermining their resource base. This is fertile ground for foresters in Amazonia who, over a 30-year-long research tradition, have largely ignored the possibilities of integrating their work with rural populations. Extractive reserves offer a challenging social agenda as well: how can they develop more co-operative modes of social organization? How can forest products be more efficiently transported and marketed? How can education and health care needs be addressed?

In the final analysis, implementing alternatives to tropical deforestation requires the involvement of rural populations. Extractive reserves represent a unique opportunity to develop a potentially sound development agenda in areas where, for the moment, a rich resource base and a receptive population coexist.

References

Allegretti, M H (1990). Extractive reserves: an alternative for reconciling development and environmental conservation in Amazonia. In A B Anderson (ed), *Alternatives to Deforestation: Steps Toward Sustainable Use of the Amazon Rainforest.* Columbia University Press, New York

Anderson, A B (1990). Extraction and forest management by rural inhabitants in the Amazon estuary. In A B Anderson (ed), *Alternatives to Deforestation: Steps Toward Sustainable Use of the Amazon Rainforest.* Columbia University Press, New York

Anderson, A B, A Gely, J Strudwick, G L Sobel and M G C Pinto (1985). Um sistema agroflorestal na várzea do estuário amazônica (Ilha das Onças, Município de Barcarena, Estado do Pará). *Acta Amazonica,* Supl., 15(1-2): 195-224

Anderson, A B and E M Ioris (1989). The logic of extraction: resource management and income generation by extractive producers in the Amazon estuary. Paper presented at the workshop, *Traditional Resource Use in Neotropical Forests,* The Center for Latin American Studies, University of Florida, Gainesville, Florida, 19th-22nd January 1989

Anderson, A B and M A G Jardim (1989). Costs and benefits of floodplain forest management by rural inhabitants in the Amazon estuary: a case study of açaí palm production. In J Browder (ed), *Fragile Lands in Latin America: The Search for Sustainable Uses.* Westview Press, Boulder, Colorado, pp 114-129

Browder, J (1991). Beyond the limits of extraction: tropical forest alternatives to extractive reserves. Paper presented to the Conference, *The Rainforest Harvest,* Friends of the Earth, Royal Geographical Society, 15-17th May 1990

Denevan, W M and C Padoch (1987). Swidden Fallow Agroforestry in the Peruvian Amazon. *Advances in Economic Botany,* The New York Botanical Garden, Bronx, New York

Flohrschutz, G H H (1983). Análise econômica de estabelecimentos rurais do Município de Tomé-Açu, Pará: Um estudo de caso. *Documentos* 19. EMBRAPA/CPATU, Belem, Brazil

IBGE (1976). *Produção Extrativa Vegetal* (1974). Fundação Instituto Brasileiro de Geografia e Estatística, Rio de Janeiro, Brazil

IBGE (1981). *Produção Extrativa Vegetal* (1978). Fundação Instituto Brasileiro de Geografia e Estatística, Rio de Janeiro, Brazil

IBGE (1984). *Produção Extrativa Vegetal* (1982). Fundação Instituto Brasileiro de Geografia e Estatística, Rio de Janeiro, Brazil

IBGE (1988). *Produção de Estração Vegetal e da Silvicultura* (1986). Fundação Instituto Brasileiro de Geografia e Estatística, Rio de Janeiro, Brazil

Kitamura, P C and C H Muller (1984). Castanhais nativos de Marabá (PA): Fatores de depredação e bases para a sua preservação. *Documentos* 30. EMBRAPA/CPATU, Belém, Brazil

Peters, C M, M J Balick, F Kahn, and A B Anderson (1989). Oligarchic forests of economic plants in Amazonia. *Environmental Conservation* 3(4): 341-349

Padoch, C, J Chonta Inuma, W de Jung, and J Unruh (1985). Amazonian agroforestry: a market-orientated system in Peru. *Agroforestry Systems* 3: 47-58

Posey, D A (1983). Indigenous knowledge and development: an ideological bridge to the future. *Ciência e Cultura* 35(7): 877-894

Schwartzmann, S (1989). Extractive reserves: the rubber tappers' strategy for sustainable use of the Amazon rainforest. In J Browder (ed), *Fragile Lands in Latin America: The Search for Sustainable Uses.* Westview Press, Boulder, Colorado, pp 150-165

Subler, S and C Uhlo (1990). Japanese agroforestry in Amazonia: a case study in Tomé-Açu, Brazil. In A B Anderson (ed), *Alternatives to Deforestation: Steps Toward Sustainable Use of the Amazon Rainforest.* Columbia University Press, New York

Weinstein, B (1983). *The Amazon Rubber Boom 1850-1920.* Stanford University Press, Stanford, California

Extractive Reserves and The Future of the Amazon's Rainforests: Some Cautionary Observations

Dr John Browder
Virginia Polytechnic Institute and State University, Blacksburg, Virginia 24061 USA

Summary

This paper challenges the widespread view that "extractive reserves offer a mode of forest use that is both immediately economically competitive and sustainable in the long-run" (Gradwohl and Greenberg, 1988). After a review of the characteristics of extractive reserves, two questions are raised. First, can market-orientated extractive systems be developed on a scale that will effectively reduce the present rates of natural forest destruction? Second, do the diverse social experiences of forest product extraction found in Amazonia today provide a tangible basis for a general framework of market-oriented extraction from which replicable land use planning models might emerge?

The paper addresses these questions in the context of corporate enterprise and traditional household-based strategies of extraction. Various social and economic constraints on both strategies are outlined. The paper argues that extractive reserves are unlikely to significantly reduce pressures on tropical forests and that exploitative social relations of production typically found in extractive economies are not conducive to sustainable natural forest management. Natural forest conservation would be better served by actions that stabilize existing farms and ranches, the principal perpetrators of deforestation in Amazonia, by encouraging rural property owners to engage in a greater diversity of land uses, including natural forest management and agroforestry.

Introduction

In recent years a great deal of international attention has focused on finding 'sustainable alternatives' to tropical deforestation. Figuring prominently among such alternatives are various proposals to establish 'extractive reserves', or natural tropical forest areas that are reserved for the extraction of renewable forest products (*eg* rubber latex, fruits, nuts, fibres, timber) by traditional resident populations. These proposals have been largely informed by the specific historical experience of the 'Rubber Tappers Movement' in the western Brazilian state of Acre (Allegretti, 1990). However, several recent studies suggest that 'extraction' may have broader applications in achieving complementary objectives of natural forest conservation and income generation for rural inhabitants. Indeed, it is argued that extraction generates higher financial returns than most conventional uses (*eg* cattle ranching and commercial farming) that destroy tropical forest. *"Without question, the sustainable exploitation of non-wood forest resources represents the most immediate and profitable method for integrating the use and conservation of Amazon forests"* (Peters *et al.*, 1989:656). "*Extractive reserves offer a mode of forest use that is both immediately economically competitive and sustainable in the long-run"* (Gradwohl and Greenberg, 1988:150).

This paper critically examines these assertions as they apply to the Brazilian Amazon and challenges the growing view among conservation groups and donor organizations that extractive reserves will help save the tropical forests on a meaningful scale. It is not my intention to criticize social movements (*eg* the rubber tappers of the western Amazon), that have legitimate claims to forest lands they have occupied for decades. While extractive reserves may play a useful, but minor, role in natural forest conservation, much greater emphasis must be given to strategies that go beyond the limits of extractive reserves, to stabilize existing farms and ranches, the principal agents of forest destruction in the Amazon.

De-mythicizing extraction and extractive reserves

'Extractive Reserves' are defined by the Brazilian Ministry of Agrarian Reform and Development (MIRAD) as *"forest areas inhabited by extractive populations granted long-term usufruct rights to forest resources which they collectively manage"* (Schwartzman, 1989:151). From this rather straight-forward definition of a common property right has emerged a series of expectations linking tropical forest conservation to extractive reserves that are bound to disappoint many. I believe it is important to question the following assertions that have been virtually canonized by the conservationist campaign to save the tropical forests based on the extractive reserves experience.

Myth 1. *Extractive reserves will protect tropical forest biodiversity.* Extractive reserves cannot be expected (and are not intended) to preserve biodiversity in the tropics. Extractive reserves, by definition, are social spaces that do not necessarily coincide with areas of particular biological importance. Indeed, extractive reserves are more likely to be economically successful in (relatively) biologically poor 'oligarchic' forests, where a few marketable species dominate. Moreover, whereas the absence of humans is generally considered prerequisite to the preservation of tropical biological diversity, as in biological reserves (Foresta, 1991), a well-organized permanent human presence is always required to manage and defend extractive reserves.

Myth 2. *'Extractor' populations are defenders of tropical forests.* In fact, forest dwellers that extract forest products also clear forest for food crops, raise livestock, pan for gold, hunt wild game, extract commercial timber and engage in most of the activities of other rural Amazonian inhabitants. When the profitability of extraction declines, forest dwelling populations will shift to other, more profitable forms of resource exploitation, even those that damage the forest. Extractive reserves, when successful, protect the economic opportunities of selected forest-dwelling social groups, but do not necessarily protect the natural forest. In this regard, it is important to recognize that organized initiatives by forest dwellers to establish extractive reserves (*eg* the Brazilian National Council of Rubber Tappers) are social movements, not environmental movements (in the contemporary Euro-North American sense). Their leaders (*eg* Chico Mendes) are more accurately portrayed as labour leaders, not 'environmental activists'.

Myth 3: *Extractive reserves generate higher net financial returns than other more damaging forest land uses.* In spite of the spate of recent studies attesting to this assertion, none conclusively demonstrates that forest extractors actually earn higher incomes from sustainable forest product extraction than cattle ranchers, cash crop farmers, or other tropical forest land users (see discussion below). Indeed, at least one study comparing the financial performance of three different land use strategies (extraction, extensive agroforestry and intensive agroforestry) indicates that extractors earn the lowest income (Anderson, 1989). Rural households that rely mainly on extracted products are comparatively poor by Amazonian standards: their social relations of production typically hold them in one or more forms of debt peonage. *"Even in the days of the rubber boom seringueiros (rubber tappers) fought disease, Indians and crocodiles for months at a time and then ended up in debt. It remains a desperate existence"* (Parfit, 1989:64).

Myth 4: *Extractive economies are indefinitely self-sustaining.* There has never been even one renewable tropical forest resource, once introduced into commerce, that has provided a basis for sustained economic activity without external subsidization. As Homma (1990a, 1990b) aptly reminds us, the historical record of extractive economies in Amazonia consistently demonstrates that such economies tend to self-destruct. If the prices of extracted products rise, rapid depletion from the wild by traditional groups follows, or cultivated or synthetic substitutes are developed elsewhere by corporate groups.

Myth 5: *Extractive systems are more efficient, in terms of land and labour, than other alternative tropical forest use systems.* Given the dispersed distribution of most marketable natural forest products, extractive systems require relatively large continuous tracts of forest land. In the Brazilian States of Amazonas and Acre, for instance, extractive reserves range from 25,000 to 335,000 hectares (Schwartzman, 1989:157). The typical rubber tapper household requires between 300 and 500 hectares of forest to survive (Fearnside, 1989). Two points must be made here. First, the highly heterogeneous biological composition of most tropical forests means that more labour time is expended in lengthy and frequently interrupted collection activities. This reduces the efficiency of labour (*ie* the net return to labour) that might otherwise be gained from more land intensive forms of tropical forest land use. Second, these dimensions may not seem large in contrast to some Amazon landholdings devoted to cattle ranching and cash cropping (yet less than 17 per cent of the nearly 500,000 agricultural establishments in Brazilian Amazonia exceeded 100 hectares in 1985 - IBGE, 1989: 297). They are enormous, however, in comparison to successful traditional agroforestry systems found elsewhere in Latin America in which household property sizes range from 0.7 to 6 hectares (Alcorn, 1989; Gliessman, undated). Although the model for extraction (in the form of extractive reserves) is a recent Brazilian phenomenon, it may very well be the case that other experiences in natural forest management and agroforestry have more to offer Brazil than what

Brazilian extractive reserves offer the rest of the tropics.

Myth 6: Extractive systems 'capitalize' on the diverse array of products naturally provided by tropical forests. To be sustainable as market-orientated enterprises, extractive reserves must provide products that markets demand for a cost that competes favourably with both cultivated and synthetic substitutes. Although as many as 30 different tropical forest products from Amazonia may have foreign commercial potential (Clay, 1989), and 17 species are currently exported abroad (Schwartzman, this volume), hundreds of other potential products are poorly known to science and completely unknown to consumer markets. In the main, any single extractive reserve does not 'capitalize' on the tropical forest's biodiversity, but rather relies heavily on just one or two locally marketable commodities. In so far as extractive reserves in Amazonia are based mainly on wild rubber latex collection, it is important to note that cultivated rubber plantations in eastern Brazil (outside of Amazonia) now supplies about 60 per cent of Brazil's domestic rubber consumption.

The 're-evaluation' of a tropical forest

Several conceptual and operational factors constrain the potential for extraction (in its prevailing social context - see below) and the extractive reserves approach to large scale tropical forest conservation in Brazil that I have presented elsewhere (Browder, 1989a). In this section, I present a critique of the most widely publicized study attesting to the potential financial performance of extractive systems in the (Peruvian) Amazon.

In their benchmark commentary on the *Valuation of a Tropical Forest* (Nature, June 29th, 1989), Peters, Gentry and Mendelsohn gathered data on natural production rates of marketable tropical fruits, palm products, rubber latex and timber from a one hectare site at Mishana, in the Peruvian Amazon, located about 30 kilometres from the city of Iquitos, where local market prices for the same species were ascertained. Given natural production rates, observed labour inputs, prevailing transport costs, and current Iquitos prices, the authors calculated the net annual revenues potentially obtainable from the fruit and latex output of the one hectare inventoried at Mishana to be equivalent to $422. Assuming that commercial timbers are also selectively harvested, extractors would obtain an additional net revenue of $310 per hectare once every 20 years. Given a 5 per cent real interest rate and a relatively long planning horizon (50 years), the authors calculate a net present value of $6,820 per hectare from the local sale of extracted tropical forest products, financial returns that vastly exceed most other tropical forest land uses.

The spectacular findings of this study, and the obvious implications they have for forest conservation policy, should be re-evaluated in light of the following.

First, consider the representativeness of the study site. The authors' site at Mishana is unique, occurring in a flood plain area of so-called 'oligarchic' forests, fortuitously dominated by a few commercial fruit species (*eg Mauritia flexuosa*, Plate 5, *Myrciaria dubia*). Flood plain forests cover about 2 per cent of the Amazon basin, so the findings do not apply to the *terra firma* forests which encompasses 76 per cent of the Brazilian Amazon (EMBRAPA, 1984), where most of the Amazon's rural population resides. *"The most important point is how poorly the Peters et al Peruvian Amazon hectare represents the tropical forests. It is the rare exception rather than the rule"* (Richard A. Howard, former Vice President for Botanical Sciences, New York Botanical Garden, personal communication, 10th February 90).

Second, the study site, is unique by its location within a relatively short distance (30 kilometres) of a major urban consumer centre, the port city of Iquitos. Studies from more distant sites, such as Santa Rosa, Peru (150 kilometres from Iquitos), indicate that of a potential gross income, based on Iquitos prices, of $653 per hectare from various cultivated and extracted products, traditional agroforesters only realized a maximum income of $22 per hectare (merely 3.3 per cent of potential income). The income shortfall is due to *"the difficulty of marketing perishable produce"* over long distances (Padoch and de Jong, 1989).

Third, a 50-year planning horizon for the typical Amazonian household is unrealistic. While some indigenous and detribalized mestizo communities have documentable tenures approaching 50 years, the vast majority of Amazonian inhabitants rarely stay fixed on their land for five years (Fifer, 1982; Mahar, 1989; Moran, 1984; Ortiz, 1984). Adopting an unrealistically long financial planning horizon of 50 years vastly overstates the true potential of extractive activities.

Fourth, the key question is not the potential net present value of the forest per hectare, but rather the actual current income per workday attributable to the sustainable extraction of marketable forest produce.

In fairness to the authors, their study focused on 'potential market value'. Nevertheless, we have no way of knowing from their study whether or not rural inhabitants in the authors' research site actually engaged in sustained yield forest extraction and what their net incomes from extraction really are.

The social context of extraction

The popular appeal of the 'extractive reserves solution' is supported by the widespread misconception that traditional rainforest inhabitants live in prosperous harmony with their fragile environment. Ample evidence exists to the contrary, that most rural households engaged in natural forest extraction are poor, even by rural Amazonian standards. Moreover, small-scale extractors are fully capable of destroying commercial forest resources[1]. Periodic shortages of açaí palm hearts in Belém[2], and the degradation of extractive reserves by rubber tappers in Acre[3], bear witness to the tenuous foundation that prevailing extractive systems provide as a model of sustainable natural forest development.

Like every other form of labour, extractive activities do not exist in a social vacuum. The behaviour and incomes of rural people who extract forest products are typically determined by social and economic factors over which they have little control. Most 'extractors' are not independent economic agents, but live under various regimes of economic and social dependence to large landowners, merchants, and private companies that regulate prices and marketing opportunities for rainforest produce. Many extractors, living in long-established traditions of debt peonage, typically earn a cash income barely sufficient to ensure household subsistence. Even the much-heralded rubber tappers movement in Acre, which has been sustained by a Brazilian tariff policy that effectively fixed the domestic price of rubber at roughly three times the world average price (Fearnside, 1989), an estimated 55 per cent of Acrean rubber tapper households are typically in debt. Ironically, the principal factors determining the survival of rubber tapper households is their ability to successfully farm and raise livestock, not their success in rubber collection (Schwartzman, 1989). As Fearnside (1989) poignantly notes, *"when the value of products accrues to intermediaries, extractivists remain poor, regardless of the amount of wealth they generate"*. Under these prevailing social relations of production, like other subsistence producers, extractors minimize risk and appropriate advantageous opportunities, regardless of their ecological impacts.

These arguments do not imply that governments should fail to vigorously pursue the establishment of protected areas in tropical forests based on appropriate biological and social criteria as one component of a comprehensive strategy to curb tropical deforestation. Extractive reserves are one small part of a much larger solution and do not constitute a panacea to deforestation. Regrettably, the inordinate emphasis being given to extractive reserves as a meaningful alternative to deforestation has deflected attention from the real tasks ahead for saving tropical forests.

Beyond extractive reserves: the real tasks ahead

Most forest destruction in Brazilian Amazonia originates on the 499,775 farms and ranches that in 1985 occupied 448,800 square kilometres, (11.6 per cent) of the Brazilian north, largely in tropical forest zones. In contrast, there are only about 68,000 rubber-tapper households occupying an estimated 97,000 square kilometres (2.7 per cent) of the region's area. Since most of the future destruction of tropical forests can be expected to occur in the former, not the latter, it would behove conservationists to focus on correcting non-sustainable land use systems, and allow sustainable ones to flourish (which, by definition, they should be able to do on their own).

Stated differently, there are between one and two million rural households in Brazilian Amazonia alone, perhaps 7 million people, that derive most of their living not from the sustainable extraction of forest products, but from largely predatory land uses that deplete tropical forest ecosystems of nutrients and energy over the short-term, strategies that are rational given the social and economic constraints such as households face (Schmink, 1987). If extraction is to have a significant impact on prevailing destructive land uses, then it must be adapted to the prevalent land users.

The real question facing policy makers and conservationists is not how many more millions of hectares of tropical forests to sequester into extractive reserves, but rather how to integrate sustained yield extractive practices, along with agroforestry systems, into the production strategies of existing rural property-owners, on small farms and large ranches alike.

Toward this goal I propose the following objectives that are elaborated elsewhere (Browder, 1989b).

Tropical forest alternatives to extractive reserves

(1) *Encourage extractive utilization of natural forest remnants on existing non-extractor rural properties.* In my recent study (forthcoming) of colonist farming strategies in Rondônia, Brazil, where approximately 100,000 landless farmers have settled in 12 government colonization projects since the early 1970s, I estimate that 609 (29 per cent) of the 2100 farmers in my study site (Rolim de Moura) periodically collect natural forest products (mainly Brazil nut and palmito) on their forest remnants averaging about 65 hectares in 1990. Since this study site is believed to be poor in commercial non-wood forest products relative to other areas of Rondônia, it probably understates the potential forest area owned by colonists elsewhere in the State that might be utilized for extractive products. If only 29 per cent of Rondônia's 100,000 farms, spanning a total of about 80,000 square kilometres could be utilized profitably for extraction, then about 15,000 square kilometres on 29,000 farms in Rondônia might be spared from destruction. The problems facing colonists in this respect include; how to identify, sustainably harvest, process, and market the potentially marketable forest products that their forest remnants naturally produce. Perhaps some of the lessons being learned from existing extractive reserves could be usefully applied to the very different social context of colonists in Rondônia.

(2) *The diversification of farm production through the planting of 'useful' tree species (for cash and subsistence), especially on degraded crop fields and abandoned pastures.* I conservatively estimate that at least 25 per cent, or 150,000 square kilometres, of the nearly 600,000 square kilometres of Brazilian tropical forests deforested by 1988 are today in various stages of secondary vegetation. Most of this area is not being used for economic ends (although the environmental services provided by forest regeneration, especially for carbon fixation, should not be ignored). Very little is known about the regenerative dynamics of secondary forests and their capacity for economic utilization, although it is believed that vegetation on eutrophic soils (spanning 8 per cent to 12 per cent of the Brazilian Amazon) is both robust and resilient to periodic human interventions. Recognizing the need to balance social and economic necessities (*eg* finding land for landless farmers and meeting foreign debt and financing requirements) with environmental concerns (deflecting social and economic pressures away from less resilient primary tropical forests), a considerable potential exists in the (re-)utilization of the Amazon's extensive secondary forest biomass. Opportunities for expanding agroforestry (the planting of useful tree species in conjunction with ground crops) and forest enrichment (the planting of commercially valuable tropical hardwoods) in neotropical secondary forests have gone largely ignored in research and demonstration. Yet, it is in secondary forests that the greatest potential for combining economic development with primary forest conservation is likely to be found.

(3) *Intensification of farm cultivation opting for continuous cropping with natural rather than*

artificial fertilizers. While a considerable amount of research support has been devoted to transferring agricultural technology from temperate climate experiences to the tropics, relatively little attention has been given to the techniques employed in indigenous Amazonian soil management strategies. Yet recent research suggests that some of these traditional systems are more productive than conventional smallholder agriculture. In a comparative analysis of crop yields obtained by the Kayapo Indians (located in the Amazon State of Pará) with those of smallholder colonists and ranchers in Brazilian Amazonia, Hecht (1989) found that after a five-year period the indigenous farming system produced nearly three times the yield of all crops as colonists' farming systems and 176 times more output in weight per hectare than the beef cattle ranches surveyed. In contrast to 'western-style' solutions, such as artificial chemical fertilizers to sustain continuous cropping on nutrient poor tropical soils (Nicholaides et al., 1985), the Kayapo have traditionally relied exclusively on naturally occurring and locally available inputs (ash, mulch, termite nests, palm fronds, rice and corn stover, banana leaves, etc). Another essential difference is that the colonist system is based on the dense sequential monocropping of a single forest clearing, while the Kayapo strategy is based on simultaneous mixed cropping or 'patch intercropping' over expansive areas interspersed with natural forest that provide habitats for game animals, fish, and socially useful environmental services (clean water, soil conservation, shade) that perpetuate, rather than diminish, the capacity of these rural inhabitants (the Kayapo) to survive.

While the land-extensive production systems of the Kayapo and other traditional groups, like rubber tappers, may seem impractical on small farm units, the objective of diversifying farm production is not limited by scale (property size) or necessarily by technique. In Mexico, for example, traditional home gardens ranging in size from 0.3 to 0.7 hectares are known to produce between 33 and 55 useful species, mostly perennials, that provide forest cover for 96.7 per cent of the garden area, virtually mimicking the natural forest (Gliessman, undated). Irrigated raised fields (*chinampas* and *cameilones chontales*) of 0.5 hectares are believed sufficient in size to ensure subsistence for one rural Mexican family by providing a variety of food and cash crops (Morales, 1980). Small Huastec farms averaging only four hectares in size produce more than 200 useful species (many cultivated), retain forest cover, and generate net returns greater than those obtained from the Yurimaguas experiments (Alcorn, 1989).

In documented traditional agroforestry systems, small farm sizes of only a few hectares are not a constraint on either household income or forest conservation. I suggest we revise our expectation that meaningful forest conservation can only be obtained by protecting areal forest units that exceed some minimum critical size of gigantic proportions, and consider how best to preserve and manage small remnant forests that could serve vital economic and ecological functions within the context of the demographic realities of Amazonia today.

Finally, the research literature on neotropical forest extraction has focused almost exclusively on non-wood products. While in smaller countries, where tropical forests have been all but decimated, the cessation of tropical timber extraction might be justifiable, the omission of timber resources from discussions of sustainable extraction in the case of Brazil seems incomprehensible. Industrial timber extraction represents the single largest contributor of value to the tropical forests of Brazil (over 80 per cent of the market value of production derived from all extracted products in Amazonia). In 1975, only 14.3 per cent of Brazil's industrial roundwood production originated from the Amazon region. Today, the Amazon supplies 54 per cent of Brazil's total roundwood requirements and no world-wide boycott of tropical hardwoods will alter this fact. The number of licensed industrial wood processors in Brazilian Amazonia increased from 89 in 1952 to perhaps 4000 today. Not surprisingly, the industrial wood sector is the single largest employer of skilled and semi-skilled labour in 5 of the Amazon's 6 states and territories (before 1988). By 1980, 25.6 per cent of the Amazon's industrial labour force was employed by the industrial wood sector, which contributed 13 per cent of the region's total value of industrial production (Browder, 1989c). If it is the goal of international conservationists to make tropical forest conservation through extraction economically feasible, then timber extractors, like colonists, in Amazonia can hardly be ignored.

There are, of course, major institutional, financial, and policy impediments to implementing any tropical forest management strategy. Insecure land tenure frequently creates an incentive to clear forests in Amazonia, even though recent federal legislation in Brazil has on paper attempted to rectify the long-practiced custom of clearing forest to establish land claims. The lack of appropriate agroecological knowledge underscores the miserable state of tropical forest research due mainly to the lack of a clear research agenda and inadequate funding, and less due to the lack of qualified local scientists. Similarly afflicted are rural extension agencies which also lack staff, vehicles, funding, and most of all consistent political leadership and commitment to carry out their legislatively mandated objectives. Inadequate marketing infrastructure for forest products, many highly perishable, from remote forest locations to regional urban markets, continues to constrain the viability of extractive economies. Persistent exploitative social relations of production to which many households are subjected, and the lack of local co-operative organization among other rural inhabitants who could more fully participate in extractive activities, also remain impediments to the successful expansion of alternative forest management systems in Amazonia. Finally, the continued subsidization of 'big projects' (from hydroelectric development to sugar cane production), whether in the form of fiscal incentives or regulatory measures, will continue to distort the true social costs of clearing forests.

Conclusion

There are tremendous constraints on any single approach to arresting tropical deforestation, which argues for multiple approaches. In Brazil, burdened with the developing world's largest external debt, a rapidly expanding disadvantaged citizenry, and a labour force that is retreating *en masse* to informal (non-licensed) activities, tropical forests can only be significantly conserved in ways that balance pressing social needs. Extractive reserves may help one small segment of the rural poor hold onto their cultural heritage and economic way of life, but solutions for millions of other poor inhabitants of tropical forests need to be developed as well. We must support appropriate efforts to establish extractive reserves in response to social needs, recognizing the inherent limits of this approach to tropical forest conservation. It is high time that donor organizations and well-endowed conservation groups think and act beyond the extractive reserves paradigm and dedicate more resources to saving tropical forests which, in the case of Brazilian Amazonia, means supporting landless peasants, small farmers and even big ranchers to find financially profitable uses for tropical forests.

Footnotes

1. For instance, Bodmer, Fang, and Moya (1990) found *"that local inhabitants in* [a study site in eastern] *Peru use palm fruits in a non-renewable manner that may be more detrimental than selective timbering".*

2. *Extração de Palmito Provoca a Escasséz do Açaí em Belém* (translation: Extraction of palmito provokes açaí [fruit] shortages in Belém). *O liberal,* Belém 7/6/89, p 5.

3. By one account, *"15 per cent of extractive reserves south of Rio Branco (Acre) had been degraded by resident populations".* Anthony Anderson, paper presented at the symposium, *Extractive Economies in Tropical Forests: A Course of Action.* National Wildlife Federation, Washington, DC, November 30th to December 1st, 1989.

References

Alcorn, J B (1989). An economic analysis of Huastec Mayan forest management. In J O Browder (ed), *Fragile Lands of Latin America: Strategies for Sustainable Development.* Boulder, Westview Press

Allegretti, M H (1990). Extractive reserves: An alternative for reconciling development and environmental conservation in Amazonia. In A B Anderson (ed), *Alternatives to Deforestation: Steps Toward Sustainable Use of the Amazon Rainforest.* New York, Columbia University Press

Anderson, A B (1989). Land-use strategies for successful extractive economies. Paper presented at the symposium, *Extractive Economies in Tropical Forests: A Course of Action,* National Wildlife Federation, Washington, DC, 30th November to 1st December 1989

Bodmer, R E, T G Fang and I Moya (1990). Fruits of the forest. *Nature* 343 (January 11th, 1990): 109

Browder, J O (1989a). Social and economic constraints on the development of market-oriented extractive reserves in Amazon rainforests. Paper presented at the symposium, *Extractive Economies in Tropical Forests: A Course of Action,* National Wildlife Federation, Washington, DC, November 30th to December 1st, 1989

Browder, J O (1989b). Development alternatives for tropical rainforests. In H Jeffrey Leonard (ed), *Environmental Strategies for Meeting Human Needs: Poverty and Sustainable Development in the 1990s.* New Brunswick, Transaction Books

Browder, J O (1989c). Lumber production and economic development in the Brazilian Amazon:

regional trends and a case study, *Journal of World Forest Resource Management* 4 (1)

Clay, J (1989). Building and supplying international markets for non-wood tropical forest products. Paper presented at the symposium, *Extractive Economies in Tropical Forests: A Course of Action,* National Wildlife Federation, Washington, DC, 30th November to 1st December 1989

EMBRAPA (1984). *Amazonia: Meio Ambiente e Técnologia Agrícola.* Belém, EMBRAPA/CPATU

Fearnside, P M (1989). Extractive reserves in Brazilian Amazonia. *Bioscience* (June): 387-393

Fifer, V J (1982). The search for a series of small successes: frontiers of settlement in eastern Bolivia. *Journal of Latin America Studies* 14 (2): 408-432

Foresta, R (1991). *The Limits of Providence: Amazon Conservation in the Age of Development.* Gainesville, University of Florida Press

Gradwohl, J and R Greenberg (1988). *Saving the Tropical Forests.* Earthscan Publications Ltd, London

Gliessman, S R (undated). *Local resource use systems in the tropics: taking pressure off the forests.* Unpublished manuscript

Hecht, S B (1989). Indigenous soil management in the Latin American tropics: some implications for the Amazon basin. In J O Browder (ed), *Fragile Lands of Latin America: Strategies for Sustainable Development.* Boulder, Westview Press

Homma, A K O (1990a). *A dinâmica do extrativismo vegetal na Amazonia: uma interpretação teórica.* Unpublished manuscript

Homma, A K O (1990b). *A sustentabilidade do sistema extrativista na floresta Amazonica.* Unpublished manuscript

IBGE (1989). *Anuário Estatístico do Brasil.* Instituto Brasileiro de Geógrafia e Estatística

Mahar, D (1989). *Government Policies and Deforestation in Brazil's Amazon Region.* Environment Department Working Paper No 7. Washington, DC, The World Bank

Morales, H L (1980). Rural development and the management of tropical integrated production units. *Tropical Ecology and Development.* p 429

Moran, E F (1984). Colonization in the Transamazon and Rondônia. In M Schmink and C Wood (eds), *Frontier Expansion in Amazonia.* Gainesville, University of Florida Press

Nicholaides, J J, D E Bandy, P A Sanchez, J R Benites, J H Villachica, A J Coutu, and C S Valverde (1985). Agricultural alternatives for the Amazon basin. *Bioscience* 35 (5): 279-85

Ortiz, S (1984). Colonization in the Colombian Amazon. In M Schmink and C Woods (eds), *Frontier Expansion in Amazonia.* Gainesville, University of Florida Press

Padoch, C and W de Jong (1989). Production and profit in agroforestry: an example from the Peruvian Amazon. In J O Browder (ed), *Fragile Lands of*

Latin America: Strategies for Sustainable Development. Boulder, Westview Press

Parfit, M (1989). Facing up to reality in the Amazon: Whose hands will shape the future of the Amazon's green mansions? *Smithsonian* (November): 58-77

Peters, C M, A H Gentry and R O Mendelsohn (1989). Valuation of an Amazonian rainforest. *Nature* 339 (June 29): 656-657

Schmink, M (1987). The rationality of forest destruction. *Management of the Forests of Tropical America: Prospects and Technologies.* San Juan, Institute of Tropical Forestry

Schwartzman, S (1989). Extractive reserves: the rubber tappers' strategy for sustainable use of the Amazon rainforest. In J O Browder (ed), *Fragile Lands of Latin America: Strategies for Sustainable Development.* Boulder, Westview Press

Indigenous Peoples and the Marketing of the Rainforest

Dr Andrew Gray
International Work Group for Indigenous Affairs (IWGIA), Fiolstraede 10, 1171, Copenhagen K, Denmark

Summary

Most indigenous peoples are, in varying degrees, affected by the market economy. Indeed history has shown that they have actively sought ways of trading or bartering their produce with outsiders. In many cases this has proven to be highly destructive of their society and culture. Non-destructive relations with the market economy have only taken place where indigenous peoples have control over the production and exchange of their commodities. If these people do not have this control, they will become more and more dependent on outside forces which will inevitably lead to the destruction of indigenous societies and the rainforests.

The enthusiasm for marketing rainforest products is understandable. As we crunch our way through nutty Bio-Bars, take the hairs off our chests with ayahuasca jelly or dab tincture of opossum under our armpits, we certainly can be rest assured that we are preserving the biodiversity of the commodity market. The question is whether this has any effect on the threat to rainforest biodiversity in general or to indigenous peoples' cultural diversity in particular.

Although this paper is directed primarily at the concerns of indigenous peoples, many of the principles here relate to the concerns and demands of other forest peoples, too. Furthermore, indigenous peoples in the Americas, in the forests of South-east Asia and in Central Africa all share the concerns and problems raised with over-reliance on international marketing.

The marketing of products gathered by forest peoples of the world initially appears as an ingenious blending of conservation and development issues. On the one hand, the forest is protected by extractive or indigenous reserves while, on the other, forest peoples can produce a sustainable income to ensure their subsistence needs and long-term survival.

The argument for encouraging marketing is as follows: indigenous peoples are in trouble. They need cash resources to defend their lives and futures. This money can come from marketing their forest products which have been extracted sustainably from their lands.

This argument emphasizes the urgency of the case. People who disagree are usually termed 'romantics' who want to keep indigenous peoples in some time-warped, protected reserve under the supervision of paternalistic do-gooders. The trouble with the proponents of this view is that they are so caught up by their own hype that they ignore years of experience, discussions on development questions and, above all, the voice of indigenous peoples themselves.

Indigenous peoples want to exchange their goods and, in many cases, actively seek market opportunities. They have been trading and bartering for centuries. The exchange of extracted forest resources over long distances is nothing new. The history of the Amazon has shown that chains of exchange are the most usual routes for the introduction of exotic goods. Inca style axes in the Peruvian Madre de Dios demonstrate the likelihood of such trading taking place in Inca times when metal axes were exchanged for forest products (Aikman, 1982). Archaeological finds in Bolivia also show that, long before the Spanish conquest, highland peoples received medicinal plants from rainforest peoples.

Evidence from different parts of the Amazon shows indigenous peoples still looking for goods from outside. In the north-west Amazon, indigenous peoples receive trade goods by barter which are exchanged within and between communities (Hugh-Jones, 1987). A detailed study of the spread of colonialism among indigenous peoples by Eric Wolf demonstrates clearly the interrelation between internal and external trading practices and how these were bound up with the spread of the colonizing frontier throughout the world (Wolf, 1982).

One of the standard ways of 'attracting' indigenous peoples has been through leaving machetes or axes as offerings in the hope of luring them into seeking more. When comparing the amount of work-time saved when clearing a field through using a steel axe instead of a stone one (several hours), it is not surprising that indigenous peoples want trade goods and some cash (Colchester, 1981:56).

There are hardly any indigenous peoples in the Amazon who are completely isolated from the market economy and who would not like to take advantage of its resources. But the argument is not as simple as this. Marketing is a two-edged sword. Industrial society and markets have taken forest products to make healthy profits while, in return, contributing generously to the devastation and destruction of indigenous peoples throughout the world.

In spite of the importance of marketing in the rainforest for companies in industrial societies, many indigenous peoples don't share this priority. The Co-ordinadora of the Amazon Basin (COICA), the indigenous international organization for the South American rainforest, considers other priorities as being far more important than encouraging marketing: *"The best defence of the Amazonian Biosphere is the defence of the territories recognized as homeland by indigenous peoples, and the promotion of our models for living within that Biosphere and for managing its resources."* (COICA, 1989:4).

The priority for indigenous peoples is to ensure a secure land and resource base, and that all marketing and recognition of intellectual property rights are firmly under their control and according to their ways of life.

Indigenous peoples' territories are constantly under threat of invasion and the consequential loss of their resource base. Throughout the Amazon, less than 30 per cent of lands belonging to the nearly 500 indigenous nations are titled, while the rainforest destruction is surrounding them at the estimated rate of 65,000 square kilometres annually (see Myers, 1989:7).

Indigenous peoples' primary problem is securing and defending their land base. Without it they cannot carry out their sustainably mixed economy of hunting, gathering, fishing, horticulture and other activities. The effect of invasions on their land is that these means of subsistence are depleted through deforestation and disturbance of the flora and fauna of the region.

However, land in itself is not the answer. Nation states which recognize areas that are too small to provide a sustainable resource base produce pockets of poverty, like the 'homelands' of South Africa, which leave indigenous peoples as a surplus pool of labour. Alternatively, dividing up territories into individual plots leads to land mortgages, debt and the destruction of culture and community as has been clearly shown in the allotment system in the United States, in the Bolivian Agrarian Reform and in Chile under Pinochet.

Until indigenous peoples obtain recognition of their control over their resources and inalienable rights to these territories, any form of survival will remain precarious and the production of surplus commodities will be unstable because of the threat of invasion, deforestation and resource depletion. Thus, to discuss marketing apart from the control of the resources which will provide that market with goods is an inversion of sound economics.

Control here means the ability to make free and informed decisions for themselves and also to receive the backing and technical support to create and strengthen their own indigenous organizations.

A common assumption of the ideal model of saving indigenous peoples and the rainforest through the market economy is to presume that the market is a changeless phenomenon. Indigenous peoples are presented as a unified, standard, community-based entity which, when plugged together with the international economy, switch on a cash flow like switching on a light. However, this is to simplify marketing excessively.

Marketing is a part of exchange activities between and within communities. It has several aspects, often co-existing, based on the extent to which the community is independent or integrated into the broadly industrial market economy (Belshaw, 1965; Hodges, 1988:4-6). A simplified scheme of these features is as follows:

- exchange between communities of goods, such as resources found in specific areas, trade goods obtained from outside the area or other commodities;

- local markets existing in the form of trading posts, or nearby towns, where indigenous and other forest peoples can bring their produce to a central place and sell or exchange it for other goods;

- chains of exchange which link the indigenous community to the national and international economy. Here, goods which are found naturally in the forest such as rubber, gold, wood or other products are sold or exchanged to middlemen or merchants who sell them to outsiders, usually at considerable profit.

When we discuss marketing of rainforest products, we are talking particularly of this third aspect of the market economy. Indigenous peoples provide markets with three potential products: the surplus of their subsistence economy; products which they discover are valuable (such as gold or rubber); or else their labour (see Colchester, 1989). In the models of marketing extractive resources (Baker, 1989: 64-5) indigenous peoples provide a mixture of their labour time, subsistence goods and new products for the market.

The following examples show the range of effects that the market economy can have on indigenous peoples in the Amazon from the genocidal and ethnocidal to the less disruptive and potentially beneficial.

Genocidal

The most bitter example of market impact on the Amazonian peoples came during the rubber boom of 1894 to 1914, particularly in the Upper Amazon. In order to meet the increasing demand for rubber to provide tyres for bicycles and motor vehicles, indigenous peoples were forced into slavery or debt-bondage to produce great quantities for the market. The most notorious and well-documented example was on the Putumayo region, now in Colombia, where the Casa Arana (a Peruvian concern which later became established as the British-based Peruvian Amazon Company) was condemned internationally for its maltreatment of the Indians (Gray, 1990).

Considering the scale of the work, the environmental destruction wrought by the rubber boom was not as severe as the appalling effect on the indigenous peoples of the area, many of whom lost up to 90 per cent of their population through displacement, disease and murder.

Ethnocidal

Less intense but by no means less destructive has been the impact of the market economy on Indians faced by on-coming development projects. The effects of highways in Brazil brought many indigenous communities in contact with the market economy. A report referring to the Parakana Indians, for example, says: *"Since their pacification and resettlement team reported, these Indians had sold their cultural possessions to outsiders in exchange for guns and ammunition and were living off the dole of highway workers along the Trans-Amazon Highway."* (Davis, 1977:68). This episode is typical of many cases in Brazil and elsewhere in the Amazon.

Market control where there is some form of balance

There are examples of Amazonian peoples who have managed to deal with the market economy on their own terms. According to Paul Henley, the Panare, who have refused to participate in replacing their subsistence economy with cash-cropping but exchange handicrafts with the local Criollos, are still able to continue with their subsistence economy (Henley, 1982:224).

In Peru, the Amarakaeri have developed their gold economy on a sustainable basis. By controlling their territories with recognized land titles and emphasising their subsistence economy, they have largely escaped the devastating impact of the market economy (Gray, 1986). However, there have been some difficulties: the buying of commodities, particularly alcohol, has affected the traditional activities and prestige of the women. Even where marketing appears to be not so destructive, the introduction of a cash economy can severely disrupt the community.

Indigenous control

Examples of indigenous peoples controlling their own marketing are hard to find. In the Pichis of Peru and the Rio Negro of Brazil, indigenous peoples are looking at marketing as a process rather than as the selling of produce. They are trying to gain control of transportation, thereby cutting out the middlemen who gain so much profit. COICA describes the way in which this marketing should take place as follows: *"establishment of community controlled marketing channels; establishment of community controlled transport systems."* However, these are only ideals towards which indigenous peoples are moving. Unless they have the time and space to develop these at their own rhythm they will be drawn into a system which will control them.

We can see that markets need not, necessarily, destroy indigenous cultures but they can and do. When indigenous peoples do not control the market process they become dependent on outside bodies. Whether these are unscrupulous middlemen or well-meaning NGOs, it is this dependency that lies at the root of the destruction of indigenous cultures and society. Dependency is the means of shattering the self-determining right of indigenous peoples to control their own lives and futures. Indeed, as one commentator has recently said: *"the solution must surely lie, not in surrendering further to the lure of the market, but in systematically disentangling ourselves from its clutches."* (Hildyard, 1989:62). This need not mean that indigenous peoples should avoid the market for ever but, rather, that they should control and determine their relationship with it.

Whereas dependency is the external way of integrating and assimilating indigenous peoples into an economy over which they have no control, the internal effects are no less problematic. Indigenous economies are renowned because they are based on the principle of reciprocity and redistribution (Dalton, 1965:14). These aspects of circulation of people, products and ideas are firmly embedded in the social and cultural relations of the people concerned (Sahlins, 1974:76). The significance of this is that indigenous society controls economic exchange and therefore production and consumption.

When indigenous peoples enter the market economy and find that they are supplying outside needs apart from their own, their subsistence orientation encounters other needs - the demands of outside interests. The effect is to take the economy out of the social control of the indigenous peoples, which transforms their society greatly (Polyani, 1944). This is precisely what happened in the cases of genocide and ethnocide, mentioned above.

In contrast, the gold economy among the Amarakaeri of Peru has blended more easily into their subsistence economy because they receive money for themselves according to how much they produce. The Peruvian government-controlled mining bank buys their gold at an official price which, although exploitative, enables the Amarakaeri to mine it at their own pace (Gray, 1986). Thus the outside economy is still under the control of Amarakaeri social and cultural relations. The economy is not yet an independent institution out of the control of the people concerned.

Sustainability controlled by consumer demand leads to a fundamental contradiction between limiting and increasing demand. Who will have the upper hand in this conflict of interests - the consumers or the producers? Anthropological work in Africa has demonstrated that domestic production can supply social and economic subsistence needs but, as demands for profit increase, consumer needs force more control over indigenous labour which threatens the very domestic production unit which supports it (Meillassoux, 1981: conclusion).

These examples demonstrate clearly that marketing among indigenous peoples is not an easy matter. The control of their market process covers several areas as has been outlined in a recent series of documents by the Union of Indigenous Nations in Brazil (Hosken and Steranka, 1990: 30-31 & 65):

■ indigenous peoples have to control the processing of products before they go to the market;

■ indigenous peoples have to control the transportation of commodities to market;

■ indigenous peoples themselves have to use their own contacts through their national and international organizations to contact marketing outlets.

In addition to these conditions, some mention must be made of the importance of intellectual property rights of indigenous peoples. This issue, raised particularly by Darrell Posey (1990), is becoming increasingly important as indigenous peoples lose control of their knowledge to unscrupulous business interests who market their ideas for medicines and products for an annual turnover of as much as $43 billion a year (Posey, *op cit*).

If indigenous peoples do not have control over these aspects of the marketing process, they will speedily find themselves in dependency relations with the outside whims of the international market. Merchants and middlemen will syphon off the profits. Middlemen do not have to be local traders; multinational middlemen touting for trade have been a feature of oil, rubber and coca booms.

The relationships of dependency described here are directly analogous to those between the countries of the North and their unequal relations with those of the South. Indigenous peoples present a microcosm of the inequalities and exploitation which takes place at the level of nation states. Thus, indigenous peoples stand to lose, not only as members of nation states of the South but, also, as exploited members within those states.

The current Biodiversity Conservation Strategy of the World Resources Institute includes utilization of the resources as one of its main attributes. On page 89 of *Keeping Options Alive* (1989), the authors say: *"Many actions that can be taken to stem the loss of biodiversity do provide short-term economic benefits - say, maintaining natural forests so that wild species can be harvested for food, medicines, and industrial products or establishing protected areas so that tourists will visit."*

The conservation strategy advocates expanding the short-term utility of biodiversity to increase the potential for new products. This involves fixing 'true' economic values to biodiversity. A recent document on conserving biological diversity (McNeely *et al.*, 1990) considers evaluation one of the fundamental bases of conservation.

The promotion of evaluating the environment is particularly problematic. Not only is it extremely difficult to do, but it actively encourages new speculation in products which can be extracted from the rainforest. In the same way as the heavily criticised Tropical Forestry Action Plan is seen as an advertisement for increasing deforestation, so the Biodiversity Conservation Strategy is attracting outside interests into further rainforest exploitation (Colchester and Lohmann, 1990).

These plans present the peoples of the rainforest as passive recipients of the benefits of green capitalism. However, there are no guidelines to provide locally controlled production methods and marketing. On the contrary, the approach is based on the needs of the northern consumer, who once again will dictate their demands and desires onto the local producers. After initially taking advantage of a few limited benefits these people will, as in the past, find themselves dependent on the development models of outsiders.

Development is the concept which the World Resources Institute (WRI) hopes to wed to biological diversity conservation. Economic utilization of biological diversity will be able to contribute to national development goals. However this says nothing about the effect of 'development' on indigenous peoples.

In addition to the dangers and complexities of market economies on indigenous peoples, there is the continual problem of imposed development. Current initiatives to market the rainforest provide the indigenous and forest peoples of the area with a sustainable means of development to counteract the direction in which development has been going in the last few years. The approach used takes a very economistic vantage point whereby development is seen as a question of cash flows which automatically solve the problems facing indigenous peoples.

However, the development debate in recent years has emphasized that there are two factors which have to play a role as important, if not more important, than economic questions (Henriksen, 1989). The first is known as the 'cultural dimension of development'. This means that sustainable development in itself is not necessarily appropriate culturally. Prohibitions, social production patterns and cosmological questions could all affect a community being persuaded to sell rainforest produce. The new production processes could well enter into conflict with their own world view, causing internal community divisions.

An example of this took place in the rainforest of Peru in an Ashaninka community. They were rice growers and part of the community had decided to increase production and develop sales nationally and internationally. The result was that the community turned themselves over to rice growing exclusively and gained the money they had originally sought, but at the expense of community harmony and respect for traditions. After several major conflicts, the community threw the rice mill into the river, curtailed their profits and returned to making subsistence agriculture their priority (Segundo Macuyama, personal communication).

The second element is the 'political dimension of development', which takes several forms. The first is the idea that indigenous peoples organized in communities naturally tend to form co-operatives. This uniform view of indigenous society is quite mistaken. Over the past 10 years of working gold, the Amarakaeri of south-eastern Peru have worked as communities, as clans, as extended families and even individually. They choose whatever strategy suits them in the current conditions. The imposition of co-operatives from outside could be disastrous to the unity of the community which is frequently kept together by respecting internal divisions.

The other aspect of the 'political dimension' is the top-down approach to development, where sustainability is but a cloak for encouraging integration of indigenous peoples into the market economy, aided and abetted by the general public and unwitting companies.

This paper raises several points at variance with the idea of encouraging indigenous peoples to enter markets before they have worked out their own strategies. The economistic basis of marketing threatens to swamp cultures and societies with money-based priorities, over and above those of territorial rights, organizational strengthening and health.

Markets can destroy more easily than they can help. Only when forest peoples can control the time and space of marketing on their own terms and be able to take their own decisions can we begin to talk of fair and balanced exchanges.

The emphasis on extractive reserves and marketing at this stage is important for those forest peoples wanting immediate cash resources. However, extractive reserves and commerce may well not provide all the needs of forest peoples as their resource base becomes ever more under threat. Small-scale projects and self-development strategies are essential components of the self-determination of their lives and cultures. Without these conditions, all marketing hopes will be very uncertain.

In terms of priorities, land rights, control over resources and the self-determination of their lives and development are the basis for indigenous production without which all their marketing hopes will be very risky. Furthermore, profits for investors from abroad will also be very uncertain. The dilemma facing commercial environmentalists and indigenous marketers is that without indigenous rights and control over production, processing and marketing, there will be no consistency in productivity as outside interests scramble for whatever profits they can grab from the area.

Where companies do make profits, they will be subject to scrutiny that they are not responsible for exploiting indigenous communities or encouraging their integration into the international economy. On the other hand when indigenous peoples control the market the companies will find themselves in competition with indigenous peoples themselves and this will subsequently reduce their share of profits.

Produce gathered, grown or extracted as well as marketed and controlled by forest peoples, could be of positive benefit. Anything else will just increase the present pressures for them to change in line with the economic priorities of others. Forest peoples who wish to go ahead certainly should be free to determine their future and take the risk but we should all think of the destruction which those non-indigenous peoples have wrought in going out to the Amazon bearing gifts and promising the indigenous peoples an answer to all their problems in return for commodities.

As the Yanomami die of malaria in Roraima Brazil, the Ashaninka of Peru are emerging from years of slavery. In Venezuela, pollution of the rainforest and, in Paraguay, encroachment on indigenous lands all show that, for many of the indigenous peoples of the Amazon, marketing is not their top priority. We must not force our priorities onto them. We must listen to forest peoples from all parts of the Amazon and give them pride of place in our support and understanding.

We have to link markets to the overall demands of indigenous peoples. We have to perceive their needs from their point of view and we have to respect their ways of approaching these problems and respond to their needs. We have to be reactive to their needs for marketing, not proactive and seeking our solutions to their problems. As an indigenous leader once said to me: *"We prefer to make our own mistakes rather than having the mistakes of others thrust down our throats"*.

The days when indigenous peoples' problems are solved paternalistically should be over. They are capable of facing these difficulties themselves and we should be listening to their voices. If we do not, we will turn the marketing of rainforest products into a commercial side show as we witness the destruction of the rainforest and the extinction and assimilation of the indigenous and forest peoples who have been custodians of the diversity of species there for thousands of years.

An indigenous leader (IWGIA, 1985) once told the story of an elephant and a duck who was sitting on her eggs. He likened the elephant to environmentalists (in this case, 'green capitalists') and the duck to indigenous peoples. The duck was killed by an encroaching colonist, leaving her eggs unattended. The kind-hearted elephant decided to do his friend the duck a favour. He sat on the eggs.

Acknowledgements

This paper was written with the support of WWF-UK and the Rainforest Peoples' Fund. I am grateful to them, the Gaia Foundation, International Work Group for Indigenous Affairs, Survival International and the World Rainforest Movement for providing many useful documents. However, the opinions expressed here do not, necessarily, reflect those of the organizations concerned. The text is an extended version of the third chapter of a forthcoming report on the relationship between indigenous peoples and biodiversity. It concentrates on the impacts of the World Resources Institute's Biodiversity Conservation Strategy and its impact on indigenous peoples.

References

Aikman, S H (1982). Informe preliminar sobre hallazgos de Rio Karene (Rio Colorado). Madre de Dios. *Amazonia Peruana* 3:6. Lima

Baker, L (1989). Cultural Survival imports: marketing the rainforest. *Cultural Survival Quarterly* 13 (3):64-67

Belshaw, C (1965). *Traditional Exchange and Modern Markets.* Prentice Hall, Englewood Cliffs

COICA (1989). *To the Community of Concerned Environmentalists.* Manuscript, Lima

Colchester, M (1981). Ecological modelling and indigenous systems of resource-use: some examples from south Venezuela. *Anthropologica* 55:51-72

Colchester, M (1989). Indian development in Amazonia: risks and strategies. *The Ecologist* 19 (6):249-254

Colchester, M and L Lohmann (1990). *Tropical Forestry Action Plan: What Progress?* Friends of the Earth, World Rainforest Movement and The Ecologist

Dalton, G (1965). Primitive, archaic and modern economics: Karl Polanyi's contribution to economic anthropology and comparative economy. In, *Essays in Economic Anthropology.* American Ethnological Society, Seattle

Davis, S (1977). *Victims of the Miracle: Development and the Indians of Brazil.* C V P

Gray, A (1986). *And After the Gold Rush...? Human Rights and Self-Development in South-eastern Peru.* IWGIA Document No 55. Copenhagen

Gray, A (1990). *The Putumayo Atrocities Revisited.* Paper presented at Oxford University seminar on the State, boundaries and Indians. Manuscript

Henley, P (1982). *The Panare: Tradition and Change on the Amazon Frontier.* Yale University Press

Henriksen, G (1989). *Introduction to Indigenous Self-Development in the Americas.* IWGIA Document No 63, Copenhagen

Hildyard, N (1989). Adios Amazonia: A report from the Altamira gathering. *The Ecologist* 19(2):53-62

Hodges, R (1988). *Primitive and Peasant Markets.* Blackwell, Oxford

Hosken, L and K Steranka (eds) (1990). *A tribute to the Forest Peoples of Brazil.* The Gaia Foundation

Hugh-Jones, S (1987). *Yesterday's Luxuries, Tomorrow's Necessities: Business and Barter in the North West Amazon.* Manuscript

IWGIA (1985). *Sri Lanka: World Council Statement to UN on Vedda.* IWGIA Newsletter Nos 43 & 44, pp 291-293. Copenhagen

McNeely, J, K Miller, W Reid, R Mittermeier, and T Werner (1990). *Conserving the World's Biodiversity.* IUCN, Gland, Switzerland; WRI, CI, WWF-USA and the World Bank, Washington DC, USA

Meillassoux, C (1981). *Maidens, Meal and Money - Capitalism and the Domestic Community.* Cambridge University Press

Myers, N (1989). *Deforestation Rates in Tropical Forests and their Climatic Implications.* Friends of the Earth, London

Polanyi, K (1944). *The Great Transformation.* New York, Rinehart

Posey, D (1990). *Intellectual Property Rights and Just Compensation for Indigenous Knowledge: Challenges to Science, Business and International Law.* Paper presented to the Association for Applied Anthropology, York

Reid, W and K Miller (1989). *Keeping Options Alive: the Scientific Basis for Conserving Biodiversity.* WRI, Washington

Sahlins, M (1974). *Culture and Practical Reason.* University of Chicago Press

Wolf, E (1982). *Europe and the People without History.* University of California Press

Land Security, Self Sufficiency and Cultural Integrity in the Philippines

Reverend Delbert Rice
Kalahan Educational Foundation, Inc. Imugan, Santa Fe, 3705 Nueva Vizcaya, The Philippines

Summary

This paper outlines Reverend Rice's work with the Ikalahan tribal people who live in Nueva Vizaya in the mountains of northern Luzon in the Philippines. Fairly recently, these people pioneered with the Government what is now called the Communal Forest Stewardship Agreement which gave the Ikalahan legal control of their ancestral lands, as a result of which they implemented various land use plans. Reverend Rice closes the paper by discussing the harvesting and processing of fruits into successful product lines of jams, jellies and marmalades.

The Ikalahan people live in the Caraballo Mountains of the northern Philippines at an elevation of between 650 and 1300 metres. They are a tribal community who have managed their own lands for several centuries, with little regard to the policies of the Government or the ideologies of dominant societies in the Philippines. They have kept themselves aloof from these outside influences. They have protected their mountain resources in the knowledge and confidence that their children and grandchildren will, one day, continue these same traditions.

However, at the end of the Second World War the Philippine government attempted to exercise authority over the Ikalahan, who were suddenly threatened with the loss of their ancestral lands through the declaration of a forest reserve. Because they suddenly felt that they no longer had security over their lands, they stopped protecting them. They decided it was necessary to extract as much as they could in the shortest possible time so that they would have something to take with them if they were driven away. Degradation was the result.

A major change occurred in 1974 when the Ikalahan incorporated themselves and pioneered what is now called the Communal Forest Stewardship Agreement with the Philippine government. They were given legal control of their ancestral lands and they began to protect them once again. Today, it is easy to see that the forests are regenerating and that the water supply is returning.

The primary food of the Ikalahan is sweet potato (*Ipomea batatas*) which are grown on the steep slopes of the mountains, usually at around 45 degrees. Their agricultural techniques, however, are so well integrated with the forest ecosystem that, as long as they are free to exercise them properly, there is no damage. They have merely integrated an agricultural element into the forest cycle.

The Ikalahan have begun to plant valuable paddy rice on the small amounts of flat ground. However, as less than 1 per cent of their lands can be cultivated in this way they cannot produce enough rice to use as a basic food. Where possible, they are now also extending their terraces, and have begun using these small areas of level land for vegetable production.

As soon as the community was given control of its own land, its leaders decided to try to prevent the use of chemicals in their agricultural practices. In fact in May 1990, about 20 young farmers were visited by a professor from the University of the Philippines in Los Baños to learn how best to maximize output whilst preventing the use of chemicals.

Their goal is self-sufficiency. They manufacture their own tools and equipment whenever possible, because they do not want to be dependent on others unless it is absolutely necessary. They have known how to weave their own garments for generations, and how to teach the young the skills to produce the necessary clothing. Some of the children have also studied tailoring and dressmaking so that they can have modern clothes should they want them.

They have always collected their own housing materials from the forests using only knives and axes but recently they have begun to use handsaws to make boards, making their residences more permanent. This too is an indirect result of control over their lands. In the past the bridges they have built have been temporary. Some of the young people, however, are now graduating as engineers and teaching the villagers how to build permanent bridges, but they still work together as they have done for centuries, integrating modern technology with ancient customs.

In an effort to bring some cash into their economy they have begun to use traditional skills such as broom and basket making to produce handicrafts for sale to outside markets. To provide access to modern technology, they have established their own high school where the children study science, history and communication skills and learn about their own ancient culture. Modernization is not appropriate if it reduces the quality of life. Fortunately, this has not happened to the Ikalahan because their approach is appropriate for them.

The Ikalahan people are now expanding their horizons in many directions. Some of their people, and especially the graduates of the high school, are becoming community assistance workers in other tribal communities, for example in Aeta in Zambales province, Mangyan and Gobatnon communities on Mindoro Island, Tagbanua on Palawan, and others. In all of these, they spread the same message: be self-sufficient, protect your resources and cultural integrity.

I have already mentioned that Ikalahan agriculture is merely one phase of the forest cycle. It usually involves two years of food production followed by a long fallow period which also produces fuel and fencing materials. Because the elders now have control over the land, they are working to improve it for their grandchildren. They have discovered ways of improving food production with new varieties of sweet potato. They have also improved the fallow system by planting fertility-restoring plants that reduce the fallow period from 14 to 7 years. By integrating these methods into the ancient system, they can increase the carrying capacity of the area from 400 to 800 families while still allowing the forests to expand.

Cash is now coming from several sources. I have already mentioned baskets but that is now minimal because of the lack of rattan. There is a bigger market for brooms, and the raw materials for these are good for erosion control in the forests. They are also shipping out resins from the pine trees. They have found it advisable to 'weed' their forests by occasionally removing a few over-mature and defective trees. These are used to make lumber, which provides a small income in addition to improving the forests.

Another very important source of cash is the harvesting and processing of fruits, mostly from the wild. Most of these are turned into jams, jellies, marmalades and preserves. This is a new technology here, but they have manufactured their own equipment and have been able to integrate this technology into their own culture so that it functions without serious disruption.

The Ikalahan people are very independently-minded, so each farmer must have his own individual farm, but they also know how to work together for community benefit if necessary. This combination of individual initiative and community involvement enables them to prove that they can provide a good living for their families, whilst protecting the watershed for the nation. We must remember, however, that this happened because of the greater motivation that arose with village land security.

Building and Supplying Markets for Non-wood Tropical Forest Products

Dr Jason Clay
Director of Research, Cultural Survival, 11 Divinity Ave, Cambridge, MA O2138 USA

Summary

This paper examines Cultural Survival's role in the development of international markets for non-wood tropical forest products and the role of this development in defending the forests.

A number of Amazonian communities - Indians, rubber tappers and some peasants - are attempting to maintain their way of life and expand their sources of income by taking more products from the forests on a sustainable basis. Their efforts buttress the recommendations of botanists, anthropologists and environmentalists, who have argued that healthy forests are capable of generating more income (and more employment in the long-term) than the same areas cleared and put into pasture or crops. Unfortunately, income obtained from the forest rarely amounts to more than a fraction of what is possible. That is because on the one hand, indigenous communities cannot find markets or incentives. On the other, potential buyers do not know about forest products. Nevertheless, a sound economic as well as ecological argument can be made for harvesting from existing forests rather than clearing them for alternative economic uses.

Given some of the papers that have been presented to the Conference, I think maybe I should change my title to "Why should a human rights group get involved in creating international markets for non-wood tropical forest products?" I would like to touch on this matter a bit because I think it relates not only to why we are doing it, but also how we are doing it.

It is nice that the world has finally become aware of the destruction of rainforests. Unfortunately, not many people are aware that forests cannot be cut until you remove the people that have been indigenous to them. And that is what has been happening throughout the last century. Since 1900, one Indian tribe has disappeared from Brazil each year: 90 out of 270 groups are gone. The rate of cultural destruction is much faster than the rate of environmental degradation.

Why is this taking place? Brazil has fantastic laws for the protection of Indian rights. In the twentieth century there are also better international laws and covenants regarding indigenous people's rights to land, laws against genocide etc. I think what this should tell us is that laws and international agreements are not enough. I do not think Brazil is an exception - this is true around the world. To stop this destruction, the people who live in rainforest areas must become organized to defend themselves and not depend solely on the laws that give them title to their land, for example.

Since 1972, Cultural Survival has existed to help such peoples - indigenous peoples living in isolated areas, often rainforest. We were organized, not only to help them survive, but to find a meaningful existence of their own choosing - an existence where they can choose the degree and the speed at which they become part of larger social and economic systems. We decided very early on that advocacy, publicity and press releases would not be enough to save these people, and that most of our efforts and monies would have to be spent on projects. These projects are designed and run by the indigenous people themselves. This allows them to organize politically to push for, and then defend, their land and resource rights. We also fund sustainable development projects which allow groups to maintain the resource base that they will depend on today and in future generations. I might add, it is in this defence of the resource base that they are also defending our global environment.

Like most human rights groups, we stopped right there - we thought our job was done. In fact, it was becoming increasingly clear that, if you help people who have material needs produce for the market more efficiently from an environmental and social point of view but then do not get involved in the hard negotiations to give them a better price for their product, you have stopped too soon. All that you will have done is to ensure that this group enters the market economy on the bottom rung and stays there forever.

Even the most isolated groups living in rainforest areas, with very few exceptions, have material needs that today can only be met in the market-place. Furthermore, these groups' populations are increasing. This is true of the Amazonian basin and it's true of Africa and South-east Asia as well. We could try to leave such groups alone but nobody else would. We could build a fence around them, or even think about building a fence around the entire Amazon but these are not workable options. Yet, if things continue as they have done so in the last few years, it will all be over for such groups very soon.

So what can we do? Clearly we do not abandon our work on land rights, political organizing and sustainable development. What we must do, in fact, is add to it. Our approach has been to see if there are markets for sustainably harvested rainforest products which can be used to support those who live in rainforest. Incidentally, it is our goal not to stop with rainforest groups but to work with indigenous groups in other ecosystems, as well, and not just in the Amazon Basin but eventually in Africa and Asia, too.

We have made a strategic decision not to work with wood products because we are concerned about the sustainability of harvesting wood in tropical forests. Nevertheless, I think an excellent case can be made about how timber harvesting in the Philippines is proceeding in what seems to be a very sustainable way. So we may have to begin to reconsider this position as more data comes in. Similarly, we will not trade medicinal plants. Our position on this issue is not permanent either, but rather one where we shall wait until we can see what kinds of rights we can negotiate - *eg* patent rights and royalties - for the people who live in the rainforest. They have, after all, protected these ecosystems and often identified the plants with the very properties that pharmaceutical companies want. These rights need to be paid for if they are going to be used in the West for medicines. It is this payment, this transfer, that needs to be made if people who live in the rainforest are going to have the kinds of income that will allow them to live there, sustainably, whilst at the same time protecting a valuable global resource.

Hence, our approach has been to focus on non-wood and non-medicinal forest products. In the last 18 months, I purchased approximately 350 different products from existing markets in the Amazon and these have been shown to 92 different companies in North America and Europe. We have decided only to purchase those commodities that already exist on markets in the Amazon because we are not interested in creating new markets - we think that this could be extremely destructive. We also decided not to go to producer groups, initially, until we found out from companies which of the products we had brought in sample form might actually have markets outside the region. We were not interested in creating a lot of enthusiasm only to have it dashed if none of the sample products actually did have markets.

The types of products we focused on are nuts, fruits, oils, resins, essences, pigments and flours. Of the nearly 50 products that have been identified so far by the various businesses, we have had orders placed on nearly 25. The companies we are working with range from Fortune 500 companies to very small, start-up companies created just to market rainforest products and to put profits back into the rainforest. They have agreed, in the short-term, to accept whatever quantities and qualities we can provide them with, in the hope that we will be willing to work with them and the suppliers to both increase the quantity from various sources and the quality from all sources.

Once we have identified these products, we approach local organizations - in the first instances, Indians and rubber tappers - to see which of these products they would be interested in producing for sale, in whatever quantities, and processing locally in the forest or nearby towns, thereby allowing them to earn far more than from the production of raw materials. At the same time, we turn to botanists and ask them which of the shortlisted products that are of interest to companies can be produced sustainably, which should not be produced at all, and which ones raise questions or concerns that need to be noted or that should guide our own attempts at marketing. The information we are getting from botanists on these 50 species is put in databases and made available to other groups and scientists that, for example, are doing work on economic botany.

A tremendous amount of the botanical research in the Amazon - I doubt it is terribly different in other parts of the world - is on plant species that are not used, that have no commercial value. Ironically, we know very little about some of the most economically rewarding plants in these areas. An example of this is the Brazil nut tree. Nobody knows how long a Brazil nut tree will live. Nobody knows how they reproduce, the number of seeds that one can expect to actually take root in a forest or whether the seeds are planted by animals or Indians or simply drop to the ground. Nobody knows, really, how many nuts an average Brazil nut tree will produce and, in fact, many botanists are under the assumption that the commonly-harvested Brazil nuts are produced in less than a year.

Rubber, too, is little understood. What is the effect

of taking latex out of a rubber tree? Are those trees effectively made sterile so that they do not reproduce? Has any botanist actually looked at rubber extraction in the Amazon and seen what is happening with those plants? These are the kinds of analyses that are going to become very important as we increase markets for other commodities in the Amazon Basin and it strikes me that we, as an organization, are going to have to look long and hard to find the botanists willing to do the research that is so essential in this kind of project.

When the information is back from the potential producer groups and the botanists, we begin to look at the current market structures for each of the commodities, as each has a different production and marketing system. Copaiba oil is different from andiroba or babassu oil and they are each different from any Brazil nuts or cupuassu seeds that may be harvested. Each product usually has a different set of producers and certainly a different set of merchants and processors. You have to understand this to know where to intercede in the system to make it more productive (and add more value closer to the forest), when it is possible for local people to process the products, and when it is not worth either your or their time.

One example of the commonly known products that we are beginning to market is a major commodity - Brazil nuts. It involves a restructuring of the existing market so that people who collect Brazil nuts can actually get more money from their activities. In 1989, we found that the people who gathered Brazil nuts in Xapuri, a co-operative in Acre in western Brazil, received about 4 to 5 cents per pound or 2 to 3 per cent of the New York wholesale price for the nuts they collected. At that low return, these people still earned 3 to 5 times as much per area as for beef produced for sale in the market-place locally. Very clearly, if we can increase the return that these people are getting from 2 or 3 per cent to an amount closer to that on the New York market, we can make their returns over meat production in that area higher still.

I need to point out that this calculation is based only on Brazil nuts at that low price. It does not include rubber or any other commodity extracted from the area. On the other hand, the calculation for cattle does not include the costs to clear the forest, plant the pasture, build the fences, buy the breeding stock, loss of cows or any of the other costs associated with producing those kilos of beef. Between beef and nuts alone at current prices we are talking about a factor of 4 in favour of nuts. In addition, at current prices, employment generation in the nut industry is extremely high compared to that for beef production.

We have done a couple of things to change this system. The co-operative in Xapuri has already organized itself to transport nuts to a local city where, by moving the nuts, they can, at minimum, double their income. In 1990, we also financed the first nut processing plant owned by the forest residents who collect the nuts. This processing plant should allow the collectors to earn about ten times as much from their nuts while generating local employment as well.

During the past year we were able to provide working capital by advancing, through a 180 day letter of credit purchase agreement, the money needed to finance the day-to-day needs of the co-operative. We are looking for similar, innovative financial mechanisms to finance, through loans that can be repaid in produce, the expansion of this factory and construction of other similar ones in coming years. One of the overreaching assumptions of our work in developing markets is that the new systems cannot be subsidized, at least in the long-term. If they do not work financially, then they will not last because it is certain that the international interests that would allow them to be subsidized in the short-term will certainly wane in a matter of a few years.

In 1991, we will work with the co-operative to add even more value to their produce. For example, with a small oil press, the co-operative will be able to process rancid nuts for their oil, thus producing an internationally tradable item from an otherwise worthless byproduct. We are also working with the Xapuri co-operative on a new shelling system which would allow members to shell nuts in their own houses and then bring the finished, more valuable product to the factory for classification, drying, and packing for export. This system not only allows the factory to be used more efficiently, it also reduces the number of nuts lost through spoilage and reduces the weight and volume of the nuts to be transported by about 60 per cent, thus reducing overall transportation costs by about the same measure.

Of course, another way to increase the long-term viability of co-operatives such as the one at Xapuri is to diversify their production and hence their source of income. For that reason, in 1991, we will begin to look at the viability of other products from the co-operative - *eg* rubber produced at a co-operative- owned processing plant, copaiba, vanilla, and vegetable ivory. The less dependent each co-operative is on either a single product or a single purchaser, the more they reduce their overall risk of financial failure.

In 1991 we will begin to work with other local co-operatives to harvest, process and export babassu oil, cashew nuts and dried fruit and copaiba oil, to name but a few. In each instance the goal will be to create a market for these goods which is larger than the co-operatives can produce. In this way, they are protected from any market declines. The difference can be met through purchases on the normal commercial market.

By 1990, 17 companies were producing rainforest products. Some 75 others, however, are still testing products and determining availability, quality and marketability. One to two years should be enough time in which to expand production and marketing outlets. Likewise, it will be important to begin to expand the marketing of other, non-food items as well as to identify products from other countries with rainforests.

If marketing is to expand significantly, it eventually must involve mainstream companies that have no direct political interest in tropical-forest issues. We believe that with the current high level of interest in tropical forests, such corporations can be convinced that a move to include rainforest products in existing product lines could be a wise marketing strategy. We hope these initial market efforts will demonstrate to other potential producers, exporters, international companies and governments that there is money to be made through the maintenance of tropical forests and the marketing of sustainable collected products.

Because public interest and marketing trends shift rapidly, however, it is important to move quickly to find new markets for rainforest materials. If the recent interest helps us to capture a small corner of the marketplace, we can create a taste for rainforest products and a demand that will not disappear when today's environment fad fades.

Discussion

Panel
Thomas Walschburger, Dr Andrew Gray, Dr Jason Clay, Dr Stephen Schwartzman, Dr Anthony Anderson, Antonio Macedo

Aubrey Meyer, Willesden Green. My question picks up on Dr Gray's paper. I was delighted to hear the strength with which you delivered that message, it was really inspiring. The only point I thought was missing was that if you really do want to address the problems in a fundamental (and bottom-up) way, it is possibly wrong for us here to assume that the answer is, quote 'in the Amazon'. The answer (again from a bottom-up perspective) is also right here - we have to green our societies and ways of living, in London, in Europe and so on.

There is a comparable statistic from South Africa which illustrates the problem quite well. Approximately 87 per cent of land in the country is allocated to the white population, who represent only a fifth or sixth of the total. These proportions correspond to the patterns of energy consumption when comparing the First World and the Third World. The populations of developed countries, although in the minority, are drastically over-exploiting energy and other resources. Unless we actually start to address this issue as directly relevant to the conservation of rainforests, we actually have no business to be having these discussions, because they will end up being what we fear most - which is top-down and paternalistic.

Dr Andrew Gray. I would not like to disagree with that.

Jeremy Haggar, Tropical Ecologist, University of Cambridge. I have great sympathy with what Andrew Gray has said, but is it not the unfortunate case that these Indian populations are living in countries that have governments that are market-orientated. One of the main reasons why the Indians have been losing their land is because it has been the view that land within Indian reserves has been lost to development for the benefit of the country. Maybe one of the aims of this Conference is to demonstrate and persuade governments that land handed back to indigenous peoples and turned over for extractive reserves benefits the country and should not be destroyed.

Thomas Walschburger. I believe that in Colombia the situation is different now. The President of Colombia is recognizing indigenous peoples rights over their traditional territories. We have more than 18 million hectares of Indian reserves. Obviously, that is still not enough but there is strong recognition of Indian territories in Colombia. I think that countries like Peru and Bolivia are also now working on recognizing indigenous peoples' rights.

Questioner. I was very inspired by Dr Gray's talk but there was something that I thought was lacking in spite of the overwhelming applause, much of which I think was self-denigratory because there is nothing that environmentalists like more than a bit of soul searching and finding that it is really all their own fault. We have been told that the indigenous communities of the Amazon and elsewhere do not need money, they do not need commercialization, they do not like tourism, and least of all they do not like top-down environmentalists in the guise of elephants.

But what they do want is their own cultural integrity, land integrity and so on. My feeling is that, in fact, they need all of these things if they are to obtain that integrity. They do need environmentalists, they may well need tourism, they certainly do need our concern, and I would like to see maybe some more positive suggestions from Dr Gray about what we should be doing, how we could be working together, rather than in confrontation which is very much what you seemed to be suggesting.

Dr Andrew Gray. I must say that I did not maintain that they should not have any money or any marketing; that is the very point I was really trying to make. Secondly, I was not attacking environmentalists per se, I was attacking commercialized environmentalists, who see the solution only in terms of commercialism. I do not see that as a problem generally. There are some fantastic things going on at the moment, for example organizations like the World Rainforest Movement which is the most wonderful example of environmentalists and indigenous peoples working together. COICA (Co-ordinating Body for the Indigenous Peoples' Organizations in the Amazon Basin) are also working together with environmentalists in the US and they have also been over here. Of course the solution has to come by these means.

What I am saying is start by listening to the Indians. I agree with what you have said; I am not laying into all environmentalists - quite the contrary. I am trying to encourage those very fine examples of co-operation that have already started. But I think it is very important that at a Conference like this, a slightly stronger position should be made in order to counterbalance the 'current' flow.

Questioner. There are other non-indigenous populations within the rainforest that need to be considered and their conflicts of interest are much stronger than the positive items of co-operation you have mentioned. The rainforest cannot just be for indigenous peoples. How do you reconcile the problems with pressures of land, urban communities and increasing population levels? Do you just want to keep these issues separate?

Dr Andrew Gray. Nobody ever said the rainforest was only for indigenous peoples. However, they were there first and they have got the prior claims to it and their land rights should be respected. It is also extremely important that the other populations of the rainforest should have their rights respected. The extractive reserves are extremely important and should be given as strong and inalienable rights as the Indians. The point is it is not for me to say; it is for forest people to get together as one and that is being achieved through organizations like the World Rainforest Movement. My particular talk was on indigenous peoples. Of course you have to look at the whole picture. That is why I am talking about a bottom-up approach - you have got to start at the root of local problems, you cannot just bypass them. Everybody blames the middlemen but maybe they too are caught in some sort of chain-economy. So, something has to be done that takes into consideration all aspects of the area but also respects the rights of indigenous peoples.

Dr Jason Clay. I agree with Andrew Gray in that we need to leave the decision as to whether indigenous people want to be involved with market economies to them. However, in our 20 years of existence and on-the-ground funding of projects with indigenous peoples throughout the world, we have not found any groups that are not, in some way, involved with the market economy, nor have we found groups that don't want to get a better price for goods that they are producing. In our work in Brazil we have found that groups want to increase their control over how they interact in the market and perhaps I will say more about this later. I think the point is that groups such as COICA, to the Kuna in Panama and others, have definitely recognized that their material needs can be met in the market-place. Today, however, these same people are being exploited in this same market and therefore need our support.

Questioner. I would like to direct my question to Dr Gray. He said that indigenous peoples are looking for markets with which to trade. Some of these markets create needs where none have existed before. In Nepal, there has been tremendous pressure on the forests due to the demand for firewood because people need to cook for tourists. For the first time in years, there has been hunger in Bali to meet the needs of tourists; for example, women are selling and cooking eggs for Americans which before would have gone to their children. In New Zealand, in an attempt to market the resources of the Maoris, the missionaries have created needs that did not exist before. Do you see this happening more and more?

Dr Andrew Gray. Yes, with qualifications. The market is not a fixed thing, it is very much bound up with social relations and the history of a particular area. For example, let us consider the Amarakaeri, who have traditionally worked gold. I think that rather than emphasize the goods themselves, we should be thinking of the type of production and whether they are in fact controlling the amount that they wish to produce. The Amarakaeri have always said to me, "no, we are not maximizing"; they have other things they want to do - hunt, fish and so on. And I think that whether they have gramophones, wind up record-players or the like is not as significant or important as whether they are in a position to determine whether they get these in accordance with their own traditional principles: or whether in fact they are foresaking them because of an obligation to pay off debts, or to get over exploitative relationships from another sort of external-type economy which prevents them from carrying out their own subsistence economy and turns them effectively into wage labourers. So I would turn it around; I do not disagree with you, but, I feel that perhaps we should start looking, in terms of the international markets, at relationships between production and consumption .

Dr Maria Allegretti, President - Instituto de Estudos Amazonicos. First of all, I would like to make two criticisms concerning the organization of this seminar. It is Brazilians who are creating extractive reserves but we are not asked to make presentations at this Conference. This gives me the impression that people think that others can speak better for us than we can for ourselves and that is a kind of colonialism that I do not like very much[1].

The other issue is that of simultaneous translation. People who are not fluent in English like myself and Antonio Macedo cannot participate in the discussions without simultaneous translation and consequently we become objects of observation rather than participants. I think it is time for the organizers of this seminar to take on the commitment to organize a seminar like this in Brazil. It is the second time that I have been at a conference where extremely important discussions about Brazil are going on outside the country, and I think they should help us to organize a seminar on this scale in Brazil.

Secondly, with relation to the presentations, I think there is some confusion about the concept of extractive reserves that I would like to clarify. First of all is the notion that extractive reserves, as a panacea or the salvation of the Amazon, does not have its origin among the people that are organizing and creating them. I have the impression that the concept was created by international environmental organizations that see it as some kind of salvation and something that we never thought of.

Originally, extractive reserves were conceived as a solution for people who lived by utilizing certain resources. They were not invented by us, but were created out of a social demand from the local level. Anthropologists and researchers were then called in, but the concept of extractive reserves was born of local social demand. I think that the concept of extractive reserves cannot be frozen. You cannot say, Anthony Anderson, that Cachoeira is a typical extractive reserve; each one is very different from the other. A model of a typical reserve does not exist. Cachoeira was there before the extractive reserve was created and cannot be considered to be what an extractive reserve is supposed to be. Extractive reserves are in the process of being created and one cannot say that Cachoeira will characterize them all.

Chair. The points that Maria Allegretti made are all very valid. First of all, I apologize that we simply could not afford simultaneous translation. It would have been a marvellous thing to have had but way beyond our resources. Your suggestion of a conference covering these same topics in Brazil is obviously an excellent one and maybe you could try and organize it.

Your points about the local creation of extractive reserves in Acre and idea that existing extractive reserves do not constitute frozen models but can evolve in different ways are very helpful observations. I am worried about time, but perhaps just two questions taking that very important comment from Acre into account.

Shyam Sunder, Karnataka Forestry Department. I have a suggestion which follows on from what has already been mentioned today - that a proportion of current degradation is due to uneconomic returns. Research centres around the world have developed clones of the rubber tree which yield about five times that obtained from the natural trees. Would it be worthwhile if we attempt to help the Indians plant these more productive clones in degraded areas so that their harvest yields would be much higher. This could equally apply to the rest of the tropical countries. It might be useful if better clones are made available to those people.

Dr Anthony Anderson. I think these views are shared by all of us that presented papers here - that extractive reserves are not static entities and that they will have to undergo transformations. I entirely agree with Maria Allegretti's concern in relation to the concept that extractive reserves are viewed as panaceas for the salvation of the Amazon, and that this concept is primarily a First World one where extractive reserves are seen, for example, as a way of preserving biodiversity. I have serious reservations about this, primarily because it is a development model that could potentially provide only for a group of long-term residents within the Amazon.

I also think the political battle has largely been won to the extent that extractive reserves are now a legally established entity within the Amazon and have the potential perhaps of being utilized in other countries. The next step is to fortify them and make them more viable economically, and that means bringing technologies from other rainforest areas; places like Africa where there is already a technology for utilizing edible leaves within the rainforest. What about the possibilities of bringing in crops from other areas such as rattan which I think might be very interesting for use in degraded areas? I think we have to think of a whole range of possible ways to consolidate land-uses within these areas and strengthen the position of rubber tappers.

Questioner. Given that there are a lot of problems getting extractive reserves to pay on an economic level, would there not be a case for introducing some limited but well-paying form of timber extraction alongside all the other rainforest products that exist in the extractive reserves. It seems to me that to swing from a form of timber extraction that at present is currently destroying huge tracts of Amazonia to an alternative model which totally discounts timber is having the pendulum swung too far the other way. Would this not then provide a role for the consumers who might be prepared to pay premium prices for timber, harvested in conjunction with an overall and sensible management plan for various rainforest products? Such timber could be useful and have a positive role to play alongside other rainforest products in an extractive reserve.

Dr Anthony Anderson. There might be some disagreement here amongst the panel on this, but I quite agree. If we look at the Brazilian Amazon region, we find that there are over 4000 licenced industrial wood processors in the region and probably twice that many unlicenced. They employ about 25 per cent of the region's industrial labour force and contribute to about 15 per cent of the regional product. They cannot be ignored. I find it incomprehensible that we would have a conference on extraction and simply avoid, from the outset, any discussion about timber extraction. It is a central part of extraction and it must be considered.

Questioner. Can I ask Antonio Macedo whether it is possible to integrate selective logging in extractive reserves?

Antonio Macedo. First of all, I agree with the comments made by Maria Allegretti. In this seminar there have been many positions with many ideas expressed that are going to make great contributions to the work that we are doing in the Amazon and other areas. I would like to make a few comments of my own and then I want to ask for clarification from Anthony Anderson of some of the things he said as I had difficulty understanding it all, as I do not speak English.

These discussions are very valid and the seminar has good intentions. I think it is too early at this moment to confirm whether extractive reserves are economically viable or not. First, we do not have a single extractive reserve that has been implemented from our point of view. Second, taking São Luis de Remanso as an example of an extractive reserve, this was created under government regulations, in contrast to Cachoeira where the reserve was created through the struggle of the rubber tappers. Blood was lost getting the reserve created at the time when São Luis de Remanso was expropriated by the Government. It was an extractive settlement project which did not fulfil all the criteria that we think are important for the creation of reserves.

The emergence of the proposal for the creation of extractive reserves was seen as an alternative to the disorderly process of development that was going on in the Amazon. We were trying to construct the best possible model; that is why we are participating in discussions here and in the forest.

Speaking in practical terms, not in scientific terms, I think that the extractive reserve is a solution for the occupants of the Amazon region. When you raise the issue of whether there are 300 or 500 hectares per family of land, you have to view it in the context that land had become this incredible commodity that was being turned over and sold very rapidly. One of the points of creating extractive reserves was to stop this uncontrolled speculation. I would just like to close by saying that extractive reserves, in my view, are an economic, social and political alternative for the Amazon.

Editors' footnote

1. Many Brazilians - including Antonio Macedo, Mario de Lima and Dr José Lutzenberger - were present at the Conference and Antonio Macedo gave a presentation concerning extractive reserves from a community perspective.

Sustainable Strategies for Saving Tropical Forests: The Ghanaian Case

Professor Kwabena Tufuor
Ag Chief Administrator, Forestry Commission, 4 Third Avenue Bridge, PO Box M434, Ministry Post Office, Accra, Ghana

Summary

Causes of forest land degradation in Ghana include open-cast mining, logging, illegal farming and fires. Generally it is agriculture-based development that has led to the greatest clearance, but this has been accelerated by timber operations which have improved the accessibility of migrants to previously closed forests.

Sustainable strategies for saving Ghana's tropical forests include: effective forest management; a forest inventory (including non-timber products); rationalization of the annual allowable cut; greater control of wood waste; rural and industrial tree planting; and the development of appropriate and sustainable agroforestry systems. Ghana's participation in the Tropical Forestry Action Plan is also discussed.

Introduction

The tropical high forest regions and woodlands of Ghana have a long tradition of human activity. The increasing demographic pressures on the forests are due to increases in demand for food, energy, infrastructure, fibres, housing and other commodities.

Causes of forest land degradation in Ghana include a range of activities:

- open-cast mining, for example in Akwatia and Awaso, for bauxite and manganese and deposition of waste rock in gold mining areas;

- over-exploitation through logging for timber, charcoal and fuelwood;

- illegal farming, ultimately leading to the disappearance of major strategic reserves; and

- repeated fires that convert the northern transition forest zone into derived savannah.

Generally, however, it is agriculture-based economic development that has led to the greatest clearance of forests for cultivation and pasture. This has been accelerated by logging, which generally improves the accessibility to closed high forests and facilitates the migration of farmers to cultivate virgin forest soils for cash crops such as cocoa, coffee and oil palm.

The accelerated search for new and cheap tropical wood supplies by developed countries facilitated deforestation in developing countries. The low stumpage value or royalties payable on exports for logs has led to higher profits for logging companies and increased wastage due to harvesting and processing.

Extent of Ghana's tropical high forest

The high forest zone occurs in Ghana where the rains are heavy - between 1250mm and 2150mm per year - occupying about 82,000 square kilometres or roughly one-third of Ghana. Our commercial timber comes from this zone, ranging from wet and moist evergreen forest through moist semi-deciduous to the dry semi-deciduous forests; the latter are a transition zone between the high forest and the savannah which cover the northern two-thirds of the country.

However, as a result of deforestation pressures, most of Ghana's tropical forests have been cleared at an alarming rate. According to the Ghana Forestry Department (1980 estimates), in 1954 the area of unreserved forest was slightly more than that of reserved forest - at about 15,400 square kilometres. By 1972, unreserved forest was down to 3600 square kilometres representing an annual loss of 4.3 per cent. By 1990, one would have expected the unreserved forests to be virtually liquidated, but remnants of high forest still exist in sacred groves and bush fallows.

Generally, uncontrolled clearance of forests in the tropics is tantamount to anti-development. Therefore, where possible, areas of high forest land which are already degraded by various causes are being reclaimed and replanted, mainly because some of these areas are critical for the maintenance of watersheds and biological diversity. Forest reserves and wildlife areas now cover nearly 17,000 square kilometres, or 16 per cent, of Ghana. In the tropical high forest, there are over 252 reserves which are designated as either productive or protective forests.

Marketing of Ghana's wood products in Europe - certificate of sustainability

i) A history of responsibility in forestry

Ghana's forest reserves are among the best examples of sustained yield management in Africa, which dates back to the 1920s and 1930s. Records show that Ghana's timber production has been sustained (at at least 70 to 80 per cent) from the permanent forest reserves which have been reasonably protected and managed by the Forestry Department.

The loans from the World Bank for the Assisted Forest Management Project (1988-92) will give a boost to forestry research and the on-the-ground management, and improve upon the productive capacity of our forests. The ODA supported National Forest Inventory Project will also enable the Ghana Forestry Service to determine more accurately the growing stock and thereby devise improved management plans to enable our forests to be exploited on a more sustained yield basis.

Already, a number of publicly-owned timber firms are actively engaged in 'enrichment planting' of primary timber species to replenish the bulk of wood removed from our forests for export and local use.

ii) Ban of wood exports from tropical rainforests by EEC countries

Our timber trade is now under fire because of its alleged contribution to the destruction of tropical rainforests and to global warming. As a result, a growing number of consumers in EEC countries are trying to boycott the so-called 'unsustainable' tropical countries and are looking for alternatives. The current spate of misinformation is being spread by environmental lobby groups such as the Green Parties, IUCN, Friends of the Earth, World Wide Fund for Nature and the Association of Wood Users Against Rainforest Exploitation (AWARE).

Importers in the past had only tenuous links with sources of wood, and hardly any information on what was going on in the exporting countries' forests. The green campaigners' awakening of the world's consciousness to the wanton destruction of tropical rainforests is a laudable one indeed, but the sudden requirement for a 'Certificate of Sustainability' to cover parcels of wood goods entering Europe may be tainted with bad motives which pose serious threats to timber economies in the developing world including Ghana.

iii) Threat to Ghana's timber economy

It is unfortunate, after all the supreme efforts made under our Economic Recovery Programme to resuscitate Ghana's timber industry, especially in the processing of secondary and tertiary products these threats should rear their ugly heads from the very countries which pretend to bail us out of our economic doldrums through rational exploitation of our renewable natural resources such as timber.

It will mean that we cannot export much beyond our present levels and we may even end up not being able to repay the very loans which were meant to be used to improve our timber production.

The 'Certificate of Sustainability' being issued by the Ghana Forestry Department to accompany our exports of wood products is likely to undermine Ghana's credibility, as some nations in South-east Asia and West Africa, notorious for their timber exploitation, are already issuing such certificates. In their December 1989 meeting, the Ghana Forestry Commission was quite apprehensive about the issue.

Sustainable strategies for saving tropical forests

i) Setting priorities in forest management

Among the peculiarities of forests, several reasons justify state-ownership and involvement: their spatial extent, their slow development through time and their environmental value. They provide 90 per cent of the existing terrestrial biomass and this, combined with their species-richness, makes their good management mandatory in the public interest.

Without effective management, our forest reserves will not have the capacity to sustain or increase the present levels of consumption of forest products. Forest management implies controlled and regulated harvesting combined with silvicultural and protective measures to sustain or increase the commercial value of forest stands. This chiefly involves natural regeneration of indigenous species.

The recent forest inventory (Phase I, 1986-1988) has provided estimates of the growing stock of commercial wood volumes in the forest reserves in the high forests. We are now in a position to prepare working plans incorporating harvesting schedules (allowable cuts) in production forest reserves. Phase II of the Overseas Development Administration (ODA) project will enable us to assess pockets of land remaining outside forest reserves and look into the availability and utilization of non-timber resources - the major source of products for subsistence for the majority of rural people.

Ghana's participation in the Tropical Forestry Action Plan (TFAP) is in tune with our national priorities to review our National Forest Policy and obtain vital information on our forest resource base, as a major step toward its management and sustainability. To this end, we have made supreme efforts to obtain external funding to enable us to achieve our perceived priorities. Funding for forest resource management has come from the World Bank, the ODA and the Canadian International Development Agency (CIDA). The ODA's funding has been a major catalyst in our present efforts to husband a more productive forest resource in the high forests of Ghana.

ii) Conservation of primary forest by planting

Industrial tree planting using fast-growing exotics and indigenous tree species should be encouraged. However, the urgency is to promote indigenous species in industrial plantations because of their local adaptability and well established or potential markets.

Undoubtedly only plantations could provide the resource to maintain a sustainable wood base for both export and domestic uses. Intensive plantation culture may produce 3 to 10 times the volume of wood per hectare per year and will therefore require less land. Plantations also help to take the pressure off sensitive indigenous forest ecosystems, allowing more to be preserved as nature reserves, national parks and wildlife refuges.

Rural community forestry, encouraged by the Department of Forestry, has wider conservation benefits and is desirable in terms of greater landscape diversity, water catchments, soil protection, and biological value. Tree planting by rural people will, of course, also provide them with firewood, poles, fodder, fruits and other tree products, shade, shelter from wind, and beauty in rural and urban areas.

Intensification of shifting cultivation has often been accompanied by declining yields, impoverishment and subsequent abandonment of the land. The challenge is therefore to develop agroforestry systems that are sustainable, and economically, ecologically and socially acceptable to the rural people.

iii) Maintenance of Ghana's wood production to the year 2000 and beyond

Recommendations drawn from the recent high forest inventory include an allowable cut of 1.1 million cubic metres, but of this the safe annual cut is 700,000 cubic metres. In 1989, about 600,000 cubic metres were harvested (Timber Export Development Board, 1989).

To ensure a sustainable harvest, the annual allowable cut is being rationalized and spread between at least some 40 species. Our future policy is to broaden the species base to about 61 (to include lesser-known trees) and allocate a felling quota to each species in relation to its relative abundance or 'resource life'[1]. In this way, species, such as afrormosia (*Pericopsis elata*) whose resource life is likely to be exhausted in less than 5 years, can only be exploited under special license from the Forestry Department.

A potential wood deficit could occur by the year 2005, but this condition could be offset by plantation silviculture.

iv) Control of wood waste

Improvements in the current low conversion ratio of logs into timber or veneer and reduction in logging wastes (logs left in the forest) will help to reduce forest over-exploitation. If our current conversion ratios of 30 to 40 per cent can be improved, then fewer trees would need to be cut.

Concluding remarks

■ During the visit of the UK Timber Trade Federation to Ghana in March 1990, Ghanaian timber experts tried to convince UK agents and their buyers that we can guarantee sustainably-sourced wood products.

■ Plans are already advanced to find logistical support for key conservation activists from EEC countries to visit Ghana and observe, first-hand, the positive steps we have taken towards implementation of sustainable forest policies (reviewed in 1989 through a national consultative symposium).

■ As of February 1990, the Ghana Forestry Commission was suggesting a day's seminar in London or at the Oxford Forestry Institute to bring together the Ghana Timber Export Development Board, Ghana High Commission in London, and the UK Timber Trade Federation for a meaningful dialogue with environmentalists.

■ Our invitation to this London Conference organized by the ODA and Friends of the Earth came as a welcome surprise, and a golden opportunity for an exchange of views on the tropical rainforest.

Editor's footnote

1. The ODA-sponsored inventory found that, in Ghana's forests, the extraction rate of most of the traditional export timbers was far greater than annual incremental growth, giving them a limited 'resource life'.

Resource life of Ghana's traditional export species (years)

Iroko (odum)	10
Edinam	18
Sapele	25
Utile	20
Mahogany	20
Afrormosia	0
Wawa	114

Source: Wong, JLG (ed) Forest Inventory Project Seminar Proceedings, 29th-30th March 1989, Accra, ODA, Ghana Forestry Department.

The Feasibility of Developing Borneo's Non-Timber Forest Products for the United States Market

Anthony Dixon, Hannah Roditi, Lee Silverman, Project Borneo, 88 Chandler Street, Arlington, MA 02174 USA

Summary

This paper presents a brief overview of a recent feasibility study of the development of Borneo's non-timber forest products (NTFPs) for the growing green market in the United States. The study was conducted in the context of the Harvard Business School Master of Business Administration (MBA) programme and took place in Borneo and the USA during 1990. The aim was to address the broad array of interdisciplinary questions relevant to the development of NTFPs and to present the findings in a way that would be of practical use to environmental groups seeking potential alternative forest uses and to businesses attempting to market sustainable rainforest products.

Background

The island of Borneo in South-east Asia, comprising the Malaysian states of Sarawak and Sabah, the oil-rich Sultanate of Brunei and the Indonesian province of Kalimantan, is home to some 10 per cent of the world's remaining rainforests. Despite Borneo's rich history of trade in NTFPs, their once significant economic and political role has been completely overshadowed in the last fifty years by that of timber.

Needless to say the politics of timber and forest management are highly sensitive issues in Malaysia and Indonesia, where the Governments have recently come under international scrutiny and have faced a great deal of criticism from environmental and human rights groups drawing attention to the alarming rate at which the forests of Borneo are disappearing. Given this context, the future of NTFP development in Borneo on any impactful scale is likely to depend far more on political strategy rather than factors like the availability of infrastructure, or the readiness of consumers in the West.

That said, official attitudes and policies towards NTFPs do differ considerably between the four Borneo 'states'. Brunei, for example, in an effort to become less dependent on oil, has created an entire ministry with an elaborate and ambitious five year strategic plan for the development of NTFPs. Indonesia too, in its current five year economic plan, Repelita V, aims to promote NTFPs for export and domestic consumption. Sabah and Sarawak on the other hand appear to have no official policies on the development of NTFPs, although they fund some small, academically focused research efforts.

Many other factors come into play of course, in assessing the potential of each of the Borneo states as a starting point for NTFP development efforts. In addition to official NTFP policy, we analysed the general political and economic climate, and factors such as infrastructure and the relationship between key institutional actors such as parastatals, non-government organizations and organizations of indigenous peoples. On the basis of our assessment, we concluded that Sarawak and Kalimantan would be the best places to begin NTFP development work.

Products with potential

We conducted a 5-week survey of the major coastal market towns of Borneo, documenting the non-timber forest products that were available and compiling a catalogue containing colour photographs of the products and details about their source, availability, traditional uses, and pertinent trade regulations.

The broad scope of the project necessitated a somewhat arbitrary focus on certain categories of NTFPs; we chose to exclude rattan, about which there already exists a reasonable body of information in the literature, and animal products. Once the catalogue had been compiled, we further narrowed our focus to take a close look at a few of the products we considered to have high potential for immediate development: the illipe nut (*Shorea* spp.), keruing oil (*Dipterocarpus kerrii*), rainforest mushrooms, spices, herbal tea ingredients and honey. A short description of these products follows.

■ The illipe nut

As with many of Borneo's non-timber forest products, the illipe nut has enjoyed a long history of trade both within the region and beyond, to Europe, where oil from the nuts has been used in the manufacture of candles, soap and cosmetic products, and as a substitute for cocoa butter in chocolate. Although the trees only fruit every three to five years, relatively large quantities are available at those times: some 30,000 tons were collected in west Kalimantan alone in 1987 (1990 prices are expected to be in the region of $M1,300 per ton). Local processing facilities exist in Sarawak and West Kalimantan, where a few small pilot plantations also exist.

The supply chain from collectors to exporters is relatively well developed and there are no problematic restrictions on their import into the United States in dried or preserved form.

■ Keruing oil

Also known as Garjan balsam, keruing oil has been extracted for centuries for use in oil lamps and torches and for skin ailments. Traditional methods of extraction were highly destructive and because of the high commercial value of the timber, the collection of the trees' resin was discouraged by governments. Recently, however, new techniques have been devised to tap the resin in sustainable, inexpensive and highly productive ways.

The properties of keruing oil make it attractive as a base for perfumes, astringents and as an emollient in skin conditioners.

■ Honey

Throughout Borneo, where bee-keeping is not a traditional practice, honey is harvested by smoking out the bees and cutting the hive from the tree. As a result of this practice, hives have grown more scarce in inhabited forest areas. But there is considerable potential to encourage rural people to keep domestic bees, and the economics are attractive. Recent work by Sarawak's Department of Agriculture has demonstrated that a 10 colony apiary requiring only 2 hours work per week, was capable of generating 36 kilogrammes of honey per year and net annual returns of $M1,190.

■ Herbal tea ingredients

Traditional Indonesian herbal medicines (jamu) already enjoy well developed markets in Indonesia, the People's Republic of China and the Middle East. The domestic market is supplied by large jamu factories as well as small local vendors selling unprocessed products. Although these ingredients are, as yet, mostly unknown in the West, we believe that many of them have potential as ingredients in herbal teas. In 1988, sales of herbal teas reached $179 million in the USA where the speciality tea market has enjoyed an annual growth rate of 20 per cent since 1983. Given that the jamu products have a documented history of consumption in Indonesia, regulatory approval to market them in the USA is unlikely to be a problem provided no explicit claims are made about their medicinal properties.

Because jamu may be derived from many parts of the plant from the roots to the leaves or flowers, it is imperative that the method of harvesting particular jamu products and the effect of increasing the harvest to supply a growing market, be carefully investigated before development takes place.

■ Edible mushrooms

These are another common non-timber forest product in Borneo with high potential to be marketed in the USA, where despite the rise in popularity of the shiitake mushroom, exotic mushrooms still have less than a 1 per cent market share.

■ Herbs and spices

Many of these such as cinnamon, cloves and nutmeg are already well known in the West and have potential for further development utilizing the rainforest theme in their marketing. Others that are not so well known include galangal (*Kaempferia galanga*) and temu kunci (*Gastrochilus panduratum*).

To assess the potential of all 90 non-timber forest products we researched and documented would have required more time and information than was available. While all 90 may prove to have possibilities, we believe it would be worth focusing on the following products as a priority: langir rambut, a vine used to make shampoo; limpanas puteh, an insect repellant; pula sari, a cosmetic powder; nipah palm sugar; kemiri, a nut similar in appearance and texture to the macadamia nut; kacangma, an herb; tabak barito, a leaf which can be infused to make tea; damar resin; cassava; asam, and a range of dried fruits.

Logistics of trade in the region

Three important elements of ideal NTFP trading conditions are: adequate infrastructure; trading expertise (implying that all participants along the trade channel understand the importance of quality and consistent supply); and competitive conditions among intermediaries which will ensure that collectors receive competitive prices for their products.

With the exception of Brunei, trade infrastructure in Borneo is limited and is probably the least well developed in Kalimantan. Throughout Borneo, air freight transport is unreliable and refrigerated containers are available only departing from Kuching and Kota Kinabalu, necessitating close-to-source processing of most NTFP for exports.

Although trading expertise exists in some cases, especially with products that are exported to regional markets or the Middle East, quality control requirements are likely to be less stringent for those markets than for the United States. Aside from transport difficulties, inconsistent supply will also result from natural seasons and harvest cycles and from the impact of price fluctuations on collecting activities.

Finally, trade in NTFPs is dominated by Chinese intermediaries, who typically control the only means of transporting goods down river to market and supply credit to village collectors. Under this system, collectors are likely to receive low prices for their produce.

Products with good storage properties, the ability to be processed locally, and high value end-use (enabling higher prices to be paid to collectors) will therefore have the best potential for development.

Comparison with Brazil

To date, most efforts to develop NTFPs for international markets have focused on Brazil. Given this fact, we thought it would be useful to make some comparisons between the Brazilian state of Acre, where Cultural Survival sources its Brazil nuts, and the Borneo states.

Among the similarities are: relatively undeveloped local and export markets for NTFPs; young or nascent indigenous and non-governmental organizations; high levels of corruption amongst government officials, particularly in the forest sector; and highly diverse forests with low species densities, resulting in high costs of NTFP collection. The principal differences include the degree of politicization and legal status achieved by indigenous groups; the more extensive cataloguing of NTFPs that has taken place in Borneo due to its longer documented history of NTFP trade; and the better infrastructure in Brazil.

Marketing issues

There is no doubt in our minds that there exists in the United States a market of relatively informed consumers willing to pay a premium for sustainably harvested rainforest products. This is evidenced not only by the results of a 1989 Gallup poll on the environment and a 1989 Harris poll on consumer attitudes to organic produce, but also by the rapid growth in recent years in the membership of environmental organizations. Growth in the natural foods and natural cosmetics industries further supports this claim, and a number of companies we interviewed in these industries were quick to see the possibilities of our product samples.

By far the most difficult issue which must be grappled with, however, is not whether the market exists, but whether it can be contained to avoid the possibly detrimental effects on the rainforests of greatly increased demand. Over-harvesting of

NTFPs by companies with no environmental motivation underlying their involvement in NTFP trade could just as easily lead to the kind of rampant commercial exploitation of the forests and their inhabitants that we have witnessed in the case of timber.

One reliable insurance against this outcome is the provision of secure property rights and long-term tenure to NTFP collector groups. Another, is a credible green labelling system capable of certifying to consumers that a product or its ingredient was sustainably harvested. Strategies for achieving these controls are discussed in detail in our report.

Structuring the organization

Bringing NTFPs to market in the United States requires four primary functions: source development, production, marketing and transport. We analysed four ways in which an organization might structure itself to carry out NTFP trade. We concluded that the most attractive structure would be one in which the production, marketing and source development functions are separated as subsidiaries within a holding company, and the transport function is contracted out to existing exporters.

Further reference

This paper has been based on a two-volume report entitled *From Forest to Market: A Feasibility Study of the Development of Selected Non-Timber Forest Products from Borneo for the US Market*. Copies of the report may be purchased by writing to Project Borneo, 88 Chandler Street, Arlington, MA 02174, USA. Phone: (617) 648 2740, Fax: (617) 495 1396

Appendix

The Rainforest Harvest Medicines

Indigenous people and rainforest cures

Fierce competition in the struggle to survive has created a wealth of chemical compounds used by rainforest plants, insects and animals for defence, attack, attraction, repulsion, or other purposes. The potential for using these natural properties for the benefit of humankind has often been revealed by forest dwelling tribal people, whose knowledge of medicines derived from the wild is astonishing.

To the Shwah Indians of Ecuador, the forest is an embracing natural pharmacy - they know of 250 separate medicinal plants. The shamans of the Wayana tribe in the north-east of Amazonia regularly use over 100 different plants for medicinal purposes. As well as utilizing a veritable medicine chest for major ailments and contraception, forest Indians can treat dandruff, foot rot, impotence and a host of other maladies.

In addition to tribal societies, millions of people in the Third World depend on traditional medicines for their well being. The forests' chemical library has also been utilized by Western medicine.

Western medicine

An estimated one in four of all purchases from pharmacies in countries such as Britain contain an active ingredient derived from a tropical forest species. Advanced medical treatments also rely heavily on the resources of the rainforest. These include drugs to treat cancer, malaria, heart disease, bronchitis, hypertension, dysentery and tuberculosis. The products include anaesthetics, contraceptives, enzymes, hormones, laxatives, cough mixtures, antibiotics, antiseptics and hallucinogenics. They support an industry worth £18 billion annually.

Tropical forests serve modern pharmacy in four general ways:

- Chemicals extracted from plant and animal species can be used without modification as drugs. Synthesis may be impossible if scientists cannot unravel the biochemical process, or else it may not be commercially feasible if natural sources are cheaper.
- Some extracts may serve as the starting point for the manufacture of semi-synthetic derivative drugs.
- Other extracts provide chemical models or blueprints which pharmacists use to develop purely synthetic compounds. The insights given by complex natural molecules may be beyond the creative capabilities of human researchers.
- Plant and animal species, or extracts from them may be used for research purposes.

Anti-cancer drugs

One of the most feared afflictions of the modern age is under attack from rainforest drugs. 70 per cent of the 3000 plants identified by the US National

Cancer Institute as having anti-cancer properties come from rainforests. The institute has warned that the rapid and widespread elimination of tropical forests constitutes a serious drawback in the fight against cancer.

Children suffering from leukaemia have had their chances of survival improved dramatically, from 20 per cent to 80 per cent, through chemotherapy with the drug vincristine. It also treats tumours of the breast and other organs and is one of two valuable alkaloids extracted from the Madagascan forest plant the rosy periwinkle, *Catharanthus roseus* (Plate 6). The other is vinblastine which treats Hodgkin's disease. Sales of the two vinca drugs exceed £75 million per annum.

Etoposide, a drug currently available for the treatment of small-cell lung cancer and testicular cancer, is a semi-synthetic derivative of podophyllotoxin obtained from the Indian plant *Podophyllum emodi.*

Many other extracts from tropical forest plants show considerable anti-tumour activity. Some are at an advanced stage of clinical testing including:

- Maytansine from the East African *Maytenus buchananii*;
- Bruceatin from the Ethiopian *Brucea antidysenterica*;
- Indicine from the Indian *Heliotropium indicum*;
- Baccharin from the Brazilian *Baccharis megapotamica*;
- Jacaranone from the South American *Jacaranda caucana.*

Ellipticine, from the New Guinean *Excavata coccinea* is also a powerful anti-tumour agent but because side effects have been noted a semi-synthetic derivative or synthetic analogue will have to be developed before the drug can be widely used.

Anti-malarial drugs

Malaria has killed more people throughout history than any other disease. It has been largely eradicated from the temperate regions but 350 million people in the tropics are still afflicted every year. In 1976 alone the World Health Organization estimated that 1.5 million people died from the disease.

South American Indians have traditionally treated malaria with an extract from the bark of cinchona trees, especially *Cinchona ledgeriana.* 200 years lapsed between the discovery of this treatment by Europeans and the identification of the alkaloid quinine. The chemistry of quinine has subsequently been used as a blueprint for synthetic substitutes such as chloroquine, fansidar and primaquine, but these have not proven to have lasting benefits. New strains of resistant parasite have emerged and malaria is on the increase again. So too is the demand for cinchona bark, as apart from quinine it contains over 30 other alkaloids and resistance has never surfaced to this broad spectrum treatment. Quinine now has a further use as a basis for the semi-synthetic drug quinidine, increasingly popular for treating out of sequence heartbeats.

The search for new anti-malarial drugs continues and tropical forest species could be expected to play a major role in this. Promising treatments include:

- Qinghaosa, from the Chinese herb *Artemesia annua*;
- Quassia, from the wood of the tropical American tree, *Quassia amara*;
- Extracts from the Ghanaian plant *Cryptolepis sanguinolenta*, which act as a broad spectrum antibiotic with considerable potential against malaria and other fevers. Scientists have not yet been able to identify, let alone isolate, the primary active ingredient.

In addition, following research on tribal Indians use of anti-fever plants, four Colombian species are being intensively tested as anti-malaria treatments.

Birth control

The Mexican yam, *Dioscorea*, which does not flourish outside of the rainforests, has had a profound impact on birth control methods, and on social culture. It is a source of diosgenin, the basic material for the manufacture of many steroidal drugs on the market including the birth control pill, 80 million of which are consumed daily, the sex hormones progesterone, oestrogen and androgens, as well as the semi-synthetic derivatives cortisone and hydrocortisone. These latter two treat arthritis, rheumatic fever, allergies, skin diseases and eye inflammation.

Extensive worldwide demand for diosgenin, and a tenfold rise in the price by the Mexican government, lead to a successful search for new sources of diosgenin: the West African calabar bean; and Indian and Chinese species of *Dioscorea*. 500 tonnes of diosgenin, which has not yet been synthesized, were used in 1985.

Other tropical forest species which are used locally as a contraceptive or are being investigated for their anti-fertility potential include:

- The greenheart tree, *Ocotea rodiaei*, of Guyana;
- The Indian greem flower, *Malvaviscus conzatti*, which could assist the development of the much sought after 'male pill'.

In addition four South American species, *Dieffenbachia seguine*, *Anthurium ressmanni*, *Tachigalia cavipes* and *Unonopsus veneficiorum*, are receiving closer attention.

Serving the cause of birth control in a different way are plants that induce abortions. The South-east Asian plant, *Plumbago indica*, is a notable member of this category.

Extracts from the nutmeg, *Myristica fragrans*, a Molluccan native, promote fertility by inducing ovulation.

Anaesthetics and surgical aids

Many tropical forest plant and animal derivatives are used in the vital functions of relieving pain and assisting in the performance of surgical operations.

Cocaine, from the South American coca bush, *Erythroxylon coca*, is a valuable local anaesthetic which has provided a blueprint from which safer and more efficient anaesthetics, such as novocaine and lignocaine, have been developed.

Teterodotoxin (a substance used by voodoo practitioners to turn their victims into 'Zombies'), derived from several species of Central American frog, is 160,000 times more powerful than cocaine in blocking nervous impulses. As well as being used as an anaesthetic, notably for persons suffering from terminal cancer, it is used as a neurological research tool in nerve impulse transmission experiments.

Tubocuranine, which has long been used by Indians as a hunting poison, and is extracted from the roots and stems of the Amazonian vine *Chondodendron tomentosum*, has been vital in the development of modern surgical techniques. It performs the critical function of immobilizing muscles during operations and shock therapy, and plays a similar anti-convulsive role in the treatment of Parkinsons disease, tetanus, multiple sclerosis and cerebral palsy.

Picrotoxin from the seeds of the South-east Asian Levant berry, *Liquidambar orientalis*, is also anti-convulsive in the treatment of epilepsy and schizophrenia.

The gum gutta percha, from South-east Asian *Pallaquium* species, serves surgery in a different way through its use in the manufacture of surgical instruments.

The Madagascan weed, *Centella asiatica*, has been refined into the wound healing drug, Madecassol.

Tranquillizers and heart-drugs

Four out of five of all preparations used to treat the serious affliction of hypertension/high blood pressure contain alkaloids from the serpentine root, *Rauwolfia serpentina* of India. Traditional Hindu doctors have used this plant for 4000 years but it was only in the early 1950s that Western scientists isolated from it reserpine, the principal active ingredient, and started using it as the basis for tranquillizers. Apart from hypertension, it is used to treat anxiety, schizophrenia and menstrual tension.

Although reserpine can be synthesized, it is a laborious and expensive process and natural sources remain paramount. The lesser used African variety, *Rauwolfia vomitoria*, holds promise for interbreeding as it contains higher concentrations of the drug. Ajalmine, a second serpentine root extract, has the same function as quinidine in controlling out-of-sequence heartbeats.

Captopril from the Brazilian *Jacaracea* snake and compounds from the Ghanaian Ashanti pepper are two further potential treatments for hypertension.

Many people owe their lives to drugs that stimulate weak and ailing hearts. The main constituent of these cardiac glycosides is digoxin from the European foxglove, *Digitalis purpurea*, but Stropanthidin, from the seeds of the West African plant, *Stropanthus gratus*, has the same effect. Also from this latter plant comes sarmentogin, an alternative starting point for the semi-synthetic drug cortisone.

A promising aid for heart surgery is cunaniol, a traditional hunting poison from the Guyanan plant, *Clibadium sylvestre*.

Extracts from the Kola plant, *Cola nitida* and *C. acuminata*, native to the West African rainforests and used as soft drinks' ingredients, also include the heart stimulant kolanin.

Dysentery and digestive complaints

Emetine from the roots of the South American ipecac plant, *Cephaelis ipecacuanha*, has long been known as a cure for dysentery. It is now commercially synthesized but this would not have been possible without the chemical model provided by the natural drug. It is also used in a number of bronchitis preparations.

Conessine is another important cure for dysentery. It is obtained from the Kurichi tree, *Holarrhena antidysenterica*, of India and Africa.

Three plants, more commonly considered as foods are also extensively traded for their medicinal applications. The seed husks of the plantain, *Plantago orata*, a native of South-east Asia, are a popular ingredient in many laxatives including the branded Serutan. The papaya, *Carica papaya* (Plate 23), originally from Central America, yields the enzyme papain which treats chronic diarrhoea and indigestion as well as helping to detect stomach cancer. Another medicinal enzyme is the anti-inflammatory bromelain, obtained from the pineapple, *Ananus comosus*, native to Amazonia.

Many tropical forest plants are used in their native localities to treat diarrhoea, worms and other digestive complaints. Some have found wider acceptance including the South-east Asian galangal, *Alpinia officinarum*, and the tropical American condurango, *Marsdenia condurango*, both treatments for chronic indigestion. Extracts from the tropical American turpentine tree, *Bursera simaruba*, are used to treat diarrhoea and general indigestion. The South-east Asian kamala tree, *Mallotus philippensis*, is exploited for its effectiveness against worms and parasitic skin infections.

The betel nut, *Areca catechu*, native to South-east Asia, is traditionally chewed as a stimulant but its fruit can also cure diarrhoea, worms, dysentery and indigestion. Cancer researchers exploit its tumour-inducing properties in laboratory experiments for anti-tumour drugs.

The Madagascan forest plant, *Haronga madagascariensis*, has been refined in German laboratories into the drug harunganin, used to treat stomach disorders.

Ophthalmology and neurology

Although it is also a source of diosgenin, the West African calabar bean, *Physostigma venonosum*, is most highly prized for another extract, physostigmine. Ophthalmologists use this to constrict the pupils of the eye and to treat glaucoma. It is also anti-spasmodic in arthritis and fibrositis and cardiologists have found that it reduces blood pressure. A third extract from the plant is neostigmine, an antidote to curare. Pilocarpine from the South American *Pilocarpus jaborandi* is also used in the treatment of glaucoma.

Two important alkaloids, atropine and hyoscine, are present in both the Australian corkwood tree, *Duboisia myorporoides*, and the South American jimson weed, *Datura stramonium*. Atropine is used to dilate the pupils. It is also intestinally anti spasmodic in cases of diarrhoea. Hyoscine, in small doses, is a sedative and a common ingredient in travel sickness pills. In large doses it is a powerful hallucinogenic. Having played its part in the South American Indian's mystical tradition, it is now used in neurological research and to treat several forms of mental illness.

A vehicle for carrying other drugs in eye drops is oil from the castor bean, *Ricinus communis*, a native of Africa. This oil is also used in contraceptive jellies and creams and from it is extracted undecylenic acid, a popular ingredient in anti-fungal preparations like athlete's foot ointment. Castor oil is traditionally a purgative and these properties are now utilized in treatments for food poisoning and in preparing patients for intestinal surgery.

Respiratory disorders

Apart from emetine from the ipecac plant, a cure for bronchitis, there are several other tropical forest plant extracts that provide relief from respiratory ailments.

Tolu balsam, from the Central American tree, *Myroxylon balsamum*, is a commonly used expectorant in cough sweets and mixtures and in inhalants effective against bronchitis. Its antibiotic properties are harnessed against tuberculosis and its antiseptic properties are utilized in ointments.

Benzoin tincture from the South-east Asian tree, *Styrax benzoin*, is a treatment for bronchitis and laryngitis. When applied externally it is an antiseptic.

Anethole, the essential component of the oil of the South-east Asian star anise, *Illicium verum*, is an expectorant used in cough preparations and a principal flavouring agent in oral pharmaceuticals.

The Indian water navel wort, *Hydrocotyle asiatica*, has the potential to treat tuberculosis due to the diuretic (water reducing) properties of its main extract asiaticoside.

A respiratory stimulant, which treats colds and fatigue and is analgesic (pain killing) is obtained from the West Indian plant *Piscidia erythrina*.

Other medicines derived from tropical forest plants

These include:

- Strychnine, from the South-east Asian tree *Strychnos-nux-vomica*, administered in small doses acts as a stimulant and convulsant used to treat overdoses of morphine, barbiturates and alcohol.

- L-dopa, from a South American legume, *Mucuna* sp., is a neurotransmitter naturally occurring in the human brain which is used to combat the disabling effects of Parkinson's disease.

- Sarsapogenine, from the South American sarsparilla plant, *Smilax regilil*, is used in conjunction with other medicines to facilitate their absorption through the digestive tract.

- Catechin, extracted from the Malaysian plant, *Uncaria gambier*, is effective against hepatitis but its potential has yet to be fully exploited.

- Camphor, from the South-east Asian *Cinnamomum camphora*, is a counter-irritant with local anaesthetic properties. It appears in itching ointments and TCP formulations.

■ The seed kernels of the fast growing Amazonian guaraná plant, *Paullinia cupana* (Plate 4), contain caffeine, tannins and other alkaloid and non-alkaloid compounds. Though 75 per cent of the crop is used by the soft drinks industry, it is also a sustaining food substitute and a useful organic medicine. In the form of syrups, pills and powders it acts as a general tonic and a treatment for diarrhoea, fevers, cramps and headaches.

■ Extracts from an Amazonian species of oak are being used by scientists in their attempts to develop a vaccine to counter AIDS. American researchers have also been testing a new drug isolated from the seeds of the black bean, *Castanospermum australe*, an Australian rainforest tree.

Primates and research

Being the closest living relatives of mankind, primates from the rainforests have often been used in research for the testing of new drugs, the development of vaccines and in studying the diseases of various organ systems.

Polio vaccines have been developed from research involving the Indian rhesus monkey, *Macaca mulatta*, and the African green monkey, *Cercopithecus aethiopes*. The Celebes macaque, *Macaca fascicularis*, is used in diabetes research, the South American squirrel monkey, *Saimiri sciureus*, in cardiovascular research and the tropical American owl monkey, *Aotus trivirgatus*, in malarial and immunology studies. The African mangabey monkey, *Cercocebus* sp., is being used in research to develop a leprosy vaccine, (as is the non-primate armadillo), and Brazilian marmosets, *Hepale* sp., are contributing to cancer and hepatitis research. The African chimpanzee, *Pan troglodytes*, is used in hepatitis research and, being a very close relative to *Homo sapiens*, also in general psychobiological studies.

The ethical nature of much of this research is highly controversial. Research using primates and other animals could be reduced by closer scrutiny of traditional medicines, where humans themselves have been the research subjects, often over periods of hundreds of years.

Industrial Products

Industrial uses

Industry relies on tropical forest species for the manufacture of a host of products used in everyday life. These products include processed foods, drinks, confectionaries, perfumes, soaps, cosmetics, paints, varnishes, fabrics, furniture, tyres and paper.

Some products, like rubber and palm oil, are now mostly obtained from plantations which may have replaced the natural forest. However, the wild relatives of industrial plantation species are important in providing genetic material for crop improvement. Other products, like rattans (Plate 8) and waxes, are still harvested from the wild, but the forest need not be destroyed in the process. Some of the contributions that tropical forest species have made to industrial processes are described below.

Exudates

i) Latexes

The rubber tree, *Hevea brasiliensis* (Plates 24, 25 and 26), was disregarded outside of its native Amazonia until little over a century ago. Now it is one of the most important materials of the industrial world, and a major agro-industrial export from the Third World, with trade worth more than £2.5 billion annually.

Two thirds of the rubber crop is consumed by the tyre industry, as its characteristics of heat resistance and elasticity are unrivalled by synthetic substitutes. The remaining third is used in hundreds of household and industrial products.

Most rubber is obtained from plantations in South-east Asia which have nearly all descended from just a handful of seedlings originally smuggled there from Brazil. Some of the several wild Amazonian *Hevea* species have resistance to blight, some the potential for improving yields, and two species, *H. benthamiana* and *H. guianensis* produce commercially useful latexes that are, as yet, unexploited. However, all these potentially crucial genetic resources are threatened by deforestation in the heart of *Hevea*'s native territory.

Another important latex-producing species is the South-east Asian pallaquium tree, which produces the tough, durable and elastic gutta-percha. This was strongly in demand at the turn of the century for electric and submarine cable insulation until the development of synthetic substitutes. It is now used for the manufacture of surgical instruments and golf-ball covers, and has potential as a thermoplastic and thermosetting resin.

Cheaper brands of chewing gums now use synthetic materials but most higher grade gums contain chicle, the latex of the Central American sapodilla tree, *Archras zapota*. Other chewing gums that are latexes of rainforest trees include:

- Crown gum, *Archras chicle* and chicle faison, *Dipholis stevensonii*, sorva gum, *Couma macrocarpa*, and letchi capsi, *Couma rigida* (Latin America);
- Gutta hangkang, *Ficus platyphylla*, and gutta ketiau, *Pallaquium leicaroum* (Indonesia).

Some bubble gums too come from the rainforest, with most based on the latex of the South-east Asian *Dyera* tree species.

The guar plant, *Cyamopsis tetragonoloba*, of South-east Asia, is an important new source of useful gum. With up to eight times the thickening capacity of starch it is demanded as a stabilizer for food products, a filter aid in mining operations, a strengthener in paper making, an agent to reduce water resistance in fire hoses and a thickener in cosmetics and pharmaceuticals.

ii) Waxes

Waxes, vital for many industrial processes and the manufacture of household products, are complex to synthesize and are mostly obtained from natural, mainly wild, sources. Though most wax comes from arid-zone species, the Amazonian plant, *Calathea lutea*, yields the high quality cauassa wax. This is used for treating fine furniture and applications requiring hard rather than liquid waxes. The Amazonian licuri palm, *Syagrus coronata*, also yields a leaf wax with commercial potential.

iii) Resins

Many paints, varnishes and lacquers contain products refined from the resins of rainforest plants.

One source is the Central American turpentine tree, *Bursera simaruba*. Others include *Agathus* sp. and *Dipterocarp* sp., both from South-east Asia, which yield copal and damar resin respectively. These resins are particularly suitable as they are hard with high melting points. Damars, being lighter coloured and soluble in turpentine and coal tar hydrocarbons, are especially appropriate for white-paper varnishes, spirit varnishes, enamels, caulking materials for boats and binding constituents in ointments.

iv) Tannins

Tannin, for treating leather, is mainly derived from minerals but vegetable tannins do satisfy 30 per cent of the market. One third of these come from three rainforest plants: quebracho, *Shinopsis lorentzii*, of South America, mangroves, *Rhizophora* species, of Asia and Africa, both of which have tannin in their bark, and myrobalans, *Terminilia* species, of India, which yields a top quality tannin from its dried fruit.

v) Dyes

Today, most commercial dyes are synthetic petrochemicals but some still come from the wood, bark, leaves, flowers or roots of rainforest plants.

The annatto bush, *Bixa orellana* (Plate 22), of Central America and Africa, yields the orange-red pigment bixin. Its non toxic properties make it suitable for colouring cosmetics and foods like butter, cheese, rice, yoghurts, margarine, coleslaw, bakery products and sponge puddings, where it is labelled as additive E 160(b).

Kamala, used for dyeing silk and wool, and colouring foods and cosmetics, is obtained from the South-east Asian kamala tree, *Mallotus philippensis*. Purple dye comes from the Asian logwood tree. Orange-brown cutch is derived from the Indian tree *Acacia catechu*.

vi) Other exudates

The Amazonian timbo tree, *Lonchocarpus* species, is one source of the important insecticide, rotenone, traditionally use by tribal people as a fish poison. Other sources include 60 species of legume from South-east Asia and the Amazon which have rotenoids in their roots.

The bark of the Indian tree, *Terminilia ardjuna*, contains calcium oxalate which is extracted for the manufacture of oxalic acid.

The industrial uses of Tolu balsam, from the Central American tree *Myroxylon balsamum*, include the flavouring of cough syrups, sweets, chewing gums and ice cream, and the extracted oil appears in soaps and cosmetics.

Apart from its medicinal uses, benzoin from the South-east Asian tree *Benzoin styrax*, is used in cosmetics, confectionary, perfumery and incense.

Fibres and canes

In South-east Asia, the most valuable forest product after timber is rattan, *Calamus* sp. (Plate 8). Its end value in world trade exceeds £1 billion annually, earning 15 countries over £15 million each in exports. The stems of these climbing plants are used in furniture, wickerwork, screens, blinds, ropes, baskets and matting. The leaves are used for weaving, thatching and cigarette papers, while some species yield jernang ('dragons blood') for dyes and varnishes. Almost all rattan is harvested from the natural forest. Unfortunately many rattan areas are now threatened by modern development, and some species have been over-exploited.

Bamboos, from the more seasonal forests of South-east Asia, are exceptionally useful plants with over 100 commercial applications. These include furniture, agricultural implements, household utensils, irrigation and general piping, paper making, construction and food.

Jute and sisal are major fibre crops native to the rainforests though they are now obtained from plantations. Jute from the South-east Asian *Corchorus capsularis*, is a soft-stem fibre used in clothing, sacking, carpets, tents, cables and twine. Sisal, *Agave sisalana*, originally from Mexico, is a hard leaf fibre suitable for ropes, twine, nets, upholstery and carpets. Two sisal relatives, cantala, *Agave cantala*, of South-east Asia, and salvador henequen, *A. letonal,* of Central America, also yield useful fibres.

Kapok, the elastic and water repellant fibre used in soundproofing, insulation and the stuffing for life jackets and belts is obtained from the seeds of the tropical tree, *Ceiba pentandra*, and the Indian tree, *Bombax malabaricum*.

The prolific growth of kenaf, *Hibiscus cannabinus*, yields five times as much cellulose per hectare as pine. It is thus potentially an alternative source of paper pulp.

Fibre from the South-east Asian ramie, *Boehemeria nivea*, is long, lustrous, water and chemical resistant and eight times stronger than cotton. Used in clothing, upholstery, fine bedding, fire hoses, parachutes and carpets, it could become a major economic species if the technology was developed to extract the fibre more easily.

Raffia comes from the upper surface of the young leaves of the *Raphia* palm of Africa. Being cheap and resistant it is a favourite in horticulture to tie up plants. It is also used for mats, baskets, thatch, rope, cord, wickerwork, handicrafts and clothing. When mixed with water the leaf forms piassava for the bristles of brooms and brushes.

The leaves of the tendu tree, *Diospyros melanoxylon*, of India, support a £300 million per annum cigarette paper industry. Harvested from the wild, they are used in the manufacture of the popular beedies.

Encephalarctos sp. and *Dicranotepis usambarica*, both of Africa, are used for wickerwork and baskets. The South American palm, *Leopoldina pissaba*, is used for ropes, cables and brooms.

Edible and industrial oils

An important category of products derived from

rainforest plants are the edible oils, used in the manufacture of industrial goods. In the Third World they serve as cooking oils and butter substitutes, where they play a valuable nutritional role, and as lighting fuels.

Most oil on the commercial market comes from a few species in plantations but many other unexploited species can offer the same economic potential.

i) Oil and coconut palms

The harvest from the plantations of oil palms, *Elaeis guiniensis*, native to West Africa, and coconut palms, *Cocus nucifera*, native to South-east Asia, satisfy over 20 per cent of the industrial market for edible oils. It is used in foods such as margarine, mayonnaise, confectionary, ice cream and bakery products; in items such as candles, detergents, lipstick, sun-tan lotions, tinplate and glycerine, (itself used in cosmetics, cellophane and explosives), and in lubricants for jet engines and precision machinery.

The genetic base of the vast South-east Asian oil palm plantations rested on only four plants, making it even narrower than that of rubber. Plant breeders have improved yields of oil palm by cross-breeding with the plant's wild West African relatives, but the natural habitat of the palm is disappearing very rapidly, sometimes due to the expansion of plantations.

ii) Oil-rich palms of the Amazon

Many wild species of Amazonian palm could become major commercial sources of oil, as important as the coconut palm or oil palm. Often these palms are an important resource for local industry. The oils are extracted from either the kernel or fruit pulp, or both, and some species also provide useful fibre, fuel and other products. Amongst these palms, and some of their uses, are;

■ Babussa, *Orbignya* species, which yield prolific quantities of high grade, colourless kernel oil suitable for margarine, shortening, general edibles, soap, plastic, emulsifiers and detergents. Almost two thirds of Brazil's edible oil production comes from these species. The seed cake is a good animal food, the leaves produce a high value wax and the kernel can be burnt as fuel or turned into charcoal.

■ Milpesos, *Jessenia polycarpa* produces a clear and golden oil resembling olive oil. It has potential for use in the manufacture of soaps, cosmetics and general edibles. Also has applications in folk medicine.

■ The light green pulp oil from the seje palm, *Jessenia bataua*, is held in high esteem by the local population. Suitable for cooking and salads but its commercial potential is presently ignored.

■ The swamp loving miriti palm, *Mauritia flexuosa* (Plate 5), yields a high quality, vitamin rich oil from its pulp and kernels, similar to oil from the African oil palm. The young leaves provide a useful fibre for string, nets, thatch and sacking and the leaf stalks are turned into cork. Its habitat is particularly threatened by development schemes. The related palm, *Mauritia vinifera*, also thrives in swamps, and yields a light yellow oil. Research into the commercial use of wild stands is underway.

■ All parts of the ubussa palm, *Manicaria saccifera*, are used by local Indians. The kernel and pulp oil resemble coconut oil, the leaves are used for thatch and fibre and the trunk provides starch.

■ *Acrocomia sclerocarpa* oil is excellent for soaps and general edibles and is the basis of small local industries.

■ The mbocaya, *Acrocomia totai*, thrives on cleared land and the dark orange kernel oil has potential, especially for soap and food manufacture. Other useful products include kernel meal and cake.

■ Several *Astrocaryum* palms have potential. The tall awarra palm, *A. vulgare*, produces light and tasty oils used locally for soaps and foods. The jauari palm, *A. jauari*, yields a reddish kernel oil and a cream coloured pulp fat, both with commercial potential. The Tucuma palm, *A. tucuma*, of the drier Amazon, is used by natives for its pulp oil and kernel fat, and the kernel oil of *A. murumuru* is locally traded.

■ The yellow pulp oil from the pejibaye palm, *Bactris gasipaes* (Plate 29), is obtained from primitive plantations as wild sources do not exist. The fruit may also be eaten directly.

■ The yoli, or American oil palm, *Elaeis oleifera*, is a relative of the African oil palm. Its pulp oil serves as a butter substitute and its kernel oil, rich in Vitamin A, is suitable for cooking, soap and lighting. Being low growing and preferring wetter areas, it could be a candidate for commerce as well as for hybridizing with its African cousin.

■ Oil from the bacaba and landi palms, *Oenocarpus bacaba* and *O. distichus*, is similar to olive oil. Bacaba oil is suitable for cooking and lighting. Landi oil has not yet been commercially exploited.

■ The large corozo palm, *Scheelea excelsa*, and the coroba palm, *S. macrocarpa*, produce a high yield of kernel oil. Corozo pulp has little oil but is burnt as fuel and being sweet is a popular local food.

■ The licuri palm, *Syagrus coronata*, gives an edible, yellow kernel oil, similar to coconut oil, which is also suitable for soaps. Its best commercial prospect however is as a source of leaf wax.

iii) Oils from other areas

The Amazon is not the only rainforest area harbouring plants with edible oils:

■ The Indian sal tree, *Shorea robusta*, gives a seed oil used in soaps, cooking and as a butter substitute;

■ Nuts from the Indonesian illipe tree, *Shorea stenoptera*, yield a fat popular in chocolate making. They are the basis of a £2 million per year export trade but the gene bank is thought to be diminishing and no plantations have ever been established, and;

■ The shea-butter tree, *Butyrospermum parkii*, native to West Africa is prized for its seed fat which is the basis of local commercial production and a small but growing export trade. Another African native, the tallow tree, *Pentadesima butyracea*, is a popular local oil source.

iv) Industrial oils

Oil from the castor bean, *Ricinus communis*, a native of Africa, contains lipase and is used to manufacture soap and lubricate machinery. Sebacic acid, extracted from the oil is used to make synthetic fibres, inks, candles and cosmetics.

Oil from the Indian *Vernonia anthelmintica* and *V. galamensis* is particularly adhesive, tough and chemically resistant, making it suitable for protective coatings.

Essential oils

The essential oils are important industrial materials with a global trade value exceeding £1 billion annually. Over half of them come from rainforest plants. The oil is essential in that it contains an aroma or essence, which is volatile, compared to the stable edible oils, and they are widely used in perfumery, cosmetics, pharmaceuticals and flavourings.

Sandalwood, *Santalum album*, from India, is one of the best known and longest established perfumery oils. The wood chips are distilled into a pale yellow liquid with a woody aroma. It is impossible to synthesize sandalwood as its main constituent, santalol, cannot be derived from other starting materials.

Oil from the flowers of the tall ylang-ylang tree, *Cananga odorata*, native to South-east Asia, is so volatile it must be collected early in the morning before it is evaporated by the sun. It is very expensive and a prime ingredient in the finest French perfumes.

Guaiac wood oil, from the Paraguayan *Bulnesia sarmienti,* has long been known, but has only recently been systematically exploited. Rising demand has been due to the increased popularity of mens' toiletries with leather type aromas and woody/floral perfumes and soaps. The wood is becoming more difficult and expensive to obtain, as near and convenient sources have been over-exploited.

The South American rosewood tree, *Aniba roseadora*, yields a useful essential oil. Because its main constituent linalol can be synthesized, demand for the natural oil declined, (though demand for the tree's reddish wood did not), but it has again become more economic with its new role as a perfumery oil in its own right.

Sassafras oil, from the Brazilian *Ocotea pretiosa*, has only recently been traded but is already a valuable foreign exchange earner. Its primary constituent safrole, which converts to heliotropin, appears in soaps, cosmetics and disinfectants. It is also used in pyrethrum-based compounds as a synergist to improve the overall effectiveness of the preparation.

The South-east Asian camphor tree, *Cinnamomum camphora*, yields a multi-purpose oil used in perfumes, soaps, deodorants, detergents, flavourings, celluloid, explosives, disinfectants and insecticides. It also acts as a solvent in paints, varnishes and inks.

Cymbopogon species produce oils popular for cosmetics and perfumery. Citronella, *C. citratus,* which contains citronellal and geraniol, Palmorosa, *C. martini*, also with geraniol, and lemongrass, containing citral.

The oil of the South-east Asian star anise, *Illicium verum*, contains anethole, a common flavouring agent in oral pharmaceuticals.

Other essential oils used in perfumery, cosmetics, confectionary and flavouring include, from South-east Asia: nutmeg; *Myristica fragrans;* cardamon; *Elleteria cardamomum*; ginger; *Zingiber officinale*; cassia; *Cinnamomum cassia*; cinnamon; *Cinnamomum zeylandicum*; clove; *Eugenia caryophyllus*; and patchouli, *Pogostemon cablin*; and from Central America: vanilla, *Vanilla planifolia.*

Having gone through a severe decline, the market for plant-derived essential oils is currently expanding. In 1900, 90 per cent of perfumes were plant based but in the era of cheap petroleum by-products this fell to 15 per cent. By the end of the 1970s it reached 25 per cent and by the year 2000 it could rise to 50 per cent again. There is much scope for improving the quality and quantity of oil yields through genetic manipulation with wild genes if species diversity can be maintained in the face of deforestation.

Energy plants

Plant-derived sources of energy, which are theoretically renewable, are likely to become increasingly important in the future. There are two basic forms of bio-energy: latex from hydrocarbon trees which serves as a petrol; oil or diesel substitute; and general biomass (vegetation) which can be used directly, as in wood burning, or can be converted to a variety of usable fuels like ethanol and gas.

i) Biomass conversion

Three main biomass conversion techniques exist: biomethanation to produce methane, which is a particularly appropriate technology for village level energy production; fermentation to produce ethanol, already a common, cheap and relatively clean-burning petrol additive in countries such as Brazil and Zimbabwe; pyrolisis, yielding several high quality fuels and by-products, including methanol, wood oil and light tar, charcoal, gas, acetic acid, creosote oil, esters and pitch.

Fast growing species with high yields of biomass (plant material) are required to fuel these techniques. Starch crops, eg corn and cassava, sugar crops and swamp reeds are all very productive but one of the most promising candidates is the prolific South American tree the ipil-ipil, *Leucana leucocephala.* It yields 35 cubic metres of biomass per hectare per year and it has been estimated that a 12,000 hectare plantation could provide the equivalent to 1 million barrels of oil every year. Generators in the Philippines and Hawaii are already running on this fuel. Biomass yields could be raised through genetic improvements, and ipil-ipil also yields a gum with commercial potential as a thickener, a dye and its leaves can be used for forage or green manure.

ii) Hydrocarbon trees

Instead of producing carbohydrates, some plants produce hydrocarbons, which can be used directly as fuels or be readily converted into them. Rubber is a hydrocarbon though its particular properties do not make it suitable as a fuel. Important hydrocarbon trees of the rainforest include the following:

- The Central American copaiba tree, *Copaiba langsdorfii*, whose latex flows at the rate of 10 litres per tree per hour from a single tap and can be used directly to fuel a diesel engine. The tree grows on swampland unsuitable for other uses and exhibits the genetic diversity necessary for yield improvements.

- The high quality, inflammable extract from the nuts of the Philippine's petroleum nut tree, *Pittospermum reiniferum*, was used to fuel Japanese tanks in World War Two. Although it can power engines its best prospects are as a household cooking and lighting oil. Six backyard trees can produce 300 litres of fuel each year. The tree thrives in secondary forests and could provide a valuable economic opportunity for degraded lands.

- The Amazonian *Eucalyptus trigoma* yields a hydrocarbon latex with economic potential.

Agriculture and food

Foods from the rainforest

The human population now obtains 90 per cent of its calories from only 30 crop species, with 4 major grain species accounting for 50 per cent of total calorie intake. Two of these, maize and rice, originated in the tropical forest. Of the 3000 or so species of plant that have been cultivated throughout history, only 150 have been farmed on a large scale. Yet there are an estimated 75,000 potential food species and many of these reside in the equatorial tropics. Deforestation threatens the vital genetic diversity needed to maintain presently exploited food sources and may cause the extinction of future food species.

Modern agriculture has been successful in generating large yields, but apart from the huge inputs of fertilizer and energy required, its reliance on monocultures leaves it highly vulnerable to disease and environmental stress. Plant breeding, using new infusions of wild genes, is essential to maintain cultivation. Increased intensity of production requires more and more genetic manipulation. It has been estimated that 50 per cent of the increases in yields obtained in the last 50 years are due to successful hybridization.

The need for new germplasm is expanding, not diminishing, and the greatest reservoir of such material lies in the rainforests. Their protection may be crucial if the expanding human population is to be fed in the years ahead.

Cereals

Cereals are humankind's staple food. Maize and rice each account for one-quarter of global cereal consumption. We rely on genetic infusions from their wild relatives to keep them commercially viable.

Throughout much of the Third World maize flour is a staple dish. In the West maize is used for cornflakes, (and the many variations thereof), popcorn, other snacks, salad dressings, soft drinks, beer and bourbon whiskey. It is also a principal feed for farm animals.

Originating in the tropical forests of Central America, it was probably first domesticated in Mexico. It was from here that wild strains, resistant to blight, were obtained and used in hybrids to rescue the United State's maize industry in the 1970s. One half of the enormous maize yield increases obtained this century in the USA can be attributed to plant breeding.

Recently a perennial variety of maize, thought to be extinct, was re-discovered on a few hectares in Mexico. The potential of a perennial hybrid to Third World farmers may be considerable, and the wild strain exhibits resistance to some of the major international maize diseases for which no other source of immunity exists. Other wild strains of maize are, as yet, uninvestigated but are threatened by the expansion of ranches and overgrazing.

Rice, *Oryza sativa*, is the staple food in South-east Asia, the most populous region of the planet, and it is from here that the species originated. The experience of the 'Green Revolution' illustrated the importance of conserving wild rice varieties.

The first Green Revolution cultivar, known as IR8, was planted widely but the whole crop was soon under threat from the grassy stunt virus. Resistant genes were uncovered in a mere two individual specimens of the wild Indian rice, *Oryza nivara*. However, hybridization produced a plant with a weak stem and further crosses were required with a Taiwanese variety. The required wild specimens were found to be almost extinct, replaced by plantings of IR8. Fortunately, some were found and the overall resulting hybrid IR36 has been highly successful. It is resistant to all four major rice diseases, but every single specimen has obtained its resistance to grassy stunt virus from just two solitary plants.

Finger millet, *Eleusine coracana*, is native to the wetter African tropics. Along with the related Bullrush millet, *Pennisetum americanum*, of the drier areas, it is an important staple food throughout the continent.

Beverages and sugar

The second most valuable commodity in international trade, after petroleum, is coffee. More than 750,000 farmers throughout 40 developing countries depend on it for their income. There are two main varieties of coffee, *Coffea arabica*, originally from East Africa and accounting for 80 per cent of world trade, and *Coffea canephora*, native to Zaire which accounts for the rest.

Most commercial production today takes place in South America, but wild African genes have saved the industry and kept the world's coffee drinkers content. The spread of rust disease in the 1970s threatened the American crop but resistant strains in Ethiopia's dwindling forests were found and hybrids developed.

Cocoa, *Theobroma cacoa*, is an Amazonian native though two thirds of present production occurs in Africa. The cocoa bean is the basis of chocolate and beverage cocoa. Demand for it is expanding but there have been problems with increasing supply. Wild strains from the Amazon have played a vital role in raising yields. Only these new hybrids are now used in commercial production.

A scarce but very promising variety has recently been uncovered in Ecuador but it is threatened, along with other wild cocoas, from logging, forest colonization and oil exploration. Some species are already extinct and the richest reservoir of cocoa diversity is diminishing.

Sugar cane, *Saccharum officinale*, is native to the forests of Indonesia. The modern crop is a complex hybrid and the industry would not have survived without genetic infusions from wild strains. In the 1920s the mosaic virus was controlled by breeding with wild Javanese varieties and since then resistance to other diseases such as red rot and gummosis has been incorporated by plant breeders. Yields have been doubled and new areas opened up to sugar production. The benefits of further hybridization are being undermined by the extinction of wild species through development schemes.

Natural sweeteners

Tropical forest plants may yield non-nutritive (non fattening) alternatives to sugar, without the side effects of synthetic chemicals like saccharin. Some are much sweeter than sucrose. Three West African rainforest plants yield sweet proteins and another comes from South America:

■ The miracle fruit, *Synsepalum dulcificium,* contains the sweetening agent monellin;

■ The accidentally discovered serendipity berry, *Dioscoreophyllum cuminsii,* is 3000 times sweeter than sucrose;

■ Katempfe, *Thaumatococcus danielli* is already commercially exploited. The sweet protein Thaumatin, marketed as Talin, is used in sweets, chewing gum, soups, jellies, pickles, fish, meat, coffee additives and in industrial fermentation;

■ Stevoiside, from the leaves of the Paraguayan stevia plant, *Stevia redaudiana*, is commercially established in Japan as a food additive;

Roots and tubers

An important Amazonian native is cassava, *Manihot esculenta*, also called tapioca or manioc, which is a subsistence staple and a cash crop for industrial starch. Crossing with wild varieties has raised protein levels, improved drought and insect resistance and increased yields 18-fold. Natural diversity is threatened by the expansion of agriculture.

The yam, *Dioscorea* species, has evolved separately in Africa, Asia and the Americas and today it is a widespread staple with a high protein content. One-half of subsistence farmers in West Africa depend on it. Only a little species interbreeding has occurred, but the natural genetic diversity is being eroded worldwide. Despite the importance of the yam as a source of the steroidal drug diosgenin, its main contribution to humanity is as a food crop.

Sweet potato, *Ipomoea batatas*, native to tropical America, are now a popular food throughout the Third World and increasingly common in Western markets. Cross-breeding with wild Mexican varieties has provided nematode resistance, and further research is underway to improve ease of harvesting.

Cocoyams, *Xanthomosa* species, native to tropical America, and taro, *Colocasia esculenta*, native to South-east Asia, are underexploited potato-like tubers with considerable economic potential. Both are now increasing in popularity and a taro crisp is being marketed in the USA.

Beans

The common (or haricot) bean, *Phaseolus vulgaris*, the runner bean, *Phaseolus coccineus*, and the butter bean, *Phaseolus lunatus*, all originated in the South American tropics. They are now nutritious dietary ingredients in Africa and America and popular in the West, particularly processed as baked beans. The genetic base of cultivated varieties is narrow, and there is considerable potential for hybridization to increase yields.

The wing bean, *Psophocarpus tetragonalobus*, has become a vital source of protein in over 50 countries. It is native to New Guinea, where it has long been used by local people, and its international spread has only occurred in the last 15 years. All parts of the plant can be eaten: the seeds, tubers, pods, leaves, stems and flowers, and it also has a high protein and oil content.

The mung bean, *Vigna radiata*, has great potential as a food but it is not yet well known outside of its native India. Apart from being cooked directly it also makes a nutritious and versatile flour.

Fruits

Many of the most popular fruits originated in tropical forests, yet many species remain unexploited. Of the 2500 rainforest fruits identified, only 50 are well known and a mere 15 commercially traded on a large scale. Some of the tastiest fruits in the world are not yet available outside of their native localities.

The pineapple, *Ananus comosus*, originated in the Amazon but it is now grown and enjoyed worldwide. Wild genes from its native habitat have been used to improve the growth characteristics of the plant including longevity and root strength.

The banana, *Musa* species, is a major export commodity and an important food in the areas in which it is grown. Originally from the rainforests of Malaysia it is now widely cultivated, yet all commercial production uses one particular variety, the Cavendish clones. It is thus vulnerable to pest and disease, and a hybridization programme is underway.

The papaya, or paw-paw, *Carica papaya*, a softwood tree native to the lowlands of tropical America, is now grown throughout the tropics. The large orange fruit is rich in minerals and vitamins. As well as being a popular fruit, it is a source of the medicinal and industrial enzyme papain.

Citrus fruits are amongst the world's most prized. More than 55 million tonnes are consumed annually, either as fresh fruits or juices. Oranges, lemons, limes, grapefruits and tangerines are all evergreen trees native to South-east Asia, although now grown throughout the world. Significant natural genetic diversity exists, although it is increasingly threatened, and the plants cross freely.

The largest citrus of all is the pummelo and although it is still uncommon outside of its wet lowland habitat, the future prospects for its commercial expansion are good.

Considered by some to be the tastiest fruit in the world, and one that is increasingly in demand, is the mango, *Mangifera indica*, originally from India. It is now a valuable export in many parts of the tropics.

The guava, *Psidium guajava*, is a small tree native to tropical America. The yellow/green fruits about the size of a tennis ball have a pink and juicy interior. They are eaten raw or made into juice.

The two varieties of climbing plants that produce passion fruits, *Passiflora edulis*, and *P. quadrangularis*, both originated in South America. The former is mainly used for juice while the later is a popular eating fruit as well.

Other lesser-known, but often locally enjoyed, tropical forest fruits include:

- The mangosteen, *Garcinia mangostana*, which has been described as the world's best tasting fruit. It is common in the villages of its native Malaysia but is little known elsewhere;

- Durian, *Durio zibethinus*, an unusual tasting fruit also native to the rainforests of Malaysia;

- The naranjilla, *Solanum quitoense*, known as the golden fruit of the Andes;

- The pineapple-like soursop, *Annona muricata*;

- The feijoa, a relative of the guava with a taste like a pineapple;

- The sapodilla tree, *Archras zapote*, yields a tasty fruit which can be eaten directly or used for jams and flavouring.

Vegetables

The hugely popular tomato, *Lycopersicon esculentum*, is a native of the higher Amazon. Crossbreeding with wild strains has transformed the plant and ensured its commercial viability. Vitamin levels, colour, flavour, ease of harvesting and environmental adaptation have all been improved. Resistance to 12 diseases has been incorporated into hybrids, including freedom from wilt as a result of breeding with wild Peruvian varieties.

The avocado, *Persea americana*, originally from Central America but now widespread, is a very important food. It is high in protein, vitamins, minerals and unsaturated oils. Wild varieties have been used to breed in resistance to root rot.

The most important species of sweet pepper, *Capsicum annum*, is a native of tropical America. It is a vitamin-rich vegetable and an important spice in the form of chillies, cayenne and paprika. Insect resistance in the cultivated forms comes from wild Mexican genes. Another species, *Capsicum frutescens*, yields tabasco.

The eggplant, aubergine or brinjal, *Solanum melongena*, is a popular tropical vegetable native to India. There is considerable natural variety and crossbreeding has improved disease resistance.

Members of the cucurbit group of plants include the cucumber, *Cucumis sativis*, an early Indian domesticate, the melon or muskmelon, *Cucumis melo*, from Africa, the pumpkin, *Cucurbita maxima* and various squashes, *Cucurbita* species, initially cultivated by tropical American Indians.

The breadfruit family are used for their fruit, fibre, latex and timber. The true breadfruit, *Artocarpus altilis*, originated in Malaysia and is now an important staple throughout Oceania and the Caribbean where it is eaten after cooking or used as dough. Two related species, the jackfruit, *Artocarpus heterophyllus*, and the champedak, *Artocarpus integer*, are also native to Malaysia but have spread less widely.

Okra, *Abelmoschus esculentus*, is a bean-like vegetable whose extracted oil is also used for margarine.

The three species of amaranths, *Amaranthus* species, are leafy vegetables with an early history of domestication in South America. They have since become important in India and Southeast Asia. Apart from the leaves, the seed grains are very nutritious and make good flours and thickeners.

The South American tarwi, *Lupinus mutabilis*, is a nutritious vegetable with a high protein and oil content. It can be slightly bitter but cross breeding could overcome this.

An underexploited plant with economic potential is the wax gourd, *Benincasa hispida*, a juicy melon-like vegetable, originally from the forests of Southeast Asia.

The chayote, *Sechium edule*, is a Central American vine which yields both a vegetable and a fruit. It has become a commercial commodity in the region.

Sago is a starchy food made from the trunks of certain palm trees including *Manicaria saccifera*, and the miriti, *Mauritia flexuosa*, both of South America, and various *Metroxylon* species of South-east Asia.

The seeds of the West African akee tree, *Bughia sapida*, are eaten after cooking. They are now a popular food in Jamaica.

Nuts

The ever popular Brazil nut, *Bertholettia excelsa* (Plates 27 and 28), is one of the Amazon's most important trees with 50,000 tonnes of nuts being harvested annually. Apart from being a food, its extracted oil is used for cooking, lighting and soap. The nuts can only be obtained from the wild as fertilization of the tree depends on complex interrelationships with local animal and insect species. All attempts to start plantations have failed. The annual harvest from a single tree can sustainably support many people, but the trees are threatened in many areas by unsustainable development schemes.

The peanut or groundnut, *Arachis hypogaea*, native to South America is an important commercial crop for its protein-rich seed and its extracted oil. Wild genes from the Amazon have been used to conquer leaf spot, adding $500 million a year to the value of production, but in general the breeding potential of the natural diversity has been unexplored.

A valuable nut and vitamin rich fruit is obtained from

the cashew, *Anacardium occidentale* (Plate 21), originally from tropical America. Genetic diversity is considerable though little breeding has been done.

The West African rainforest is the home of the tall kola trees, *Cola nitida* and *Cola accuminata*, whose nuts are a valuable commodity. They contain caffeine and are used to flavour soft drinks like coca-cola. The main centre of production is now South America.

Sesame, *Sesamum indicum*, is an ancient oil seed plant originally from Africa whose main commercial centre is now South-east Asia. The seed is highly nutritious and the extracted oil is of top quality and used for culinary purposes.

The increasingly sought-after macadamia nut, *Macadamia* species, is native to the rainforests of Queensland, Australia, though it is now being cultivated elsewhere. Other nuts from the region offering the same commercial potential include the bush walnut, the red bopple and the Daintree nut.

From the Philippines comes the pili nut, *Canarium ovatum*, which can be eaten directly, used for oil extraction or roasted to provide the basis for confections.

Another promising addition to the commercial nut range is the Paradise nut, *Lecythis zabucajo*, a native of Brazil.

Spices

The nine major rainforest spices earn over $150 million per annum in international trade. These are:

- Cloves, *Eugenia caryophyllus*, native to the Southeast Asian Molluca Islands and now grown extensively in Zanzibar, Madagascar and Indonesia. The aromatic flower buds from the tropical evergreen tree are used for flavouring and the manufacture of alternative cigarettes;

- Nutmegs, *Myristica fragrans*, also from the Molluca Islands which are the seeds of a tree. A second spice, mace, is derived from the nutmeg;

- Black pepper, *Piper nigrum*, which evolved in the hot, wet parts of the Indian subcontinent. Peppercorns are the dried fruit of this climbing plant and the spice is an essential condiment on many dinner tables;

- Pimento or allspice, *Pimenta dioica*, which is the dried unripe fruit of a Central American tree. It is mostly harvested from the wild but plantations have been established in Jamaica. It is from these that the highest quality spice is obtained;

- Cardamon, *Elleteria cardamomum*, is a native to India and the third most expensive spice after saffron and vanilla. Wild substitutes include the bastard cardamon, *Amomum xanthioides*, from South-east Asia, and the Melegueta pepper, *Aframomum melegueta*, from West Africa;

- Vanilla is obtained from a climbing orchid, *Vanilla planifolia*, of the Central American rainforests and is the most important spice of the New World;

- Cinnamon, *Cinnamomum zeylandicum*, and cassia, *Cinnamomum cassia*, are two popular and extensively traded spices native to South-east Asia.

Two further important spices are turmeric, *Curcuma longa*, used for flavouring, colouring and dyeing, and native to South-east Asia, and the tonka bean, *Dipteryx odorata*, a wild South American plant used for flavouring food and tobacco.

Animals

Wild animals are an important source of meat in many parts of the world but their main contribution to modern agriculture could come from cross-breeding with domesticated species. However only a little work has been done in this field, and many of the wild species with breeding potential are endangered.

There are approximately 6 thousand million domesticated chickens, *Gallus gallus*, in the world providing valuable nutrition for millions of people in the form of meat and eggs. They are descended from the wild red jungle fowl of India, also *Gallus gallus*, with some genetic input from the West African Guinea fowl, both birds being rainforest natives.

The wild ancestor of the common domesticated cow, *Bos taurus*, is now extinct but other wild bovids could provide important breeding stock. Domestic cattle in India are descended from the gaur, *Bos gaurus*, and the Indonesian madura is a cross between *Bos taurus* and the banteng, *Bos javanicus*. The kouprey, *Bos sauveli*, is an extremely rare bovid of the forests of South-east Asia which displays immunity to rinderpest and has potential for use in hybridization programmes. The West African n'dama seems resistant to the dreaded sleeping sickness carried by the tsetse fly. It is also a highly endangered animal.

The water buffalo, *Bubalus arnee*, is prized in South-east Asia as the principal work animal and a source of meat. Descended from its wild counterpart of the same name, it could be further improved by crosses with the wild tamarau, *Anoa mindorensis*, and the anoa, *Bubalus depressicornis*.

Of the many species of wild pig from around the world, one in particular shows great promise for upgrading the domesticated stock. It is a rudimentary ruminant called the babirusa, *Babyrousa babyrussa*, which is a native of the South-east Asian rainforests.